PROBLEMS AND SOLUTIONS

International Olympiads on Astronomy and Astrophysics

Second Edition

PROBLEMS AND SOLUTIONS

International Olympiads on Astronomy and Astrophysics

Second Edition

Edited by

Aniket Sule

(On behalf of the IOAA International Board)

Dr. rer. nat. (Doctor of Natural Sciences) in Astrophysics (Germany)
Academic Coordinator, Indian Astronomy Olympiad Programme
Regional Coordinator (Asia-Pacific), International Olympiads on Astronomy and Astrophysics
Reader, Homi Bhabha Centre for Science Education
Tata Institute of Fundamental Research, Mumbai

Universities Press

PROBLEMS AND SOLUTIONS International Olympiads on Astronomy and Astrophysics

UNIVERSITIES PRESS (INDIA) PRIVATE LIMITED

Registered Office
3-6-747/1/A & 3-6-754/1, Himayatnagar, Hyderabad 500 029, Telangana, India
info@universitiespress.com; www.universitiespress.com

Distributed by
Orient Blackswan Private Limited

Registered Office
3-6-752 Himayatnagar, Hyderabad 500 029, Telangana, India

Other Offices
Bengaluru, Chennai, Guwahati, Hyderabad,
Kolkata, Mumbai, New Delhi, Noida, Patna

© 2016 International Olympiad on Astronomy and Astrophysics (IOAA)

First published in Romania by Cygnus Publishing House 2014
Second edition published by Universities Press 2016
Reprinted 2017, 2019, 2023, 2024

Cover, book design and illustrations
© Universities Press (India) Private Ltd 2016

502136

ISBN: 978-81-7371-980-6

Typeset in Palatino 10/12 *by*
MacroTex Solutions, Madipakkam, Chennai 600 091.

Printed in India by
Avantika Printers Private Limited, New Delhi 110 020

Published by
Universities Press (India) Private Limited
3-6-747/1/A & 3-6-754/1, Himayatnagar, Hyderabad 500 029, Telangana, India

Preface

International Olympiads are high-school competitions where each country sends a team of students accompanied by mentors; the students compete individually in a set of tests and are awarded medals based on their performance. Currently, such olympiads exist for Physics, Chemistry, Biology, Mathematics, Astronomy and Astrophysics, Informatics, Earth Sciences and Linguistics. There are also special olympiads like International Junior Science Olympiads aimed at middle-school and early high-school students. These International Olympiads have also given birth to smaller, regional events like Asian Physics Olympiad, Latin American Astronomy and Astrophysics Olympiad and European Girls' Mathematics Olympiad, to name a few.

International Olympiad on Astronomy and Astrophysics (IOAA) was started in 2007. We have had eight Olympiads thus far. They were hosted by Thailand (2007), Indonesia (2008), Iran (2009), China (2010), Poland (2011), Brazil (2012), Greece (2013) and Romania (2014). The next two Olympiads will be hosted by Indonesia (2015) and India (2016). Currently, roughly 45 countries participate in IOAA. Each team consists of up to five students chosen through a national-level selection process in the respective country and it is accompanied by two mentors. There are three rounds of tests: theoretical problems, data analysis problems and night sky observation test. The theoretical problems round typically has 15 short questions and 2–3 long questions to be solved in five hours. Data analysis usually comprises two problems to be solved in four hours while the night sky observation round consists of 4–5 tasks with typically up to 5 minutes for each task.

The scores obtained by each participant in each of the three rounds are added up, with 50% weightage given to theory and 25% each for the other two. Post totalling, the scores are renormalised by the average score of the top three participants. As per these renormalised scores, participants scoring more than 90%, 78%, 65% and 50% qualify for Gold Medal, Silver Medal, Bronze Medal and Honourable Mention certificates, respectively. Additional special certificates are awarded for outstanding performances in one or more tests. Since 2011, an additional team competition has been included, where all the members of the team work together on one or more problems.

This compilation includes problems from all the eight IOAAs held so far. The problems in the respective years were originally designed by the respective host countries. A sketch of possible solutions was also provided. Post IOAA, these problems were also made available on the respective IOAA websites. This compilation, however, aspires to present the problem set in a pedagogically more useful way. The problems are classified according to the concepts involved and also graded by difficulty level. In some places, sub-questions have been added to stimulate the thought process. Additional notes have been provided in the solutions to make them self explanatory. IOAA statutes demand that original solutions not involve calculus. However, sometimes the same problem can be solved more elegantly using calculus.

Sometimes, a problem may be solved in more than one way. In such cases, both solutions are included. In some cases, numerical values from original problems are tweaked slightly to make the problems more realistic. If a problem involves concepts spread across multiple chapters, it is included in the last of these chapters. Numerical values use the SI system of units wherever applicable. It is implicitly expected that students use the proper number of significant digits and at least have a rough estimate of the amount of error in their answer. The problems and solutions remain the property of IOAA and reproduction in any language should carry proper acknowledgements.

   The current syllabus of IOAA is appended to this book. As can be seen, apart from the non–calculus-based solutions restriction, the syllabus more or less covers the same range of topics as covered in any typical undergraduate astrophysics course in any university. Thus, we hope that this book can serve as a useful problem set for those courses too. Needless to say, potential Astronomy and Astrophysics Olympiad participants would find this compilation extremely handy for their preparation.

Happy solving!

Aniket Sule
astronomy@hbcse.tifr.res.in

Acknowledgements

I would like to thank the International Board of International Olympiad on Astronomy and Astrophysics (IOAA); in particular, the President of the Board, Professor Chatief Kunjaya, and Professor Gregorz Stachowaski, for entrusting this task to me. I acknowledge the hard work done by the respective year's problem setters in designing the problems. I am also grateful to all the host countries of IOAA for graciously granting permission to use these problems in this book. As a mark of acknowledgement, I have listed the names of the problem setters for each year on the next page. All the members of the international board of IOAA are thanked for their support and suggestions. All IOAA participants are thanked for their ingenious solutions to the problems, some of which you will see in this book. I would also like to thank Ms Sheetal Chopde for typesetting the initial draft and proofreading the final version, and Mr Swapnil Jawkar and Mr Prasad Adekar for their constructive suggestions.

Aniket Sule

Academic Committees of Previous IOAAs

The following academic committees were responsible for designing problems and solutions for IOAA in the respective years:

IOAA 2007, Chiang Mai, Thailand

- Professor Boonrucksar Soonthornthum, NARIT - Chair
- Mr Nipon Saipetch, The Royal Institute - Vice-chair
- Mr Aree Sawasdee, The Thai Astronomical Society
- Dr Wudhiban Prachyabrued, POSN Foundation
- Professor Kao Muanwong
- Professor Piyapong Sittikong, Mahidol University
- Dr Busaba Kramer, NARIT

IOAA 2008, Bandung, Indonesia

- Dr Chatief Kunjaya, Institut Teknologi Bandung - Vice-chair (Academic), Organising Committee
- Dr Hakim L Malasan, Institut Teknologi Bandung - Convener, Academic Committee
- Dr Premana W Premadi, Institut Teknologi Bandung - Chair, Jury Council
- Dr Dhani Herdiwijaya, Institut Teknologi Bandung - Coordinator, Observational Equipments
- Dr Djoni N Dawanas, Institut Teknologi Bandung - Coordinator, Theoretical Round
- Dr Moedji Raharto, Institut Teknologi Bandung - Coordinator, Practical Round
- Dr Suhardja D Wiramihardja, Institut Teknologi Bandung
- Dr Freddy P Zen, Institut Teknologi Bandung
- Dr Triyanta, Institut Teknologi Bandung
- Dr Agus Yodi Gunawan, Institut Teknologi Bandung
- Dr Zaki Su'ud, Institut Teknologi Bandung
- Dr Bobby Eka Gunara, Institut Teknologi Bandung
- Dr Wono Setiabudhi, Institut Teknologi Bandung
- Dr Oki Neswan, Institut Teknologi Bandung
- Dr Udjianna S Pasaribu, Institut Teknologi Bandung

IOAA 2009, Tehran, Iran

- Professor Mohammad Taghi Mirtorabi, Alzahra University, Tehran - Chair, Academic Committee
- Professor Mahdi Khakian Ghomi, Amirkabir University of Technology, Tehran - Chair, Jury Council
- Professor Alireza Molaeinezhad, Institute of Physics and Mathematics, Tehran - Coordinator, Observational Round
- Professor Saeed Shami - Coordinator, and Practical Round
- Professor Sohrab Rahwar, Sharif University of Technology, Tehran
- Professor Hossein Haghi, Institute for Advanced Studies in Basic Sciences, Zanjan
- Professor Shahram Abbasi, Ferdowsi University, Mash'had
- Professor Mohammad Malekjani

IOAA 2010, Beijing, China

- Dr Jin Jhu, Beijing Planetarium - Chair
- Dr Dongi N Chen, Beijing Planetarium

IOAA 2011, Krakow & Katowice, Poland

- Professor Waldemar Ogloza - Chair, Jury Council
- Professor Gregorz Stachowski, Krakow Pedagogical University
- Professor Andrzej Soltan
- Professor Jerzy Kuczyński
- Marek Szczepański
- Professor Jerzy Kreiner
- Stefan Janta

IOAA 2012, Vassouras and Rio de Janeiro, Brazil

- Bruno L'Astorina, Colégio Etapa, São Paulo
- Professor Carlos Alexandre Wuensche, INPE/Divisão de Astrofísica, S. José dos Campos, São Paulo
- Eduardo Fernandez del Peloso, Instituto de Ciências Náuticas, Rio de Janeiro
- Felipe Augusto Cardoso Pereira, Universidade de São Paulo / Instituto de Física, São Paulo
- Fernando Vieira, Fundação Planetárioda Cidadedo Riode Janeiro
- Jorge Márcio Carvano, Observatório Nacional, Rio de Janeiro
- Julio Cesar Neves Campagnolo, Observatório Nacional, Rio de Janeiro
- Marcos Mataratzis, Colégio Pedro II / Grupo NGC-51, Rio de Janeiro
- Professor Thais Mothé Diniz, Universidade Federal do Rio de Janeiro / Observatório do Valongo, Rio de Janeiro
- Thiago Saksanian Hallak, Escola Politécnica da USP, São Paulo

IOAA 2013, Volos, Greece

- Dr Seiradakis John, Professor, Aristotle University of Thessaloniki (AUTH)
- Dr Chatzidimitriou Despina, Associate Professor, University of Athens (UOA)
- Dr Apostolatos Theocharis, Assistant Professor, UOA
- Dr Tsiganis Kleomenis, Assistant Professor, AUTH
- Dr Stergioulas Nicolaos, Associate Professor, AUTH
- Dr Tsikoudi Vassiliki, Professor Emeritus, University of Ioannina
- Dr Plionis Manolis, Professor, AUTH
- Dr Preka-Papadima Panagiota, Assistant Professor, UOA
- Voulgaris Aristides
- Voutiras George

IOAA 2014, Suceava, Romania

- Dr Sandu Mihail, Technological Highschool, Calimanesti
- Dr Christian Pirghie, University Stefan cel Mare, Suceava
- Dr Ana Camelia Pîrghie, University Stefan cel Mare, Suceava
- Dr Sorin Trocaru, Ministry of Education, Bucharest

President's Message

The growing population and limited natural resources on earth has motivated scientists to explore outer space to facilitate the existence of human humankind in the future. Exploration of outer space requires that many brilliant young people work in this field, attracting bright young people to learn about space sciences. It is a competitive event for high-school students in the field of Astronomy and Astrophysics.

IOAA was initiated in 2007 and since then, member countries have hosted the event by turn. During the event, the participating students are required to solve theoretical, data analysis and observational problems. Before the actual event, many astronomers from host countries collect their briliant ideas, data and knowledge to prepare problems to be posed in IOAA. They spend a lot of time discussing ideas for designing high quality astronomical problems. Later they are reviewed by many astronomers from participating countries in the meeting of the International Board. This long and difficult process ensures the delivery of high quality problem sets for the olympiad rounds.

Till now, a lot of problems have been accumulated and reported in the olympiad proceedings of each year's event. The problems will be very valuable for several purposes such as training national teams projected to participate in IOAA, training young astronomy students in universities and knowledge enrichment of high-school physics teachers. Therefore, the effort to collect the problems and solutions in a published book is laudable. I thank the editor who has spent a lot of his valuable time to make the publication of this book a reality. I support the publication of the IOAA problems and solutions book for the future of IOAA and for its contribution to the world of astronomy.

Chatief Kunjaya
Institute of Technology, Bandung, Indonesia
IOAA President 2012–present

A Note about the Problems

You will find a code in parenthesis after each problem, e.g., (I07 - T20 - C). The first number gives the year in which this problem was posed, e.g., I07 means IOAA2007. The second number gives information about the test and question number. T stands for theory, D for data analysis, O for observation and G for group tasks. In theory, numbers greater than 15 denote long questions. The last letter denotes the difficulty level of the question, as perceived by the editor, A being the simplest and D the most difficult.

The prefix *EA* before a line in a problem indicates that this was not part of the original question but is an addition by the editor.

General Marking Principle

1.	Correct answer without detailed calculation	Deduct 50% of the marks for that part
2.	Minor mistakes in the calculations, e.g., wrong signs, symbols, substitutions	Deduct 20% of the marks for that part
3.	Units missing from final answers	Deduct 10% of the marks for that part
4.	Too few or too many significant digits in the final answer	Deduct 10% of the marks for that part
5.	Using incorrect physical concept (despite correct answers)	**No points given**
6.	Error propagated from earlier parts: minor errors	Full points (i.e., no deductions)
7.	Error propagated from earlier parts: major errors	Deduct 20% of the marks for the final answer

Table of Constants

The Sun	
Mass	$M_\odot = 1.9891 \times 10^{30}$ kg
Radius	$R_\odot = 6.955 \times 10^8$ m
Luminosity	$L_\odot = 3.826 \times 10^{26}$ W
Apparent magnitude at mid-day	$m_\odot = -26.72$
Absolute V-band magnitude	$M_{v\odot} = 4.82$
Absolute bolometric magnitude	$M_{bol} = 4.72$
Apparent angular diameter	$\theta_\odot = 32'$
Temperature on the surface	$T_\odot = 5778$ K
Solar constant (at Earth)	$S = 1366$ W/m^2

The Earth	
Mass	$M_\oplus = 5.9736 \times 10^{24}$ kg
Radius	$R_\oplus = 6.3708 \times 10^6$ m
Mean density	$\rho_\oplus = 5515$ kg/m^3
Gravitational acceleration on the surface	$g = 9.81$ m/s^2
Inclination of the axis	$\epsilon = 23°26'$
Orbital eccentricity	$e_\oplus = 0.0167$
Albedo	$\alpha_\oplus = 0.39$

The Moon	
Mass	$M_M = 7.3477 \times 10^{22}$ kg
Radius	$R_M = 1.7374 \times 10^6$ m
Mean distance from Earth	$d_M = 3.78 \times 10^8$ m
Synodic period	$P_{sy} = 29.5306$ days
Apparent magnitude (full moon)	$m_{moon} = -12.74$

Albedo	$\alpha = 0.14$
Inclination of the lunar orbit w.r.t. the ecliptic	$= 5°9'$

Venus

Radius	$R_v = 0.949\, R_\oplus$
Orbital semi-major axis	$a_{Venus} = 0.723$ AU
Orbital period	$T_{Venus} = 224.70$ days
Albedo	$\alpha = 0.87$

Mars

Mass	$M_{Mars} = 6.421 \times 10^{23}$ kg
Radius	$R_{Mars} = 3393$ km
Orbital semi-major axis	$a_{Mars} = 1.524$ AU
Rotational period	$P_{Mars} = 24.623$ hr
Orbital radius of Phobos	$a_{Ph} = 9380$ km

Jupiter

Mass	$M_J = 1.898 \times 10^{27}$ kg
Orbital semi-major axis	$a_{Jup} = 5.204$ AU
Number of arcseconds in a rad.	$= 206\ 265''$
1 sidereal day	$= 23^h\ 56^m\ 4^s.1$
1 sidereal year	$= 365.2564$ solar days
1 tropical year	$= 365.2422$ solar days
	$= 3.1557 \times 10^7$ s
1 astronomical unit (AU)	$a_\oplus = 1.4960 \times 10^{11}$ m
1 light-year (ly)	$= 9.46 \times 10^{15}$ m
	$= 6.324 \times 10^4$ AU
1 parsec (pc)	$= 3.0856 \times 10^{16}$ m
	$= 3.262$ ly
Distance to the galactic centre	$d_{GC} = (8.3 \pm 0.3)$ kpc
Speed of light	$c = 2.997924\,58 \times 10^8$ m/s

Universal gravitational constant	$G = 6.6741 \times 10^{-11}\,\mathrm{Nm^2/kg^2}$
Planck constant	$h = 6.62 \times 10^{-34}\,\mathrm{Js}$
Hubble constant	$H_0 = (67.80 \pm 0.77)\,\mathrm{km/(s\ Mpc)}$
Age of the universe	$t_0 = 13.77 \times 10^9\,\mathrm{years}$
Stefan–Boltzmann constant	$\sigma = 5.67 \times 10^{-8}\,\mathrm{W/m^2/K^4}$
Boltzmann constant	$k_B = 1.38 \times 10^{-23}\,\mathrm{j/K^2}$
Universal gas constant	$R = 8.314\,\mathrm{J\ mol^{-1}\ K^{-1}}$
Wien's displacement law	$\lambda_m T = 2.898 \times 10^{-3}\,\mathrm{mK}$
Charge of a electron	$e = 1.602 \times 10^{-19}\,\mathrm{C}$
Mass of a electron	$m_e = 9.1 \times 10^{-31}\,\mathrm{kg}$
Mass of a proton	$m_p = 938.27\,\mathrm{MeV/c^2}$
Mass of a neutron	$m_n = 939.56\,\mathrm{MeV/c^2}$
Mass of a deuterium atom	$m_D = 1875.60\,\mathrm{MeV/c^2}$
Mass of a helium-3 atom	$m_{He3} = 2808.30\,\mathrm{MeV/c^2}$
Mass of a helium-4 atom	$m_{He} = 4.002\,603\,\mathrm{a\,m\,u}$
	$= 3727.40\,\mathrm{MeV/c^2}$
Mass of a carbon atom	$m_c = 12.000000\,\mathrm{a\,m\,u}$
Rest wavelength of Balmer Hα line	$\lambda_\alpha = 656.3\,\mathrm{nm}$
Rest frequency of spin-flip transition of hydrogen	$\nu_{21} = 1420.406\,\mathrm{MHz}$
Distance of Barnard's star	$d_{Barnarad} = 1.83\,\mathrm{pc}$
Coordinates of northern ecliptic pole (J2000.0)	$(\alpha_E, \delta_E) = 18^h\,00^m\,00^s,\ 66°33.6'$
Coordinates of northern galactic pole (J2000.0)	$(\alpha_G, \delta_G) = 12^h\,51^m,\ 27°8'$
Diameter of human pupil	$= 6\,\mathrm{mm}$
Height of Christ the Redeemer	$= 39.60\,\mathrm{m}$
Height of Eiffel Tower	$= 324\,\mathrm{m}$

Basic equations of spherical trigonometry (for a spherical triangle ABC)

$$\sin a \sin B = \sin b \sin A$$

$$\cos a = \cos b \cos c + \sin b \sin c \cos A$$

$$\sin a \cos B = \cos b \sin c - \sin b \cos c \cos A$$

Moment of inertia for

1. Homogeneously filled sphere of radius R and mass M, $I = \dfrac{2}{5} MR^2$

2. Thin spherical shell of radius R and mass M, $I = \dfrac{2}{3} MR^2$

3. Thin, homogeneously filled disk of radius R and mass $I_z = \dfrac{1}{2} MR^2$ in x–y plane

Contents

1

Celestial Mechanics

1.1 Theory

1. A Sun-orbiting periodic comet is farthest from the Sun at 31.5 AU and closest to the Sun at 0.5 AU. What is the orbital period of this comet? (I07 - T06 - A)

2. For the comet in Question 1 above, what is the area (in square AU per year) swept by the line joining the comet and the Sun? (I07 - T07 - A)

3. Most single-appearance comets enter the inner Solar System directly from the Oort Cloud. Estimate how long it will take a comet to make this journey. Assume that in the Oort Cloud, 35 000 AU from the Sun, the comet was at aphelion. (I11 - T01 - A)

4. Estimate the radius of a planet such that a person can escape its gravitation by jumping vertically. Assume that the density of the planet and that of the Earth are the same. (I09 - T03 - A)

5. A spacecraft landed on the surface of a spherical asteroid with negligible rotation. The diameter of the asteroid is 2.2 km and its average density is 2.2 g cm^{-3}. Can the astronaut complete a circle along the equator of the asteroid on foot in 2.2 hr? (I10 - T06 - A)

6. Estimate the number of stars in a globular cluster of diameter 40 pc, if the escape velocity at the edge of the cluster is 6 km s^{-1} and most of the stars are similar to the Sun. (I11 - T02 - B)

7. Estimate the mass of a globular cluster with radius $R = 20$ pc when the root mean square velocity of the stars in the cluster is 3 km s^{-1}. (I09 - T08 - B)

8. On 9 March 2011, the Voyager probe was 116.406 AU from the Sun and moving at 17.062 km s^{-1}. Determine the type of orbit the probe is on:

   (a) elliptical, (b) parabolic or (c) hyperbolic.

   What is the apparent magnitude of the Sun as seen from Voyager? (I11 - T03 - B)

9. Calculate the ratio between the average densities of the Earth and the Sun, using ONLY the dataset given below:

   - The angular diameter of the Sun, as seen from the Earth.
   - The gravitational acceleration on the Earth's surface.
   - The length of the year.
   - The fact that one degree in latitude at the Earth's surface corresponds to 111 km.

   (I12 - T05 - B)

10. A spacecraft is orbiting the near-Earth asteroid Seneca (staying continuously very close to the asteroid), transmitting pulsed data to the Earth. Due to the relative motion of the two bodies (the asteroid and the Earth) around the Sun, the time it takes for a pulse to arrive at

the ground station varies approximately between 2 and 39 minutes. Assuming that the Earth moves around the Sun on a circular orbit and that the orbit of Seneca does not intersect the orbit of the Earth, calculate:

(a) The semi-major axis a_s and the eccentricity e_s of Seneca's orbit around the Sun.

(b) The period of Seneca's orbit T_s and the synodic period T_{syn} of the Earth–Seneca couple.

(c) An approximate value for the mass of the planet Jupiter M_J (assuming this is the only planet in our Solar System with non-negligible mass compared to the Sun). Assume that the presence of Jupiter does not influence the orbit of Seneca and that Jupiter's orbital period is 11.8618 years.   (I13 - T17 - B)

11. Assuming that dust grains are black bodies, determine the diameter of a spherical dust grain which can remain at 1 AU from the Sun in equilibrium between the radiation pressure and the gravitational attraction of the Sun. Take the density of the dust grain to be $\rho = 10^3$ kg/m^3.   (I11 - T08 - B)

12. Tidal forces impart a torque on the Earth. Assuming that during the last several hundred million years, both this torque and the length of the sidereal year were constant and had values of 6.0×10^{16} Nm and 3.15×10^7 s, respectively, calculate how many days there were in a year 6.0×10^8 years ago.   (I11 - T06 - B)

EA: Estimate the number of days in a year when the Mesopotamians developed their calender (about 5000 years ago).

13. A spacecraft is due to make a close pass of an object in space and scientists would like to investigate the object more carefully using the onboard telescope. For simplicity, let us reduce the problem to two dimensions and assume that the position of the spacecraft is stationary at (0,0) and the shape of the object is a disk and its boundary has the equation

$$x^2 + y^2 - 10x - 8y + 40 = 0 \qquad (1.1)$$

Find the exact values of the maximum and minimum of $\tan \phi$, where ϕ is the elevation angle of the telescope with respect to the horizontal direction (x-axis) during investigation from one edge to the other.   (I08 - T13 - C)

14. Consider a potential hazardous object (PHO) moving in a closed orbit under the influence of the Earth's gravitational force. Let u be the inverse of the distance of the object from the Earth and p be the magnitude of its linear momentum. As the object travels through points A and B, values of u and p are noted, as shown in the following table. Find the mass and the total energy of the object and sketch the shape of the u curve as a function of p from A to B.   (I08 - T14 - C)

	p ($\times 10^9$ kgm s^{-1})	u ($\times 10^{-8}$ m^{-1})
A	0.052	5.15
B	1.94	194.17

15. Derive a relation for the escape velocity of an object launched from the centre of a proto-star cloud. The cloud has uniform density with mass M and radius R. Ignore collisions between the particles of the cloud and the launched object. You are given the fact that if the object were allowed to fall freely from the surface, it would reach the centre with a velocity equal to $\sqrt{\dfrac{GM}{R}}$.   (109 - T06 - C)

16. Gravitational forces of the Sun and Moon lead to the raising and lowering of sea water surfaces. Let ϕ be the difference in longitude between points A and B, where both points are at the equator and A is on the sea surface. Derive the horizontal acceleration of sea water at position A due to the Moon's gravitational force at the time when the Moon is above point B according to observers on the Earth (express it in terms of ϕ, the radius of the Earth $R_\oplus$, and the Earth–Moon distance $a_\oplus$). (I08 - T08 - C)

17. **Lagrange points:** The Lagrange points are the five positions in an orbital configuration, where a small object is stationary relative to two big bodies, only gravitationally interacting with them. For example, an artificial satellite relative to the Earth and Moon, or relative to the Earth and Sun. Find out if the Lagrange point L_3 is located inside the Earth's orbit or outside and its separation from the centre of the Sun, using the length of 1 AU and the masses of the Earth and Sun. (I14 - T1 - C)

18. **Sun gravitational catastrophe!** In a gravitational catastrophe, the mass of the Sun suddenly decreases to half its present value. Find the new orbital period of the Earth if the catastrophe occurs on: (a) 3 July (b) 3 January. (I14 - T2 - C)

19. **High-altitude projectile:** A projectile which starts from the surface of the Earth at sea level is launched with an initial speed of $v_0 = \sqrt{\dfrac{GM_\oplus}{R_\oplus}}$ and with a projecting angle (with respect to the local horizon) of $\theta = \dfrac{\pi}{6}$. Ignore the air resistance and rotation of the Earth.

    (a) Show that the orbit of the projectile is an ellipse with a semi-major axis of $a = R_\oplus$.

    (b) Calculate the highest altitude of the projectile with respect to the Earth's surface (in units of $R_\oplus$).

    (c) What is the range of the projectile (surface distance between launching point and falling point) in units of $R_\oplus$?

    (d) What is the eccentricity (e) of this elliptical orbit?

    (e) Find the time of flight for the projectile. (I09 - T16 - C)

20. **From Romania to antipode with a ballistic messenger:** The organisers of the 8th IOAA plan to send the official flag to the antipode (the point on the Earth's surface diametrically opposite the launch position) using a ballistic projectile ($r = 40$ cm). You can assume that the projectile is a perfectly metallic sphere with a perfectly reflective surface. The projectile will be launched from Romania, and we assume the Earth to be a non-rotating body. The maximum height attained by the projectile is approximately $6R_\oplus$ and it reaches maximum height if the Sun is at meridian at antipode point. (I14 - T17 - C)

    (a) Calculate the coordinates of the target-point if the launch-point coordinates are: $\phi_{Ro} = 44°$ North; $\lambda_{Ro} = 30°$ East.

    (b) Determine the elements of the launching-velocity vector, with respect to the centre of the Earth, in order that the projectile should reach the target.

    (c) Calculate the speed of the projectile when it hits the target.

    (d) Calculate the minimum speed of the projectile on its trajectory.

    (e) Calculate the flying time of the projectile, from launch to impact.

    (f) By comparing the intensity of light reflected by the projectile with the Moon, estimate if it is possible to see this projectile with the naked eye when it is at maximum distance from the Earth.

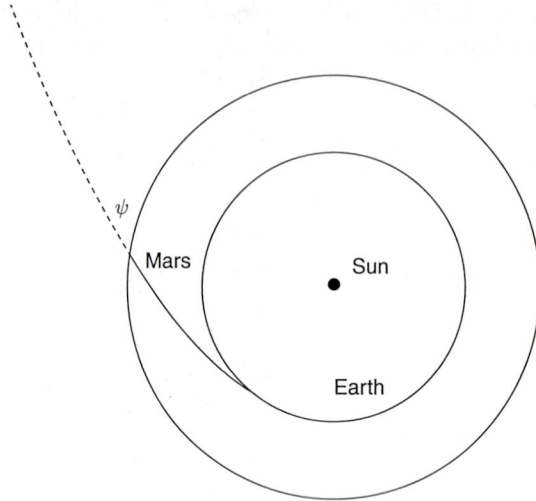

Fig. 1.1 *The trajectory of the spacecraft (not in scale, seen from the north ecliptic pole). The inner circle is the orbit of the Earth, the outer circle is the orbit of Mars.*

EA: The maximum height of the projectile was not specified in the original question. Thus, a vast number of solutions were possible.

21. A spacecraft is launched from the Earth and it is quickly accelerated to its maximum velocity in the direction of the heliocentric orbit of the Earth, such that its orbit is a parabola with the Sun at its focus point and grazes the Earth's orbit. Take the orbit of the Earth and Mars as circles on the same plane. Make the following approximation: during most of the flight, only the gravity from the Sun needs to be considered.   (I10 - T16 - D)

    (a) What is the angle (ψ) between the path of the spacecraft and the orbit of Mars (see Fig. 1.1) as it crosses the orbit of Mars, without considering the gravity effect of Mars?

    (b) Suppose Mars happens to be very close to the crossing point at the time of the crossing, from the point of view of an observer on Mars, what is the approaching velocity and direction of approach (with respect to the Sun) of the spacecraft before it is significantly affected by the gravity of Mars?

22. A satellite orbits the Earth on a circular orbit. The initial momentum of the satellite is given by the vector $\vec{p}$. At a certain time, an explosive charge is set off which gives the satellite an additional impulse $\Delta\vec{p}$, equal in magnitude to $|\vec{p}|$.

    Let α be the angle between the vectors $\vec{p}$ and $\Delta\vec{p}$, and β between the radius vector of the satellite and the vector $\Delta\vec{p}$.

    By thinking about the direction of the additional impulse $\Delta\vec{p}$, consider if it is possible to change the orbit to each of the cases given below. If it is possible, then give the values of α and β for which it is possible. If the orbit is not possible, mark NO.

    (a) A hyperbola with perigee at the location of the explosion.

    (b) A parabola with perigee at the location of the explosion.

    (c) An ellipse with perigee at the location of the explosion.

(d) A circle.

(e) An ellipse with apogee at the location of the explosion.

Note that for $\alpha = 180°$ and $\beta = 90°$, the new orbit will be a line along which the satellite will free-fall vertically towards the centre of the Earth. (I11 - T07 - D)

1.2 Data Analysis

1. **Galilean moons:** A computer simulation of the planet Jupiter and its four Galilean moons is shown on the screen, similar to the view you may see through a small telescope. After observing the movement of the moons, please identify the names of the moons that appear at the end of the simulation. (Simulation was played on screen during the first fifteen minutes and the last fifteen minutes of the exam). (I07 - D01 - A)

EA: It is not possible to present this question in the same form here. The question given below is an alternative formulation.

Here we have given three snapshots taken on successive nights of the planet Jupiter and its four Galilean moons. Identify these moons.

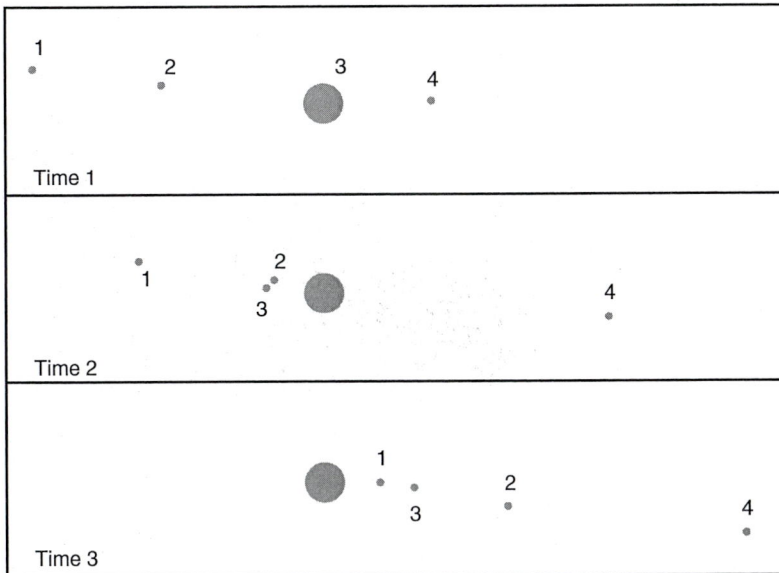

2

Celestial Coordinate Systems

2.1 Theory

1. Two persons on the equator of the Earth, separated by 180° in longitude, observe the Moon's position with respect to the background star field at the same time. If the declination of the Moon is zero, sketch the situation and calculate the difference in apparent right ascension as seen by those two persons. (I08 - T01 - A)

   EA: In reality, what is the maximum longitude separation possible between the two observers such that both will see the Moon at the same time?

2. Damavand Mountain is located in the northern part of Iran, on the south coast of the Caspian Sea. Consider an observer standing on top of Damavand Mountain (latitude = 35°57' N; longitude = 52°6' E; altitude 5.6×10^3 m from mean sea level) and looking at the sky over the Caspian Sea. What is the minimum declination for a star to be seen marginally circumpolar for this observer? The surface level of the Caspian Sea is approximately equal to mean sea level. (I09 - T05 - A)

3. In typical Persian architecture, on the top of south side windows lies a structure called tabeshband (shader), which controls the amount of light entering the rooms in summer and winter. In summer when the Sun is high, the tabeshband prevents sunlight from entering the rooms and keeps the inside cool. Modern studies have verified that the tabeshband saves about 20% of energy costs. Fig. 2.1 shows a vertical section of this design at latitude 36.0° N with window and tabeshband. Using the parameters given in the figure, calculate

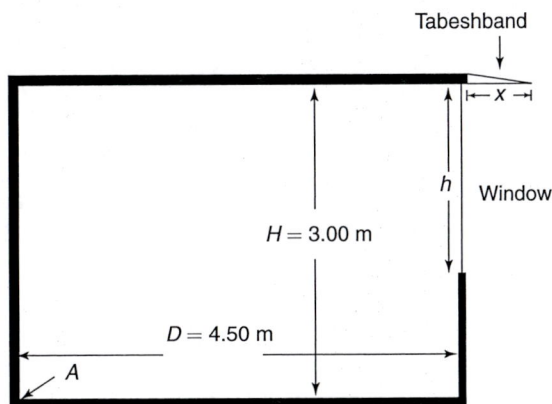

Fig. 2.1 *Tabeshband*

the maximum width of the tabeshband (x) and the maximum height of the window (h) in such a way that:

(a) No direct sunlight can enter the room on summer solstice at noon.

(b) Direct sunlight reaches the end of the room (indicated by point A in the figure) on winter solstice at noon.

(I09 - T04 - A)

4. For an observer at latitude 42.5° N and longitude 71° W, estimate the time of sunrise on 21 December if the observer's civil time is −5 hours from GMT. Ignore refraction by the atmosphere and the size of the solar disc.

(I07 - T01 - B)

EA: What is the error (in minutes) introduced by the atmospheric refraction and the size of the solar disc and equation of time?

5. At Brazil's National Observatory, located in the city of Rio de Janeiro (22°54' S, 43°12' W), there is a sundial above the door of the dome of the 32-cm telescope, facing north. The dial lies on the plane East–Zenith–West and the rod of the sundial is parallel to the Earth's axis. For which declinations of the Sun and during what period of the year (months and seasons) does the clock:

(a) Not work during at least some fraction of the day?

(b) Not work at all during the day?

(I12 - T01 - B)

6. A full moon occurred on 19 June 2008 at 00^h30^mWest Indonesian time (local civil time for the western part of Indonesia with reference geographic longitude as 105° E). Calculate the extreme possible durations of the Moon above the horizon for an observer at Bosscha Observatory (longitude: 107°35'0.0" E, latitude: 6°49'0.0" S, elevation: 1300.0 m, time zone = UT + 7^h30^m).

(I08 - T03 - B)

7. What is the maximum altitude a_M (max) of the full moon as observed from Thessaloniki (geographical latitude $\phi = 40°37'$)? Take into account as many factors as possible.

(I13 - T11 - B)

8. An observer tries to measure the field of view (FOV) of the eyepiece of his/her telescope, using the rotation of the Earth. To do this, the observer points the telescope towards Vega (α Lyr, RA: 18.5^h, Dec: + 39°), turns off its clock drive and measures trace out time to be $t = 5.3$ minutes. Trace out time is the time taken by a star to cross the full diameter of the FOV. What is the FOV of this telescope in arcminutes?

(I09 - T07 - B)

9. **Stars with Romanian names:** Two Romanian astronomers, Ovidiu Tercu and Alex Dumitriu from Galati, Romania, discovered two variable stars in September 2013. The galactic coordinates of the two stars are: Galati V1 ($l_1 = 114.371°$; $b_1 = -11.35°$) and (Galati V2 $l_2 = 113.266°$; $b_2 = -16.177°$). Estimate the angular distance between the stars Galati V1 and Galati V2.

(I14-T10-B)

10. Find the equatorial coordinates (hour angle and declination) of a star at Madrid (geographic latitude $\phi = 40°$) at the instant when the star is at zenith angle $z = 30°$ and azimuth $A = 50°$ (azimuth is measured from the South).

(I13 - T9 - B)

11. What is the hour angle H and the zenith angle z of Vega ($\delta = 38°47'$) in Thessaloniki ($\lambda_1 = 1^h 32^m$, $\phi_1 = 40°37'$), at the moment it culminates at the local meridian of Lisbon ($\lambda_2 = -0^h 36^m$, $\phi_2 = 39°43'$)?

(I13 - T14 - B)

12. **Nocturnal:** Circumpolar stars describe a full circle around the celestial pole over 24 hours. This fact can be used to make a simple clock. You are given a blank card with a movable ring, along with a clear strip with a central circle.

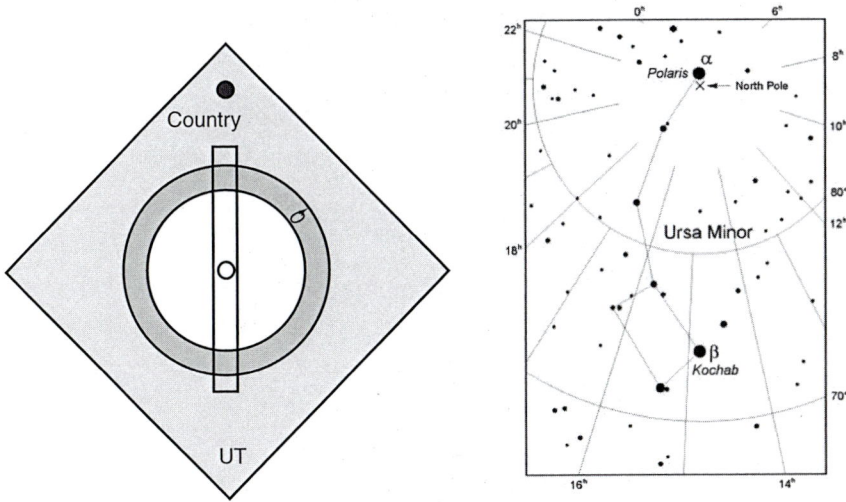

Fig 2.2   *Sky map of Ursa Minor and clock card*

If the card has a suitable scale, the clear strip is attached as in Fig. 2.2 (left) and the Pole Star is visible through the central circle, then the position of the star Kochab (β UMi) on the inner edge of the ring will give the current time.

Design and mark on the card and ring, suitable inner and outer scales (as required) such that, in Katowice, Poland, for any night of the year, the side of the clock marked UT can be used to show current Universal Time, and the other side (marked ST) can be used independently to show current Local Sidereal Time. For August 27, in Katowice, the lower culmination of Kochab is at 05:15 Central European Summer Time (UT+2). The coordinates of Kochab (β UMi) are: α : 14^h51^m, δ : $74.2°$.   (I11 - T05 - C)

Notes:
- The blank card is marked with a line which should be held horizontally when the device is used.
- The clear strip will be attached later, after marking of the scale is finished.

13. The equation of the ecliptic in equatorial coordinates (α, δ) has the form:

$$\delta = \tan^{-1}(\sin \alpha \tan \epsilon) \qquad (2.1)$$

where ϵ is the angle of the celestial equator to the ecliptic plane. Find an analogous relation $h = f(A)$ for the galactic equator in horizontal coordinates (A, h) for an observer at latitude $\varphi = 49°34'$ at local sidereal time $\theta = 0^h51^m$.   (I11 - T13 - C)

14. Due to the precession of the Earth's axis, the region of sky visible from a location with fixed geographical coordinates changes with time. Is it possible that, at some point in time, Sirius will not rise as seen from Krakow, while Canopus will rise and set?   (I11 - T12 - C)

Krakow is at latitude 50.1°N; the current equatorial coordinates (right ascension and declination) of these stars are:

Sirius (α CMa): 6^h45^m, $-16°43'$

Canopus (α Car): 6^h24^m, $-52°42'$

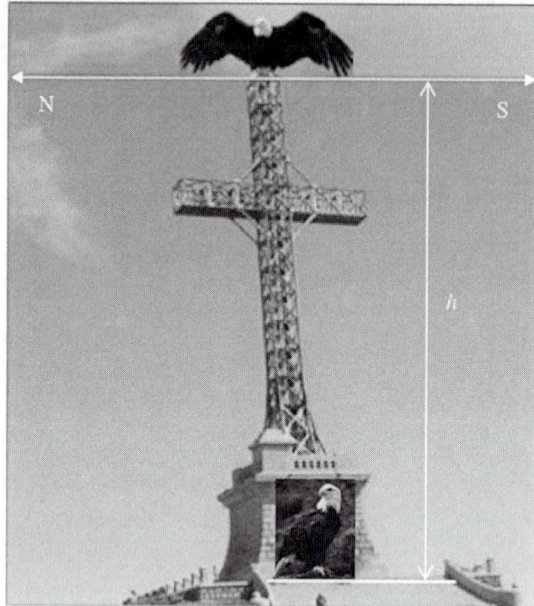

Fig. 2.3   *Eagles on the Caraiman Cross*

15. **Eagles on the Caraiman Cross:** The tallest cross built on a mountain top is located on a plateau situated at the top of a peak called Caraiman in the Bucegi Mountains in Romania at altitude $H = 2300$ m from sea level. Its height, including the base-support, is $h = 39.3$ m. The horizontal arms of the cross are oriented in the N–S direction. The latitude at which the cross is located is $\phi = 45°$.   (I14 - T16 - C)

   (a) On the evening of 21 March 2014, vernal equinox day, two eagles come to the cross; the first near the base of the monument, and the second on the top of the Cross, as seen in Fig. 2.3. The two eagles are along the same vertical line. The sky was very clear, so the eagles could see the horizon and observe the sunset. Each eagle began to fly right at the moment it observed that they entire solar disk had disappeared below the horizon.

   At the same time, an astronomer is located at sea level, at the base of the Bucegi Mountains. Assume that he is in the same vertical line as the two eagles. Assuming the atmospheric refraction to be negligible,

   i. Calculate the duration of sunset, measured by the astronomer.

   ii. Calculate the duration of sunset measured by each of the two eagles?

   iii. Which of the eagles leaves the Cross first and what is the time interval between the moments of the flights of the two eagles?

   Note: Duration of sunset is defined as the time taken by the solar disk to completely disappear below the horizon, from the moment it first touched the horizon.

   (b) On the very next day, 22 March 2014, the two eagles come back to the same Cross. One of the eagles lands on the top of the vertical pillar of the Cross and the other one lands on the horizontal plateau, just at the tip of the shadow of the vertical pillar of the Cross, at the time when the shadow length is minimum.

     i. Calculate the distance between the two eagles and the second eagle's distance from the Cross.

    ii. Calculate the length of the horizontal arms of the Cross l_b, if the shadow of one of the arm of the Cross at this moment has the length $u_b = 7$ m.

(c) At midnight, the astronomer visits the Cross and, from its top, he identifies a bright star at the limit of circumpolarity. He names this star Eagles Star. If the atmospheric refraction causes the horizon to dip by $\xi = 34'$,

     i. Calculate the declination of the Eagles Star.

    ii. Calculate the maximum altitude above the horizon for the Eagles Star.

16. Christ, the Redeemer, is the most famous monument in Brazil. But there are similar statues in other Brazilian cities and across the world. Imagine that an exact copy of the monument was built on Borradaile Island, at latitude $\varphi = -66.55°$, the first place on the Antarctic circle, or to the south of it, reached by humans.

Assume that the island is exactly on the Antarctic Circle, and define a Cartesian coordinate system (O_{xy}) on the horizontal plane, with the origin O being at the base of Christ, the O_x axis in the East–West direction and the O_y axis in the North–South direction. Determine the equation of the curve described by the tip of the shadow of Christ's head on the horizontal plane on a sunny solstice day and the minimum length of the shadow during that day (neglect the motion of the Sun in declination during the day). Neglect the atmospheric effects. (I12 - T15 - C)

17. An observer in Salonika ($\varphi = 40.65°$), Greece, quietly contemplates the starry sky. Suddenly, he realizes that a very bright object ($\alpha = 5^h55^{min}$, $\delta = 7.41°$, $m = 0.45$), when reaching its upper culmination, mysteriously detaches from the celestial sphere and continues moving at the same tangential speed, remaining in this movement for all eternity. Assume that the Earth stands still and the celestial sphere rotates. Then, determine the final alt–azimuthal coordinates of the object. How long will it take for its apparent magnitude to change to 6.00? (I12 - T14 - D)

18. An astronomer in the southern hemisphere contemplates the rise of the south ecliptic pole and wonders how much fun it would be if the sky started spinning around the ecliptic pole, instead of the usual celestial pole.

Sketch the displacement of this observer over the Earth's surface, to observe the stars revolving around the south ecliptic pole in the same direction and with the same period that they usually revolve around the south celestial pole. Sketch the observer's trajectory for one entire day. Determine its velocity (direction and speed) when crossing the equator for the first time. (I12 - T13 - D)

2.2 Data Analysis

1. **Solar System objects**: A set of data containing the apparent positions of four Solar System objects over a period of 1 calendar year is given in Table 2.1. The latitude of the observing location was 18°47'0.0"N and longitude was 98°59'0.0"E.

(a) Identify objects A, B, C and D.

(b) During the period of observation, which object could be observed for the longest duration at night?

(c) What was the date corresponding to the situation in Question 1b?

(d) Assuming the orbits are coplanar (lie on the same plane) and circular, indicate the positions of the four objects and the Earth on the date in Question 1c in an orbit diagram. The answer must show one of the objects as the Sun at the centre of the Solar System. It should also mark the direction of the vernal equinox by an arrow originating from the Sun. Other objects including the Earth must be specified together with the correct values of elongation on that date.   (I07 - D03 - D)

Table 2.1

Date		Object A							Object B							Object C							Object D						
		RA			Dec				RA			Dec				RA			Dec				RA			Dec			
		h	m	s		°	'	"	h	m	s		°	'	"	h	m	s		°	'	"	h	m	s		°	'	"
Jan	1	18	44	7.11	–	23	3	11.92	9	18	19.95	+	16	30	33.13	15	28	49.55	–	15	14	51.76	15	9	15.05	–	16	57	57.2
	2	18	48	32.14	–	22	58	18.94	9	17	59.44	+	16	32	19.98	15	32	37.4	–	15	27	53.69	15	11	50.45	–	17	8	47.63
	3	18	52	56.86	–	22	52	58.47	9	17	38.28	+	16	34	9.51	15	36	27.82	–	15	40	56.32	15	14	26.14	–	17	19	30.7
	4	18	57	21.21	–	22	47	10.65	9	17	16.5	+	16	36	1.63	15	40	20.75	–	15	53	58.28	15	17	2.13	–	17	30	6.3
	5	19	1	45.16	–	22	40	55.67	9	16	54.11	+	16	37	56.27	15	44	16.12	–	16	6	58.27	15	19	38.41	–	17	40	34.32
	6	19	6	8.68	–	22	34	13.69	9	16	31.11	+	16	39	53.34	15	48	13.9	–	16	19	55	15	22	14.98	–	17	50	54.66
	7	19	10	31.74	–	22	27	4.91	9	16	7.53	+	16	41	52.72	15	52	14.02	–	16	32	47.23	15	24	51.85	–	18	1	7.23
	8	19	14	54.3	–	22	19	29.54	9	16	43.38	+	16	43	54.33	15	56	16.44	–	16	45	33.75	15	27	29.01	–	18	11	11.93
	9	19	19	16.35	–	22	11	27.82	9	15	18.68	+	16	45	58.07	16	0	21.12	–	16	58	13.38	15	30	6.46	–	18	21	8.68
	10	19	23	37.84	–	22	2	59.97	9	15	53.45	+	16	48	3.82	16	4	28.02	–	17	10	44.96	15	32	44.21	–	18	30	57.4
	11	19	27	58.77	–	20	54	6.25	9	14	27.71	+	16	50	11.49	16	8	37.09	–	17	23	7.37	15	35	22.25	–	18	40	38.02
	12	19	32	19.11	–	20	44	46.94	9	14	1.47	+	16	52	20.98	16	12	48.29	–	17	35	19.51	15	38	0.58	–	18	50	10.46
	13	19	36	38.84	–	20	35	2.3	9	14	34.75	+	16	54	32.19	16	17	1.59	–	17	47	20.2	15	40	39.21	–	18	59	34.64
	14	19	40	57.93	–	20	24	52.64	9	13	7.57	+	16	56	45.02	16	21	16.94	–	17	59	8.65	15	43	18.13	–	19	8	50.51
	15	19	45	16.37	–	20	14	18.25	9	13	39.96	+	16	58	59.62	16	25	34.31	–	18	10	43.57	15	45	57.34	–	19	17	57.99
	16	19	49	34.14	–	20	3	19.44	9	12	11.92	+	17	1	15.15	16	29	53.66	–	18	22	4.02	15	48	36.85	–	19	26	57.02
	17	19	53	51.23	–	21	51	56.52	9	12	43.49	+	17	3	32.27	16	34	14.95	–	18	33	9.01	15	51	16.65	–	19	35	47.51
	18	19	58	7.61	–	21	40	9.83	9	11	14.66	+	17	5	50.62	16	38	38.13	–	18	43	57.56	15	53	56.73	–	19	44	29.41
	19	20	2	23.28	–	21	27	59.67	9	11	45.47	+	17	8	10.11	16	43	3.17	–	18	54	28.7	15	56	37.11	–	19	53	2.63
	20	20	6	38.23	–	21	15	26.38	9	10	15.93	+	17	10	30.64	16	47	30.03	–	19	4	41.47	15	59	17.76	–	20	1	27.09
	21	20	10	52.44	–	21	2	30.27	9	9	46.06	+	17	12	52.1	16	51	58.65	–	19	14	34.95	16	1	58.7	–	20	9	42.71
	22	20	15	5.91	–	19	49	11.67	9	9	15.88	+	17	15	14.38	16	56	29.01	–	19	24	8.21	16	4	39.91	–	20	17	49.4
	23	20	19	18.63	–	19	35	30.9	9	8	45.41	+	17	17	37.36	17	1	1.06	–	19	33	20.35	16	7	21.4	–	20	25	47.08
	24	20	23	30.6	–	19	21	28.3	9	8	14.68	+	17	20	0.93	17	5	34.74	–	19	42	10.51	16	10	3.16	–	20	33	35.67
	25	20	27	41.8	–	19	7	4.21	9	7	43.7	+	17	22	24.96	17	10	10.02	–	19	50	37.83	16	12	45.19	–	20	41	15.1
	26	20	31	52.24	–	18	52	18.99	9	7	12.51	+	17	24	49.36	17	14	46.85	–	19	58	41.5	16	15	27.49	–	20	48	45.31
	27	20	36	1.91	–	18	37	13.01	9	6	41.12	+	17	27	14.01	17	19	25.16	–	20	6	20.74	16	18	10.04	–	20	56	6.22
	28	20	40	10.79	–	18	21	46.66	9	6	9.57	+	17	29	38.82	17	24	4.91	–	20	13	34.8	16	20	52.84	–	21	3	17.77
	29	20	44	18.87	–	18	6	0.34	9	5	37.86	+	17	32	3.69	17	28	46.04	–	20	20	2.93	16	23	35.88	–	21	10	19.89

Date	Object A RA h	m	s	Object A Dec	°	'	"	Object B RA h	m	s	Object B Dec	°	'	"	Object C RA h	m	s	Object C Dec	°	'	"	Object D RA h	m	s	Object D Dec	°	'	"
30	20	48	26.19	–	17	49	54.45	9	5	6.03	+	17	34	28.52	17	33	28.49	–	20	26	44.44	16	26	19.15	–	21	17	12.5
31	20	52	32.68	–	17	33	29.39	9	4	34.1	+	17	36	53.21	17	38	12.21	–	20	32	38.66	16	29	2.65	–	21	23	55.54
Feb 1	20	56	38.36	–	17	16	45.58	9	4	2.1	+	17	39	17.64	17	42	57.13	–	20	38	4.93	16	31	46.35	–	21	30	28.92
2	21	0	43.22	–	16	59	43.43	9	3	30.03	+	17	41	41.7	17	47	43.19	–	20	43	2.65	16	34	30.26	–	21	36	52.57
3	21	4	47.25	–	16	42	23.36	9	2	57.94	+	17	44	5.28	17	52	30.35	–	20	47	31.23	16	37	14.36	–	21	43	6.44
4	21	8	50.46	–	16	24	45.77	9	2	25.85	+	17	46	28.25	17	57	18.54	–	20	51	30.12	16	39	58.66	–	21	49	10.46
5	21	12	52.84	–	16	6	51.09	9	1	53.78	+	17	48	50.51	18	2	7.72	–	20	54	58.81	16	42	43.13	–	21	55	4.57
6	21	16	54.4	–	15	48	39.75	9	1	21.76	+	17	51	11.93	18	6	57.82	–	20	57	56.81	16	45	27.79	–	22	0	48.74
7	21	20	55.14	–	15	30	12.16	8	0	49.82	+	17	53	32.4	18	11	48.8	–	21	0	23.68	16	48	12.63	–	22	6	22.92
8	21	24	55.06	–	15	11	28.75	8	0	17.97	+	17	55	51.84	18	16	40.61	–	21	2	19	16	50	57.63	–	22	11	47.07
9	21	28	54.18	–	14	52	29.96	8	59	46.26	+	17	58	10.13	18	21	33.18	–	21	3	42.39	16	53	42.8	–	22	17	1.17
10	21	32	52.49	–	14	33	16.2	8	59	14.69	+	18	0	27.18	18	26	26.46	–	21	4	33.49	16	56	28.13	–	22	22	5.19
11	21	36	50	–	14	13	47.91	8	58	43.29	+	18	2	42.91	18	31	20.41	–	21	4	51.99	16	59	13.62	–	22	26	59.09
12	21	40	46.73	–	13	54	5.52	8	58	12.1	+	18	4	57.23	18	36	14.96	–	21	4	37.58	17	1	59.26	–	22	31	42.86
13	21	44	42.68	–	13	34	9.45	8	57	41.12	+	18	7	10.05	18	41	10.07	–	21	3	49.99	17	4	45.04	–	22	36	16.48
14	21	48	37.86	–	13	14	0.13	8	57	10.38	+	18	9	21.31	18	46	5.67	–	21	2	29.01	17	7	30.95	–	22	40	39.92
15	21	52	32.29	–	12	53	37.99	8	56	39.9	+	18	11	30.93	18	51	1.73	–	21	0	34.4	17	10	17	–	22	44	53.15
16	21	56	25.98	–	12	33	3.42	8	56	9.7	+	18	13	38.84	18	55	58.17	–	20	58	5.99	17	13	3.17	–	22	48	56.15
17	22	0	18.94	–	12	12	16.82	8	55	39.79	+	18	15	44.94	19	0	54.95	–	20	55	3.6	17	15	49.46	–	22	52	48.88
18	22	4	11.2	–	11	51	18.6	8	55	10.21	+	18	17	49.18	19	5	52.02	–	20	51	27.1	17	18	35.86	–	22	56	31.32
19	22	8	2.76	–	11	30	9.12	8	54	40.97	+	18	19	51.45	19	10	49.33	–	20	47	16.36	17	21	22.36	–	23	0	3.42
20	22	11	53.65	–	11	8	48.75	8	54	12.08	+	18	21	51.69	19	15	46.83	–	20	42	31.31	17	24	8.96	–	23	3	25.17
21	22	15	43.89	–	10	47	17.87	8	53	43.58	+	18	23	49.81	19	20	44.46	–	20	37	11.89	17	26	55.66	–	23	6	36.54
22	22	19	33.5	–	10	25	36.85	8	53	15.48	+	18	25	45.76	19	25	42.17	–	20	31	18.08	17	29	42.44	–	23	9	37.52
23	22	23	22.49	–	10	3	46.09	8	52	47.81	+	18	27	39.46	19	30	39.93	–	20	24	49.93	17	32	29.29	–	23	12	28.11
24	22	27	10.89	–	9	41	45.98	8	52	20.58	+	18	29	30.88	19	35	37.65	–	20	17	47.49	17	35	16.21	–	23	15	8.29
25	22	30	58.7	–	9	19	36.93	8	51	53.82	+	18	31	19.96	19	40	35.31	–	20	10	10.87	17	38	3.17	–	23	17	38.08
26	22	34	45.95	–	8	57	19.35	8	51	27.53	+	18	33	6.66	19	45	32.84	–	20	2	0.17	17	40	50.17	–	23	19	57.46
27	22	38	32.64	–	8	34	53.67	8	51	1.75	+	18	34	50.93	19	50	30.18	–	19	53	15.57	17	43	37.18	–	23	22	6.42
28	22	42	18.78	–	8	12	20.29	8	50	36.47	+	18	36	32.71	19	55	27.29	–	19	43	57.23	17	46	24.21	–	23	24	4.97

Date	Object A RA h	m	s	Object A Dec	°	'	"	Object B RA h	m	s	Object B Dec	°	'	"	Object C RA h	m	s	Object C Dec	°	'	"	Object D RA h	m	s	Object D Dec	°	'	"
Mar 1	22	46	4.4	−	7	49	39.63	8	50	11.73	+	18	38	11.96	20	0	24.12	−	19	34	5.36	17	49	11.22	−	23	25	53.1
2	22	49	49.5	−	7	26	52.12	8	49	47.54	+	18	39	48.61	20	5	20.63	−	19	23	40.19	17	51	58.21	−	23	27	30.81
3	22	53	34.1	−	7	1	58.15	8	49	23.91	+	18	41	22.6	20	10	16.76	−	19	12	41.98	17	54	45.18	−	23	28	58.1
4	22	57	18.21	−	6	40	58.15	8	49	0.86	+	18	42	53.9	20	15	12.49	−	19	1	10.99	17	57	32.1	−	23	30	14.99
5	23	1	1.85	−	6	17	52.52	8	48	38.41	+	18	44	22.44	20	20	7.76	−	18	49	7.55	18	0	18.98	−	23	31	21.49
6	23	4	45.05	−	5	54	41.66	8	48	16.58	+	18	45	48.18	20	25	2.56	−	18	36	31.97	18	3	5.79	−	23	32	17.62
7	23	8	27.8	−	5	31	26	8	47	55.38	+	18	47	11.08	20	29	56.84	−	18	23	24.62	18	5	52.54	−	23	33	3.42
8	23	12	10.14	−	5	8	5.92	8	47	34.81	+	18	48	31.12	20	34	50.58	−	18	9	45.85	18	8	39.21	−	23	33	38.92
9	23	15	52.09	−	4	44	41.83	8	47	14.91	+	18	49	48.26	20	39	43.75	−	17	55	36.07	18	11	25.8	−	23	34	4.16
10	23	19	33.65	−	4	21	14.14	8	46	55.67	+	18	51	2.48	20	44	36.31	−	17	40	55.69	18	14	12.3	−	23	34	19.18
11	23	23	14.85	−	3	57	43.23	8	46	37.11	+	18	52	13.76	20	49	28.26	−	17	25	45.14	18	16	58.7	−	23	34	24.04
12	23	26	55.71	−	3	34	9.51	8	46	19.24	+	18	53	22.09	20	54	19.56	−	17	10	4.87	18	19	44.98	−	23	34	18.77
13	23	30	36.25	−	3	10	33.37	8	46	2.06	+	18	54	27.45	20	59	10.2	−	16	53	55.33	18	22	31.16	−	23	34	3.43
14	23	34	16.48	−	2	46	55.19	8	45	45.59	+	18	55	29.83	21	4	0.16	−	16	37	17.01	18	25	17.21	−	23	33	38.06
15	23	37	56.43	−	2	23	15.36	8	45	29.83	+	18	56	29.24	21	8	49.43	−	16	20	10.37	18	28	3.12	−	23	33	2.71
16	23	41	36.11	−	1	59	34.24	8	45	14.78	+	18	57	25.64	21	13	37.99	−	16	2	35.92	18	30	45.89	−	23	32	17.43
17	23	45	15.56	−	1	35	52.2	8	45	0.46	+	18	58	19.04	21	18	25.83	−	15	44	34.15	18	33	34.52	−	23	31	22.25
18	23	48	54.79	−	1	12	9.57	8	44	46.86	+	18	59	9.41	21	23	12.94	−	15	26	5.54	18	36	19.99	−	23	30	17.22
19	23	52	33.84	−	0	48	26.7	8	44	33.99	+	18	59	56.73	21	27	59.33	−	15	7	10.62	18	39	5.3	−	23	29	2.37
20	23	56	12.72	−	0	24	43.88	8	44	21.87	+	19	0	40.98	21	32	44.99	−	14	47	49.88	18	41	50.44	−	23	27	37.75
21	23	59	51.47	−	0	1	1.44	8	44	10.49	+	19	1	22.16	21	37	29.92	−	14	28	3.87	18	44	35.4	−	23	26	3.42
22	0	3	30.11	+	0	22	40.3	8	43	59.87	+	19	2	0.26	21	42	14.12	−	14	7	53.13	18	47	20.18	−	23	24	19.45
23	0	7	8.67	+	0	46	21.01	8	43	50.01	+	19	2	35.3	21	46	57.6	−	13	47	18.24	18	50	4.77	−	23	22	25.91
24	0	10	47.16	+	1	10	0.35	8	43	40.91	+	19	3	7.28	21	51	40.34	−	13	26	19.81	18	52	49.14	−	23	20	22.9
25	0	14	25.62	+	1	33	37.96	8	43	32.58	+	19	3	36.21	21	56	22.35	−	13	4	58.42	18	55	33.28	−	23	18	10.49
26	0	18	4.04	+	1	57	13.49	8	43	25.02	+	19	4	2.11	22	1	3.63	−	12	43	14.71	18	58	17.19	−	23	15	48.76
27	0	21	42.46	+	2	20	46.55	8	43	18.22	+	19	4	24.97	22	5	44.17	−	12	21	9.3	19	1	0.43	−	23	13	17.8
28	0	25	20.89	+	2	44	16.79	8	43	12.2	+	19	4	44.79	22	10	24	−	11	58	42.81	19	3	44.29	−	23	10	37.68
29	0	28	59.35	+	3	7	43.84	8	43	6.96	+	19	5	1.56	22	15	3.1	−	11	35	55.88	19	6	27.17	−	23	7	48.5

Date	Object A RA h	m	s	Dec	°	'	"	Object B RA h	m	s	Dec	°	'	"	Object C RA h	m	s	Dec	°	'	"	Object D RA h	m	s	Dec	°	'	"
30	0	32	37.85	+	3	31	7.33	8	43	2.49	+	19	5	15.27	22	19	41.49	–	11	12	49.15	19	9	10.05	–	23	4	50.33
31	0	36	16.42	+	3	54	26.88	8	42	58.8	+	19	5	25.92	22	24	19.18	–	10	49	23.26	19	11	52.52	–	23	1	43.26
Apr 1	0	39	55.06	+	4	17	42.14	8	42	55.89	+	19	5	33.51	22	28	56.18	–	10	25	38.84	19	14	34.66	–	22	58	27.4
2	0	43	33.8	+	4	40	52.73	8	42	53.76	+	19	5	38.03	22	33	32.51	–	10	1	36.56	19	17	16.48	–	22	55	2.85
3	0	47	12.66	+	5	3	58.29	8	42	52.42	+	19	5	39.49	22	38	8.18	–	9	37	17.06	19	19	57.94	–	22	51	29.71
4	0	50	51.65	+	5	26	58.45	8	42	51.87	+	19	5	37.89	22	42	43.21	–	9	12	41	19	22	39.06	–	22	47	48.1
5	0	54	30.79	+	5	49	52.85	8	42	52.09	+	19	5	33.23	22	47	17.62	–	8	47	49.03	19	25	19.82	–	22	43	58.13
6	0	58	10.09	+	6	12	41.12	8	42	53.1	+	19	5	25.55	22	51	51.42	–	8	22	41.81	19	28	0.21	–	22	39	59.92
7	1	1	49.58	+	6	35	22.91	8	42	54.89	+	19	5	14.84	22	56	24.65	–	7	57	20.01	19	30	40.22	–	22	35	53.61
8	1	5	29.26	+	6	57	57.84	8	42	57.46	+	19	5	1.14	23	0	57.33	–	7	31	44.3	19	33	19.85	–	22	31	39.3
9	1	9	9.15	+	7	20	25.56	8	43	0.8	+	19	4	44.45	23	5	29.47	–	7	5	55.32	19	35	59.08	–	22	27	17.12
10	1	12	49.27	+	7	42	45.71	8	43	4.91	+	19	4	24.8	23	10	1.1	–	6	39	53.75	19	38	37.92	–	22	22	47.21
11	1	16	29.64	+	8	4	57.93	8	43	9.78	+	19	4	2.21	23	14	32.25	–	6	13	40.24	19	41	16.34	–	22	18	9.68
12	1	20	10.26	+	8	27	1.87	8	43	15.41	+	19	3	36.69	23	19	2.94	–	5	47	15.46	19	43	54.35	–	22	13	24.66
13	1	23	51.15	+	8	48	57.18	8	43	21.79	+	19	3	8.26	23	23	33.21	–	5	20	40.04	19	46	31.94	–	22	8	32.25
14	1	27	32.34	+	9	10	43.54	8	43	28.92	+	19	2	36.92	23	28	3.08	–	4	53	54.64	19	49	9.1	–	22	3	32.58
15	1	31	13.84	+	9	32	20.62	8	43	36.79	+	19	2	2.68	23	32	32.59	–	4	26	59.89	19	51	45.83	–	21	58	25.75
16	1	34	55.67	+	9	53	48.12	8	43	45.39	+	19	1	25.55	23	37	1.77	–	3	59	56.4	19	54	22.12	–	21	53	11.88
17	1	38	37.86	+	10	15	5.74	8	43	54.74	+	19	0	45.53	23	41	30.67	–	3	32	44.81	19	56	57.97	–	21	47	51.08
18	1	42	20.43	+	10	36	13.21	8	44	4.81	+	19	0	2.63	23	45	59.3	–	3	5	25.74	19	59	33.37	–	21	42	23.48
19	1	46	3.4	+	10	57	10.23	8	44	15.61	+	18	59	16.88	23	50	27.72	–	2	37	59.82	20	2	8.32	–	21	36	49.23
20	1	49	46.78	+	11	17	56.52	8	44	27.13	+	18	58	28.31	23	54	55.96	–	2	10	27.7	20	4	42.8	–	21	31	8.5
21	1	53	30.59	+	11	38	31.75	8	44	39.37	+	18	57	36.95	23	59	24.03	–	1	42	50.04	20	7	16.8	–	21	25	21.46
22	1	57	14.85	+	11	58	55.62	8	44	52.32	+	18	56	42.83	0	3	51.99	–	1	15	7.53	20	9	50.29	–	21	19	28.26
23	2	0	59.56	+	12	19	7.78	8	45	5.97	+	18	55	45.95	0	8	19.85	–	0	47	20.83	20	12	23.27	–	21	13	29.09
24	2	4	44.74	+	12	39	7.91	8	45	20.32	+	18	54	46.34	0	12	47.66	–	0	19	30.64	20	14	55.72	–	21	7	24.09
25	2	8	30.4	+	12	58	55.66	8	45	35.36	+	18	53	43.99	0	17	15.43	+	0	8	22.38	20	17	27.62	–	21	1	13.45
26	2	12	16.55	+	13	18	30.69	8	45	51.08	+	18	52	38.91	0	21	43.22	+	0	36	17.55	20	19	58.95	–	20	54	57.33
27	2	16	3.2	+	13	37	52.67	8	46	7.49	+	18	51	31.11	0	26	11.04	+	1	4	14.18	20	22	29.72	–	20	48	35.9

Date	A RA h	A RA m	A RA s	A Dec	°	'	"	B RA h	B RA m	B RA s	B Dec	°	'	"	C RA h	C RA m	C RA s	C Dec	°	'	"	D RA h	D RA m	D RA s	D Dec	°	'	"
				Object A							Object B							Object C							Object D			
28	2	19	50.36	+	13	57	1.25	8	46	24.57	+	18	50	20.59	0	30	38.93	+	1	32	11.59	20	24	59.89	−	20	42	9.34
29	2	23	38.04	+	14	15	56.1	8	46	42.32	+	18	49	7.35	0	35	6.93	+	2	0	9.11	20	27	29.47	−	20	35	37.83
30	2	27	26.24	+	14	34	36.89	8	47	0.73	+	18	47	51.44	0	39	35.07	+	2	28	6.06	20	29	58.44	−	20	29	1.56
May 1	2	31	14.97	+	14	53	3.27	8	47	19.81	+	18	46	32.78	0	44	3.39	+	2	56	1.76	20	32	26.79	−	20	22	20.7
2	2	35	4.24	+	15	11	14.92	8	47	39.54	+	18	45	11.47	0	48	31.92	+	3	23	55.52	20	34	54.51	−	20	15	35.46
3	2	38	54.04	+	15	29	11.5	8	47	59.91	+	18	43	47.5	0	53	0.7	+	3	51	46.66	20	37	21.59	−	20	8	46.02
4	2	42	44.4	+	15	46	52.68	8	48	20.93	+	18	42	20.9	0	57	29.76	+	4	19	34.49	20	39	48.02	−	20	1	52.59
5	2	46	35.29	+	16	4	18.13	8	48	42.57	+	18	40	51.68	1	1	59.13	+	4	47	18.32	20	42	13.78	−	19	54	55.36
6	2	50	26.74	+	16	21	27.53	8	49	4.85	+	18	39	19.87	1	6	28.84	+	5	14	57.48	20	44	38.88	−	19	47	54.52
7	2	54	18.73	+	16	38	20.54	8	49	27.73	+	18	37	45.49	1	10	58.94	+	5	42	31.26	20	47	3.3	−	19	40	50.29
8	2	58	11.28	+	16	54	56.85	8	49	51.22	+	18	36	8.56	1	15	29.46	+	6	9	58.98	20	49	27.03	−	19	33	42.84
9	3	2	4.37	+	17	11	16.13	8	50	15.31	+	18	34	29.11	1	20	0.42	+	6	37	19.94	20	51	50.07	−	19	26	32.37
10	3	5	58.01	+	17	27	18.08	8	50	39.98	+	18	32	47.15	1	24	31.86	+	7	4	33.46	20	54	12.4	−	19	19	19.06
11	3	9	52.2	+	17	43	2.38	8	51	5.23	+	18	31	2.69	1	29	3.82	+	7	31	38.86	20	56	34.02	−	19	12	3.1
12	3	13	46.94	+	17	58	28.74	8	51	31.05	+	18	29	15.74	1	33	36.34	+	7	58	35.45	20	58	54.92	−	19	4	44.67
13	3	17	42.23	+	18	13	36.88	8	51	57.43	+	18	27	26.31	1	38	9.44	+	8	25	22.56	21	1	15.09	−	18	57	23.93
14	3	21	38.08	+	18	28	26.53	8	52	24.37	+	18	25	34.4	1	42	43.17	+	8	51	59.54	21	3	34.54	−	18	50	1.05
15	3	25	34.5	+	18	42	57.44	8	52	51.86	+	18	23	40.03	1	47	17.56	+	9	18	25.71	21	5	53.25	−	18	42	36.24
16	3	29	31.48	+	18	57	9.38	8	53	19.9	+	18	21	43.22	1	51	52.65	+	9	44	40.42	21	8	11.21	−	18	35	9.67
17	3	33	29.03	+	19	11	2.1	8	53	48.47	+	18	19	43.99	1	56	28.48	+	10	10	43.01	21	10	28.42	−	18	27	41.59
18	3	37	27.14	+	19	24	35.38	8	54	17.57	+	18	17	42.38	2	1	5.07	+	10	36	32.8	21	12	44.86	−	18	20	12.21
19	3	41	25.83	+	19	37	48.97	8	54	47.19	+	18	15	38.42	2	5	42.45	+	11	2	9.08	21	15	0.5	−	18	12	41.8
20	3	45	25.08	+	19	50	42.62	8	55	17.32	+	18	13	32.12	2	10	20.66	+	11	37	31.17	21	17	15.33	−	18	5	10.59
21	3	49	24.89	+	20	3	16.07	8	55	47.96	+	18	11	23.5	2	14	59.71	+	11	52	38.33	21	19	29.32	−	17	57	38.86
22	3	53	25.25	+	20	15	29.06	8	56	19.09	+	18	9	12.58	2	19	39.64	+	12	17	29.86	21	21	42.45	−	17	50	6.84
23	3	57	26.15	+	20	27	21.33	8	56	50.72	+	18	6	59.34	2	24	20.47	+	12	42	5.04	21	23	54.7	−	17	42	34.8
24	4	1	27.59	+	20	38	52.62	8	57	22.82	+	18	4	43.81	2	29	2.22	+	13	6	23.14	21	26	6.05	−	17	35	2.99
25	4	5	29.56	+	20	50	2.7	8	57	55.4	+	18	2	25.97	2	33	44.92	+	13	30	23.45	21	28	16.48	−	17	27	31.68

Date	Object A RA h	m	s	Dec °	'	"	Object B RA h	m	s	Dec	°	'	"	Object C RA h	m	s	Dec	°	'	"	Object D RA h	m	s	Dec	°	'	"
26	4	9	32.05	+	21	0	51.32	8	58	28.46	+	18	0	5.83	2	38	28.59	+	13	54	5.26	21	30	25.98	−	17	20	1.12
27	4	13	35.04	+	21	11	18.24	8	59	1.98	+	17	57	43.41	2	43	13.25	+	14	17	27.84	21	32	34.51	−	17	12	31.58
28	4	17	38.53	+	21	21	23.24	8	59	35.96	+	17	55	18.72	2	47	58.92	+	14	40	30.47	21	34	42.07	−	17	5	3.34
29	4	21	42.5	+	21	31	6.09	9	0	10.39	+	17	52	51.77	2	52	45.61	+	15	3	12.46	21	36	48.63	−	16	57	36.65
30	4	25	46.93	+	21	40	26.59	9	0	45.28	+	17	50	22.57	2	57	33.34	+	15	25	33.06	21	38	54.17	−	16	50	11.81
31	4	29	51.8	+	21	49	24.51	9	1	20.6	+	17	47	51.15	3	2	22.13	+	15	47	31.59	21	40	58.68	−	16	42	49.07
Jun 1	4	33	57.1	+	21	57	59.68	9	1	56.35	+	17	45	17.13	3	7	11.98	+	16	9	7.31	21	43	2.13	−	16	35	28.73
2	4	38	2.81	+	22	6	11.87	9	2	32.52	+	17	42	41.73	3	12	2.9	+	16	30	19.52	21	45	4.51	−	16	28	11.04
3	4	42	8.91	+	22	14	0.93	9	3	9.12	+	17	40	3.77	3	16	54.91	+	16	51	7.5	21	47	5.79	−	16	20	56.3
4	4	46	15.36	+	22	21	26.65	9	3	46.11	+	17	37	23.68	3	21	48	+	17	11	30.56	21	49	5.95	−	16	13	44.76
5	4	50	22.16	+	22	28	28.87	9	4	23.51	+	17	34	41.47	3	26	42.19	+	17	31	27.98	21	51	4.99	−	16	6	36.69
6	4	54	29.28	+	22	35	7.43	9	5	1.29	+	17	31	57.18	3	31	37.47	+	17	50	59.07	21	53	2.87	−	15	59	32.35
7	4	58	36.7	+	22	41	22.17	9	5	39.45	+	17	29	10.8	3	36	33.84	+	18	10	3.13	21	54	59.58	−	15	52	31.99
8	5	2	44.39	+	22	47	12.95	9	6	17.99	+	17	26	22.36	3	41	31.31	+	18	28	39.49	21	56	55.1	−	15	45	35.85
9	5	6	52.34	+	22	52	39.64	9	6	56.89	+	17	23	31.85	3	46	29.88	+	18	46	47.46	21	58	49.43	−	15	38	44.17
10	5	11	0.53	+	22	57	42.13	9	7	36.15	+	17	20	39.29	3	51	29.53	+	19	4	26.41	22	0	42.53	−	15	31	57.19
11	5	15	8.94	+	23	2	20.32	9	8	15.76	+	17	17	44.69	3	56	30.29	+	19	21	35.68	22	2	34.39	−	15	25	15.14
12	5	19	17.55	+	23	6	34.15	9	8	55.72	+	17	14	48.06	4	1	32.13	+	19	38	14.65	22	4	25	−	15	18	38.29
13	5	23	26.35	+	23	10	23.54	9	9	36.03	+	17	11	49.44	4	6	35.05	+	19	54	22.73	22	6	14.33	−	15	12	6.89
14	5	27	35.32	+	23	13	48.45	9	10	16.67	+	17	8	48.83	4	11	39.04	+	20	9	59.29	22	8	2.35	−	15	5	41.24
15	5	31	44.44	+	23	16	48.84	9	10	57.64	+	17	5	46.29	4	16	44.09	+	20	25	3.75	22	9	49.04	−	14	59	21.66
16	5	35	53.69	+	23	19	24.66	9	11	38.93	+	17	2	41.84	4	21	50.19	+	20	39	35.51	22	11	34.35	−	14	53	8.46
17	5	40	3.05	+	23	21	35.85	9	12	20.54	+	16	59	35.5	4	26	57.3	+	20	53	33.97	22	13	18.26	−	14	47	1.99
18	5	44	12.5	+	23	23	22.38	9	13	2.45	+	16	56	27.27	4	32	5.42	+	21	6	58.55	22	15	0.71	−	14	41	2.58
19	5	48	22.02	+	23	24	44.18	9	13	44.66	+	16	53	17.18	4	37	14.51	+	21	19	48.68	22	16	41.68	−	14	35	10.59
20	5	52	31.58	+	23	25	41.23	9	14	27.17	+	16	50	5.22	4	42	24.56	+	21	32	3.79	22	18	21.11	−	14	29	26.35
21	5	56	41.18	+	23	26	13.51	9	15	9.96	+	16	46	51.39	4	47	35.53	+	21	43	43.34	22	19	58.98	−	14	23	50.21

Date	Object A RA h	m	s	Dec	°	'	"	Object B RA h	m	s	Dec	°	'	"	Object C RA h	m	s	Dec	°	'	"	Object D RA h	m	s	Dec	°	'	"
22	6	0	50.78	+	23	26	20.99	9	15	53.04	+	16	43	35.7	4	52	47.4	+	21	54	46.83	22	21	35.25	−	14	18	22.51
23	6	5	0.37	+	23	26	3.67	9	16	36.41	+	16	40	18.16	4	58	0.13	+	22	5	13.74	22	23	9.86	−	14	13	3.58
24	6	9	9.91	+	23	25	21.57	9	17	20.04	+	16	36	58.79	5	3	13.69	+	22	15	3.59	22	24	42.79	−	14	7	53.78
25	6	13	19.39	+	23	24	14.7	9	18	3.95	+	16	33	37.59	5	8	28.04	+	22	24	15.94	22	26	13.98	−	14	2	53.44
26	6	17	28.78	+	23	22	43.09	9	18	48.13	+	16	30	14.59	5	13	43.14	+	22	32	50.35	22	27	43.41	−	13	58	2.89
27	6	21	38.05	+	23	20	46.79	9	19	32.57	+	16	26	49.8	5	18	58.94	+	22	40	46.4	22	29	11.03	−	13	53	22.48
28	6	25	47.19	+	23	18	25.86	9	20	17.26	+	16	23	23.25	5	24	15.41	+	22	48	3.72	22	30	36.8	−	13	48	52.53
29	6	29	56.15	+	23	15	40.35	9	21	2.2	+	16	19	54.96	5	29	32.5	+	22	54	41.93	22	32	0.68	−	13	44	33.36
30	6	34	4.92	+	23	12	30.34	9	21	47.38	+	16	16	24.96	5	34	50.15	+	23	0	40.69	22	33	22.62	−	13	40	25.3
Jul 1	6	38	13.47	+	23	8	55.91	9	22	32.79	+	16	12	53.27	5	40	8.32	+	23	5	59.7	22	34	42.59	−	13	36	28.63
2	6	42	21.77	+	23	4	57.16	9	23	18.42	+	16	9	19.92	5	45	26.95	+	23	10	38.66	22	36	0.54	−	13	32	43.65
3	6	46	29.79	+	23	0	34.18	9	24	4.28	+	16	5	44.94	5	50	45.98	+	23	14	37.31	22	37	16.44	−	13	29	10.63
4	6	50	37.51	+	22	55	47.09	9	24	50.34	+	16	2	8.33	5	56	5.37	+	23	17	55.4	22	38	30.24	−	13	25	49.82
5	6	54	44.9	+	22	50	36	9	25	36.61	+	15	58	30.12	6	1	25.06	+	23	20	32.74	22	39	41.92	−	13	22	41.46
6	6	58	51.94	+	22	45	1.04	9	26	23.08	+	15	54	50.31	6	6	44.99	+	23	22	29.14	22	40	51.43	−	13	19	45.76
7	7	2	58.61	+	22	39	2.35	9	27	9.74	+	15	51	8.92	6	12	5.12	+	23	23	44.46	22	41	58.74	−	13	17	2.93
8	7	7	4.9	+	22	32	40.08	9	27	36.39	+	15	47	25.97	6	17	25.38	+	23	24	18.59	22	43	3.82	−	13	14	33.16
9	7	11	10.78	+	22	25	54.41	9	28	43.62	+	15	43	41.46	6	22	45.73	+	23	24	11.45	22	44	6.62	−	13	12	16.65
10	7	15	16.25	+	22	18	45.52	9	29	30.84	+	15	39	55.43	6	28	6.12	+	23	23	23	22	45	7.12	−	13	10	13.6
11	7	19	21.28	+	22	11	13.58	9	30	18.23	+	15	36	7.9	6	33	26.48	+	23	21	53.24	22	46	5.27	−	13	8	24.21
12	7	23	25.86	+	22	3	18.81	9	31	5.8	+	15	32	18.91	6	38	46.77	+	23	19	42.18	22	47	1.02	−	13	6	48.71
13	7	27	29.99	+	21	55	1.4	9	31	53.52	+	15	28	28.48	6	44	6.94	+	23	16	49.88	22	47	54.32	−	13	5	27.32
14	7	31	33.64	+	21	46	21.54	9	32	41.41	+	15	24	36.66	6	49	26.92	+	23	13	16.39	22	48	45.13	−	13	4	20.27
15	7	35	36.82	+	21	37	19.43	9	33	29.44	+	15	20	43.45	6	54	46.66	+	23	9	1.81	22	49	33.38	−	13	3	27.81
16	7	39	39.5	+	21	27	55.24	9	34	17.62	+	15	16	48.88	7	0	6.11	+	23	4	6.24	22	50	19.03	−	13	2	50.15
17	7	43	41.67	+	21	18	9.18	9	35	5.94	+	15	12	52.95	7	5	25.23	+	22	58	29.81	22	51	2.01	−	13	2	27.5
18	7	47	43.34	+	21	8	1.43	9	35	54.39	+	15	8	55.67	7	10	43.96	+	22	52	12.7	22	51	42.27	−	13	2	20.04
19	7	51	44.49	+	20	57	32.21	9	36	42.98	+	15	4	57.05	7	16	2.25	+	22	45	15.08	22	52	19.77	−	13	2	27.93

Date	Object A RA h	m	s	Dec °	'	"	Object B RA h	m	s	Dec °	'	"	Object C RA h	m	s	Dec °	'	"	Object D RA h	m	s	Dec °	'	"
20	7	55	45.12	+ 20	46	41.72	9	37	31.7	+ 15	0	57.1	7	21	20.06	+ 22	37	37.2	22	52	54.45	− 13	2	51.3
21	7	59	45.21	+ 20	35	30.18	9	38	20.55	+ 14	56	55.83	7	26	37.34	+ 22	29	19.3	22	53	26.26	− 13	3	30.26
22	8	3	44.77	+ 20	23	57.84	9	39	9.52	+ 14	52	53.26	7	31	54.04	+ 22	20	21.68	22	53	55.16	− 13	4	24.88
23	8	7	43.77	+ 20	12	4.93	9	39	58.61	+ 14	48	49.41	7	37	10.12	+ 22	10	44.64	22	54	21.11	− 13	5	35.2
24	8	11	42.22	+ 19	59	51.7	9	40	47.82	+ 14	44	44.3	7	42	25.54	+ 22	0	28.53	22	54	44.07	− 13	7	1.22
25	8	15	40.1	+ 19	47	18.4	9	41	37.14	+ 14	40	37.96	7	47	40.25	+ 21	49	33.7	22	55	4	− 13	8	42.9
26	8	19	37.41	+ 19	34	25.29	9	42	26.56	+ 14	36	30.42	7	52	54.21	+ 21	38	0.57	22	55	20.87	− 13	10	40.18
27	8	23	34.14	+ 19	21	12.66	9	43	16.08	+ 14	32	21.71	7	58	7.38	+ 21	25	49.54	22	55	34.65	− 13	12	52.91
28	8	27	30.27	+ 19	7	40.77	9	44	5.69	+ 14	28	11.86	8	3	19.73	+ 21	13	1.05	22	55	45.32	− 13	15	20.93
29	8	31	25.81	+ 18	53	49.9	9	44	55.4	+ 14	24	0.89	8	8	31.22	+ 20	59	35.56	22	55	52.86	− 13	18	4
30	8	35	20.74	+ 18	39	40.35	9	45	45.18	+ 14	19	48.84	8	13	41.81	+ 20	45	33.56	22	55	57.26	− 13	21	1.84
31	8	39	15.06	+ 18	25	12.39	9	46	35.03	+ 14	15	35.74	8	18	51.48	+ 20	30	55.54	22	55	58.52	− 13	24	14.08
Aug 1	8	43	8.76	+ 18	10	26.33	9	47	24.95	+ 14	11	21.59	8	24	0.19	+ 20	15	42.02	22	55	56.64	− 13	27	40.32
2	8	47	1.84	+ 17	55	22.45	9	48	14.94	+ 14	7	6.44	8	29	7.91	+ 19	59	53.53	22	55	51.64	− 13	31	20.07
3	8	50	54.29	+ 17	40	1.05	9	49	4.99	+ 14	2	50.28	8	34	14.63	+ 19	43	30.62	22	55	43.53	− 13	35	12.8
4	8	54	46.12	+ 17	24	22.44	9	49	55.09	+ 13	58	33.13	8	39	20.33	+ 19	26	33.86	22	55	32.34	− 13	39	17.94
5	8	58	37.32	+ 17	8	26.93	9	50	45.24	+ 13	54	15.03	8	44	25	+ 19	9	3.84	22	55	18.1	− 13	43	34.86
6	9	2	27.91	+ 16	52	14.82	9	51	35.45	+ 13	49	55.99	8	49	28.61	+ 18	51	1.16	22	55	0.85	− 13	48	2.92
7	9	6	17.88	+ 16	35	46.45	9	52	25.69	+ 13	45	36.05	8	54	31.15	+ 18	32	26.44	22	54	40.61	− 13	52	41.44
8	9	10	7.24	+ 16	19	2.11	9	53	15.98	+ 13	41	15.25	8	59	32.63	+ 18	13	20.32	22	54	17.45	− 13	57	29.74
9	9	13	55.99	+ 16	2	2.14	9	54	6.31	+ 13	36	53.62	9	4	33.03	+ 17	53	43.44	22	53	51.39	− 14	2	27.11
10	9	17	44.15	+ 15	44	46.84	9	54	56.66	+ 13	32	31.19	9	9	32.34	+ 17	33	36.45	22	53	22.49	− 14	7	32.82
11	9	21	31.73	+ 15	27	16.5	9	55	47.03	+ 13	28	8.01	9	14	30.57	+ 17	13	0	22	52	50.79	− 14	12	46.1
12	9	25	18.72	+ 15	9	31.42	9	56	37.42	+ 13	23	44.09	9	19	27.72	+ 16	51	54.74	22	52	16.36	− 14	18	6.17
13	9	29	5.14	+ 14	51	31.88	9	57	27.83	+ 13	19	19.45	9	24	23.78	+ 16	30	21.33	22	51	39.27	− 14	23	32.2
14	9	32	51.01	+ 14	33	18.17	9	58	18.25	+ 13	14	54.1	9	29	18.76	+ 16	8	20.42	22	50	59.57	− 14	29	3.32
15	9	36	36.34	+ 14	14	50.55	9	59	8.67	+ 13	10	28.06	9	34	12.68	+ 15	45	52.67	22	50	17.36	− 14	34	38.62
16	9	40	21.14	+ 13	56	9.33	9	59	59.1	+ 13	6	1.35	9	39	5.55	+ 15	22	58.76	22	49	32.73	− 14	40	17.15

Date	Object A RA h	m	s	Object A Dec	°	'	"	Object B RA h	m	s	Object B Dec	°	'	"	Object C RA h	m	s	Object C Dec	°	'	"	Object D RA h	m	s	Object D Dec	°	'	"
17	9	44	5.43	+	13	37	14.77	10	0	49.53	+	13	1	33.97	9	43	57.37	+	14	59	39.37	22	48	45.78	−	14	45	57.91
18	9	47	49.22	+	13	18	7.19	10	1	39.97	+	12	57	5.95	9	48	48.16	+	14	35	55.16	22	47	56.61	−	14	51	39.88
19	9	51	32.51	+	12	58	46.88	10	2	30.4	+	12	52	37.33	9	53	37.94	+	14	11	46.85	22	47	5.36	−	14	57	22.01
20	9	55	15.33	+	12	39	14.15	10	3	20.82	+	12	48	8.12	9	58	26.72	+	13	47	15.13	22	46	12.15	−	15	3	3.2
21	9	58	57.69	+	12	19	29.3	10	4	11.24	+	12	43	38.42	10	3	14.51	+	13	22	20.73	22	45	17.11	−	15	8	42.35
22	10	2	39.59	+	11	59	32.65	10	5	1.63	+	12	39	8.36	10	8	1.34	+	12	57	4.36	22	44	20.41	−	15	14	18.33
23	10	6	21.05	+	11	39	24.52	10	5	51.98	+	12	34	37.64	10	12	47.23	+	12	31	26.75	22	43	22.19	−	15	19	50
24	10	10	2.08	+	11	19	5.24	10	6	42.33	+	12	30	6.2	10	17	32.2	+	12	5	28.62	22	42	22.61	−	15	25	16.22
25	10	13	42.68	+	10	58	35.13	10	7	32.64	+	12	25	34.43	10	22	16.26	+	11	39	10.72	22	41	21.86	−	15	30	35.83
26	10	17	22.88	+	10	37	54.52	10	8	22.92	+	12	21	2.34	10	26	59.44	+	11	12	33.76	22	40	20.12	−	15	35	47.67
27	10	21	2.68	+	10	17	3.75	10	9	13.15	+	12	16	29.92	10	31	41.76	+	10	45	38.48	22	39	17.56	−	15	40	50.6
28	10	24	42.09	+	9	56	3.16	10	10	3.34	+	12	11	57.19	10	36	23.25	+	10	18	25.63	22	38	14.39	−	15	45	43.48
29	10	28	21.11	+	9	34	53.09	10	10	53.46	+	12	7	24.18	10	41	3.94	+	9	50	55.93	22	37	10.8	−	15	50	25.18
30	10	31	59.78	+	9	13	33.88	10	11	43.53	+	12	2	50.9	10	45	43.85	+	9	23	10.12	22	36	7.01	−	15	54	54.62
31	10	35	38.08	+	8	52	5.86	10	12	33.54	+	11	58	17.38	10	50	23.01	+	8	55	8.93	22	35	3.2	−	15	59	10.76
Sep 1	10	39	16.06	+	8	30	29.38	10	13	23.48	+	11	53	43.64	10	55	1.46	+	8	26	53.1	22	33	59.6	−	16	3	12.63
2	10	42	53.71	+	8	8	44.78	10	14	13.36	+	11	49	9.72	10	59	39.22	+	7	58	23.36	22	32	56.38	−	16	6	59.33
3	10	46	31.05	+	7	46	52.42	10	15	3.16	+	11	44	35.65	11	4	16.34	+	7	29	40.47	22	31	53.75	−	16	10	30.06
4	10	50	8.1	+	7	24	52.63	10	15	52.88	+	11	40	1.48	11	8	52.84	+	7	0	45.16	22	30	51.89	−	16	13	44.09
5	10	53	44.88	+	7	2	45.76	10	16	42.52	+	11	35	27.25	11	13	28.77	+	6	31	38.18	22	29	50.98	−	16	16	40.8
6	10	57	21.4	+	6	40	32.14	10	17	32.08	+	11	30	53	11	18	4.15	+	6	2	20.27	22	28	51.17	−	16	19	19.65
7	11	0	57.68	+	6	18	12.1	10	18	21.53	+	11	26	18.78	11	22	39.02	+	5	32	52.15	22	27	52.64	−	16	21	40.15
8	11	4	33.74	+	5	55	45.96	10	19	10.89	+	11	21	44.6	11	27	13.42	+	5	3	14.56	22	26	55.53	−	16	23	41.9
9	11	8	9.6	+	5	33	14.02	10	20	0.15	+	11	17	10.51	11	31	47.38	+	4	33	28.22	22	25	59.98	−	16	25	24.57
10	11	11	45.3	+	5	10	36.58	10	20	49.3	+	11	12	36.53	11	36	20.96	+	4	3	33.84	22	25	6.14	−	16	26	47.85
11	11	15	20.83	+	4	47	53.94	10	21	38.34	+	11	8	2.67	11	40	54.19	+	3	33	32.12	22	24	14.14	−	16	27	51.52
12	11	18	56.25	+	4	25	6.38	10	22	27.26	+	11	3	28.95	11	45	27.12	+	3	3	23.77	22	23	24.1	−	16	28	35.38
13	11	22	31.55	+	4	2	14.22	10	23	16.08	+	10	58	55.41	11	49	59.79	+	2	33	9.5	22	22	36.15	−	16	28	59.3
14	11	26	6.78	+	3	39	17.74	10	24	4.77	+	10	54	22.06	11	54	32.24	+	2	2	50.01	22	21	50.4	−	16	29	3.17

Date	Object A RA h	m	s	Dec	°	'	"	Object B RA h	m	s	Dec	°	'	"	Object C RA h	m	s	Dec	°	'	"	Object D RA h	m	s	Dec	°	'	"
15	11	29	41.95	+	3	16	17.25	10	24	53.34	+	10	49	48.93	11	59	4.52	+	1	32	26.03	22	21	6.97	−	16	28	46.94
16	11	33	17.08	+	2	53	13.05	10	25	41.79	+	10	45	16.05	12	3	36.66	+	1	1	58.26	22	20	25.94	−	16	28	10.59
17	11	36	52.2	+	2	30	5.47	10	26	30.11	+	10	40	43.47	12	8	8.72	+	0	31	27.42	22	19	47.43	−	16	27	14.13
18	11	40	27.33	+	2	6	54.83	10	27	18.29	+	10	36	11.22	12	12	40.73	+	0	0	54.24	22	19	11.51	−	16	25	57.62
19	11	44	2.48	+	1	43	41.44	10	28	6.34	+	10	31	39.34	12	17	12.75	−	0	29	40.56	22	18	38.27	−	16	24	21.13
20	11	47	37.68	+	1	20	25.64	10	28	54.24	+	10	27	7.87	12	21	44.8	−	1	0	16.24	22	18	7.79	−	16	22	24.79
21	11	51	12.95	+	0	57	7.78	10	29	41.99	+	10	22	36.85	12	26	16.93	−	1	30	52.06	22	17	40.13	−	16	20	8.7
22	11	54	48.3	+	0	33	48.18	10	30	29.58	+	10	18	6.34	12	30	49.19	−	2	1	27.3	22	17	15.35	−	16	17	33.04
23	11	58	23.75	+	0	10	27.2	10	31	17.01	+	10	13	36.36	12	35	21.61	−	2	32	1.2	22	16	53.51	−	16	14	37.97
24	12	1	59.32	−	0	12	54.79	10	32	4.28	+	10	9	6.98	12	39	64.23	−	3	2	33.01	22	16	34.65	−	16	11	23.65
25	12	5	35.02	−	0	36	17.46	10	32	51.36	+	10	4	38.21	12	44	27.1	−	3	33	1.98	22	16	18.83	−	16	7	50.29
26	12	9	10.88	−	0	59	40.42	10	33	38.27	+	10	0	10.09	12	49	0.26	−	4	3	27.36	22	16	6.08	−	16	3	58.07
27	12	12	46.92	−	1	23	3.31	10	34	25	+	9	55	42.66	12	53	33.74	−	4	33	48.4	22	15	56.43	−	15	59	47.22
28	12	16	23.14	−	1	46	25.77	10	35	11.54	+	9	51	15.95	12	58	7.6	−	5	4	4.34	22	15	49.9	−	15	55	17.96
29	12	19	59.57	−	2	9	47.42	10	35	57.88	+	9	46	49.99	13	2	41.87	−	5	34	14.42	22	15	46.52	−	15	60	30.56
30	12	23	36.23	−	2	33	7.88	10	36	44.04	+	9	42	24.82	13	7	16.59	−	6	4	17.88	22	15	46.27	−	15	45	25.33
Oct 1	12	27	13.13	−	2	56	26.78	10	37	29.99	+	9	38	0.5	13	11	51.8	−	6	34	13.96	22	15	49.15	−	15	40	2.6
2	12	30	50.29	−	3	19	43.73	10	38	15.74	+	9	33	37.08	13	16	27.53	−	7	4	1.86	22	15	55.15	−	15	34	22.76
3	12	34	27.72	−	3	42	58.36	10	39	1.28	+	9	29	14.61	13	21	3.83	−	7	33	40.82	22	16	4.25	−	15	28	26.19
4	12	38	5.45	−	4	6	10.29	10	39	46.59	+	9	24	53.14	13	25	40.73	−	8	3	10.07	22	16	16.39	−	15	22	13.27
5	12	41	43.5	−	4	29	19.18	10	40	31.68	+	9	20	32.71	13	30	18.27	−	8	32	28.82	22	16	31.56	−	15	15	44.42
6	12	45	21.88	−	4	52	24.66	10	41	16.54	+	9	16	13.35	13	34	56.49	−	9	1	36.31	22	16	49.71	−	15	9	0.02
7	12	49	0.63	−	5	15	26.39	10	42	1.17	+	9	11	55.11	13	39	35.43	−	9	30	31.77	22	17	10.79	−	15	2	0.46
8	12	52	39.75	−	5	38	24.03	10	42	45.55	+	9	7	38.01	13	44	15.12	−	9	59	14.45	22	17	34.76	−	14	54	46.12
9	12	56	19.29	−	6	1	17.24	10	43	29.7	+	9	3	22.08	13	48	55.6	−	10	27	43.57	22	18	1.57	−	14	47	17.37
10	12	59	59.25	−	6	24	5.7	10	44	13.6	+	8	59	7.34	13	53	36.92	−	10	55	58.38	22	18	31.19	−	14	39	34.56
11	13	3	39.67	−	6	46	49.06	10	44	57.25	+	8	54	53.83	13	58	19.1	−	11	23	58.12	22	19	3.55	−	14	31	38.04
12	13	7	20.56	−	7	9	26.98	10	45	40.65	+	8	50	41.58	14	3	2.19	−	12	51	42.03	22	19	38.62	−	14	23	28.15
13	13	11	1.96	−	7	31	59.12	10	46	23.79	+	8	46	30.64	14	7	46.23	−	12	19	9.32	22	20	16.34	−	14	15	5.2

Date		Object A RA			Object A Dec				Object B RA			Object B Dec					Object C RA			Object C Dec					Object D RA			Object D Dec			
		h	m	s		°	'	"	h	m	s		°	'	"	h	m	s		°	'	"	h	m	s		°	'	"
	14	13	14	43.87	−	7	54	25.14	10	47	6.67	+	8	42	21.03	14	12	31.23	−	13	46	19.25	22	20	56.66	−	14	6	29.51
	15	13	18	26.33	−	8	16	44.66	10	47	49.29	+	8	38	12.81	14	17	17.24	−	13	13	11.01	22	21	39.55	−	13	57	41.38
	16	13	22	9.35	−	8	38	57.34	10	48	31.63	+	8	34	6.03	14	22	4.28	−	14	39	43.84	22	22	24.94	−	13	48	41.1
	17	13	25	52.95	−	9	1	2.8	10	49	13.69	+	8	30	0.73	14	26	52.39	−	14	5	56.95	22	23	12.8	−	13	39	28.93
	18	13	29	37.14	−	9	23	0.67	10	49	55.47	+	8	25	56.96	14	31	41.58	−	14	31	49.54	22	24	3.07	−	13	30	5.14
	19	13	33	21.95	−	9	44	50.55	10	50	36.96	+	8	21	54.78	14	36	31.88	−	15	57	20.82	22	24	55.7	−	13	20	29.98
	20	13	37	7.39	−	10	6	32.08	10	51	18.14	+	8	17	54.23	14	41	23.32	−	15	22	29.99	22	25	50.66	−	13	10	43.67
	21	13	40	53.48	−	10	28	4.84	10	51	59.02	+	8	13	55.36	14	46	15.91	−	16	47	16.25	22	26	47.89	−	13	0	46.43
	22	13	44	40.23	−	10	49	28.44	10	52	39.58	+	8	9	58.22	14	51	9.67	−	16	11	38.79	22	27	47.35	−	12	50	38.47
	23	13	48	27.66	−	11	10	42.47	10	53	19.83	+	8	6	2.86	14	56	4.63	−	10	35	36.81	22	28	49	−	12	40	19.26
	24	13	52	15.78	−	11	31	46.51	10	53	59.75	+	8	2	9.31	15	1	0.79	−	16	59	9.5	22	29	52.79	−	12	29	51.08
	25	13	56	4.6	−	11	52	40.15	10	54	39.34	+	7	58	17.62	15	5	58.17	−	17	22	16.07	22	30	58.69	−	12	19	11.97
	26	13	59	54.14	−	12	13	22.98	10	55	18.6	+	7	54	27.82	15	10	56.78	−	17	44	55.72	22	32	6.65	−	12	8	22.82
	27	14	3	44.4	−	12	33	54.56	10	55	57.52	+	7	50	39.96	15	15	56.63	−	18	7	7.65	22	33	16.64	−	11	57	23.8
	28	14	7	35.39	−	12	54	14.46	10	56	36.09	+	7	46	54.09	15	20	57.72	−	18	26	51.09	22	34	28.6	−	11	46	15.1
	29	14	11	27.13	−	13	14	22.27	10	57	14.32	+	7	43	10.28	15	26	0.05	−	18	50	5.24	22	35	42.48	−	11	34	56.94
	30	14	15	19.6	−	13	34	17.54	10	57	52.18	+	7	39	28.58	15	31	3.62	−	19	10	49.32	22	36	58.23	−	11	23	29.57
	31	14	19	12.84	−	13	53	59.84	10	58	29.67	+	7	35	49.06	15	36	8.41	−	19	31	2.54	22	38	15.8	−	11	11	53.21
Nov	1	14	23	6.83	−	14	13	28.75	10	59	6.79	+	7	32	11.76	15	41	14.43	−	19	50	44.14	22	39	35.12	−	11	0	8.11
	2	14	27	1.59	−	14	32	43.86	10	59	43.53	+	7	28	36.74	15	46	21.66	−	20	9	53.35	22	40	56.14	−	10	48	14.5
	3	14	30	57.13	−	14	51	44.76	11	0	19.88	+	7	25	4.03	15	51	30.09	−	20	28	29.42	22	42	18.82	−	10	36	12.61
	4	14	34	53.46	−	15	10	31.06	11	0	55.84	+	7	21	33.66	15	56	39.72	−	20	46	31.65	22	43	43.1	−	10	24	2.66
	5	14	38	50.59	−	15	29	2.37	11	1	31.4	+	7	18	5.68	16	1	50.53	−	21	3	59.31	22	45	8.93	−	10	11	44.87
	6	14	42	48.54	−	15	47	18.31	11	2	6.56	+	7	14	40.11	16	7	2.5	−	21	20	51.71	22	46	36.27	−	9	59	19.43
	7	14	46	47.31	−	16	5	18.49	11	2	41.32	+	7	11	16.99	16	12	15.62	−	21	37	8.17	22	48	5.08	−	9	46	46.56
	8	14	50	46.9	−	16	23	2.55	11	3	15.67	+	7	7	56.36	16	17	29.86	−	21	52	48.05	22	49	35.3	−	9	34	6.44
	9	14	54	47.34	−	16	40	30.1	11	3	49.6	+	7	4	38.26	16	22	45.2	−	22	7	50.7	22	51	6.9	−	9	21	19.28
	10	14	58	48.62	−	16	57	40.76	11	4	23.11	+	7	1	22.73	16	28	1.62	−	22	22	15.5	22	52	39.85	−	9	8	25.24
	11	15	2	50.76	−	17	14	34.17	11	4	56.2	+	6	58	9.83	16	33	19.09	−	22	36	1.84	22	54	14.09	−	8	55	24.52

Date		Object A						Object B							Object C							Object D						
		RA			Dec.			RA			Dec.				RA			Dec.				RA			Dec.			
		h	m	s	°	'	"	h	m	s		°	'	"	h	m	s		°	'	"	h	m	s		°	'	"
	12	15	6	53.75	−	17	31	9.93	11	5	28.85	+	6	54	59.6	16	38	37.56	−	22	49	9.13	22	55	49.6	−	8	42	17.29
	13	15	10	57.61	−	17	47	27.67	11	6	1.06	+	6	51	52.1	16	43	57.01	−	23	1	36.81	22	57	26.35	−	8	29	3.71
	14	15	15	2.32	−	18	3	27	11	6	32.83	+	6	48	47.37	16	49	17.39	−	23	13	24.33	22	59	4.29	−	8	15	43.93
	15	15	19	7.89	−	18	19	7.54	11	7	4.14	+	6	45	45.48	16	54	38.66	−	23	24	31.15	23	0	43.39	−	8	2	18.12
	16	15	23	14.33	−	18	34	28.9	11	7	34.98	+	6	42	46.48	17	0	0.79	−	23	34	56.77	23	2	23.63	−	7	48	46.41
	17	15	27	21.62	−	18	49	30.68	11	8	5.35	+	6	39	50.42	17	5	23.71	−	23	44	40.7	23	4	4.98	−	7	35	8.94
	18	15	31	29.77	−	19	4	12.5	11	8	35.25	+	6	36	57.36	17	10	47.38	−	23	53	42.48	23	5	47.42	−	7	21	25.83
	19	15	35	38.76	−	19	18	33.97	11	9	4.66	+	6	34	7.33	17	16	11.76	−	24	2	1.67	23	7	30.91	−	7	7	37.19
	20	15	39	48.61	−	19	32	34.7	11	9	33.58	+	6	31	20.4	17	21	36.78	−	24	9	37.85	23	9	15.43	−	6	53	43.13
	21	15	43	59.28	−	19	46	14.29	11	10	1.99	+	6	28	36.59	17	27	2.39	−	24	16	30.66	23	11	0.97	−	6	39	43.74
	22	15	48	10.79	−	19	59	32.38	11	10	29.91	+	6	25	55.96	17	32	28.54	−	24	22	39.75	23	12	47.51	−	6	25	39.11
	23	15	52	23.11	−	20	12	28.59	11	10	57.32	+	6	23	18.54	17	37	55.16	−	24	28	4.81	23	14	35.02	−	6	11	29.34
	24	15	56	36.24	−	20	25	2.55	11	11	24.21	+	6	20	44.39	17	43	22.19	−	24	32	45.57	23	16	23.5	−	5	57	14.54
	25	16	0	50.15	−	20	37	13.89	11	11	50.57	+	6	18	13.56	17	48	49.56	−	24	36	41.8	23	18	12.9	−	5	42	54.82
	26	16	5	4.81	−	20	49	2.26	11	12	16.41	+	6	15	46.11	17	54	17.21	−	24	39	53.3	23	20	3.22	−	5	28	30.34
	27	16	9	20.22	−	21	0	27.29	11	12	41.71	+	6	13	22.12	17	59	45.05	−	24	42	19.89	23	21	54.41	−	5	14	1.28
	28	16	13	36.34	−	21	11	28.64	11	13	6.46	+	6	11	1.63	18	5	13.01	−	24	44	1.43	23	23	46.46	−	4	59	27.79
	29	16	17	53.16	−	21	22	5.95	11	13	30.65	+	6	8	44.7	18	10	41.03	−	24	44	57.82	23	25	39.33	−	4	44	50.06
	30	16	22	10.65	−	21	32	18.92	11	13	54.28	+	6	6	31.36	18	16	9.02	−	24	45	8.97	23	27	33	−	4	30	8.26
Dec	1	16	26	28.79	−	21	42	7.23	11	14	17.35	+	6	4	21.64	18	21	36.92	−	24	44	34.86	23	29	27.45	−	4	15	22.56
	2	16	30	47.58	−	21	51	30.61	11	14	39.85	+	6	2	15.58	18	27	4.67	−	24	43	15.49	23	31	22.65	−	4	0	33.13
	3	16	35	6.98	−	22	0	28.77	11	15	1.77	+	6	0	13.2	18	32	32.18	−	24	41	10.91	23	33	18.57	−	3	45	40.13
	4	16	39	26.99	−	22	9	1.47	11	15	23.11	+	5	58	14.54	18	37	59.4	−	24	38	21.21	23	35	15.21	−	3	30	43.72
	5	16	43	47.57	−	22	17	8.46	11	15	43.86	+	5	56	19.62	18	43	26.27	−	24	34	46.51	23	37	12.54	−	3	15	44.07
	6	16	48	8.71	−	22	24	49.5	11	16	4.03	+	5	54	28.48	18	48	52.7	−	24	30	26.97	23	39	10.54	−	3	0	41.33
	7	16	52	30.39	−	22	32	4.38	11	16	23.61	+	5	52	41.16	18	54	18.65	−	24	25	22.78	23	41	9.19	−	2	45	35.66
	8	16	56	52.59	−	22	38	52.88	11	16	42.58	+	5	50	57.69	18	59	44.04	−	24	19	34.19	23	43	8.48	−	2	30	27.21
	9	17	1	15.27	−	22	45	14.81	11	17	0.95	+	5	49	18.12	19	5	8.81	−	24	13	1.45	23	45	8.39	−	2	15	16.14
	10	17	5	38.42	−	22	51	9.97	11	17	18.71	+	5	47	42.5	19	10	32.91	−	24	5	44.85	23	47	8.91	−	2	0	2.59

Date	Object A								Object B								Object C								Object D							
	RA			Dec				RA			Dec				RA			Dec				RA			Dec			
	h	m	s		°	'	"	h	m	s		°	'	"	h	m	s		°	'	"	h	m	s		°	'	"
11	17	10	2	–	22	56	38.18	11	17	35.85	+	5	46	10.85	19	15	56.27	–	23	57	44.72	23	49	10.02	–	1	44	46.71
12	17	14	26	–	23	1	39.27	11	17	52.36	+	5	44	43.24	19	21	18.84	–	23	49	1.41	23	51	11.71	–	1	29	28.63
13	17	18	50.38	–	23	6	13.07	11	18	8.24	+	5	43	19.7	19	26	40.55	–	23	39	35.29	23	53	13.97	–	1	14	8.49
14	17	23	15.11	–	23	10	19.42	11	18	23.48	+	5	42	0.27	19	32	1.37	–	23	29	26.78	23	55	16.79	–	0	58	46.43
15	17	27	40.18	–	23	13	58.18	11	18	38.07	+	5	40	45	19	37	21.23	–	23	18	36.28	23	57	20.15	–	0	43	22.54
16	17	32	5.53	–	23	17	9.21	11	18	52.02	+	5	39	33.91	19	42	40.09	–	23	7	4.27	23	59	24.05	–	0	27	56.96
17	17	36	31.16	–	23	19	52.38	11	19	5.3	+	5	38	27.05	19	47	57.91	–	22	54	51.2	0	1	28.49	–	0	12	29.78
18	17	40	57.02	–	23	22	7.57	11	19	17.92	+	5	37	24.44	19	53	14.64	–	22	41	57.58	0	3	33.46	–	0	2	58.9
19	17	45	23.09	–	23	23	54.7	11	19	29.88	+	5	36	26.11	19	58	30.25	–	22	28	23.93	0	5	38.95	–	0	18	29
20	17	49	49.32	–	23	25	13.69	11	19	41.17	+	5	35	32.07	20	3	44.69	–	22	14	10.8	0	7	44.97	–	0	34	0.43
21	17	54	15.7	–	23	26	4.47	11	19	51.78	+	5	34	42.37	20	8	57.94	–	21	59	18.78	0	9	51.51	–	0	49	33.09
22	17	58	42.17	–	23	26	27	11	20	1.72	+	5	33	57.03	20	14	9.95	–	21	43	48.47	0	11	58.56	–	1	5	6.89
23	18	3	8.7	–	23	26	21.28	11	20	10.97	+	5	33	16.09	20	19	20.7	–	21	27	40.51	0	14	6.12	–	1	20	41.71
24	18	7	35.25	–	23	25	47.28	11	20	19.53	+	5	32	39.59	20	24	30.15	–	21	10	55.58	0	16	14.18	–	1	36	17.42
25	18	12	1.77	–	23	24	45.01	11	20	27.4	+	5	32	7.57	20	29	38.26	–	20	53	34.33	0	18	22.73	–	1	51	53.87
26	18	16	28.22	–	23	23	14.49	11	20	34.56	+	5	31	40.06	20	34	45.02	–	20	35	37.47	0	20	31.76	–	2	7	30.91
27	18	20	54.55	–	23	21	15.73	11	20	41.02	+	5	31	17.07	20	39	50.38	–	20	17	5.68	0	22	41.26	–	2	23	8.38
28	18	25	20.74	–	23	18	48.79	11	20	46.77	+	5	30	58.62	20	44	54.33	–	19	57	59.68	0	24	51.21	–	2	38	46.12
29	18	29	46.75	–	23	15	53.73	11	20	51.82	+	5	30	44.69	20	49	56.86	–	19	38	20.18	0	27	1.61	–	2	54	23.98
30	18	34	12.54	–	23	12	30.64	11	20	56.16	+	5	30	35.28	20	54	57.95	–	19	18	7.93	0	29	12.46	–	3	10	1.81
31	18	38	38.09	–	23	8	39.63	11	20	59.79	+	5	30	30.4	20	59	57.59	–	18	57	23.68	0	31	23.73	–	3	25	39.47

3

Geometric Astronomy and Time

3.1 Theory

1. The largest angular separation between Venus and the Sun, when viewed from the Earth, is 46°. Calculate the radius of Venus's circular orbit in astronomical units (AU).
   (I07 - T02 - A)

2. One night during full moon, the Moon subtends an angle of 0.46° to an observer. What is the observer's distance to the Moon on that night? (I07 - T04 - A)

3. An observer was able to measure the minute differences in the positions of the stars, due to the Earth's motion around the Sun, to a star as distant as 100 parsecs away. What was the minimum angular difference in arcseconds that this observer could measure?
   (I07 - T05 - A)

4. The time interval between noon of 1 July and noon of 31 December is 183 solar days. What is this interval in sidereal days? (I07 - T03 - A)

5. What is the time interval between two consecutive oppositions of Mars? Assume the orbit is circular. (I12 - T03 - A)

6. Mars arrived at its great opposition at UT 17^h56^m on 28 August 2003. The next great opposition of Mars will be in 2018. Estimate the date of that opposition.
   (I10 - T11 - A)

7. Calculate the length of the sidereal day on the Earth. What would be the length of the solar and sidereal days in the current time measures (our solar hours, minutes and seconds), if the Earth would rotate in the opposite direction, but with the same rotation speed?
   (I12 - T02 - A)

8. A satellite is orbiting around the Earth in a circular orbit along the celestial equator, positioned at the same longitude as Tehran. An observer in Tehran at the latitude of $\varphi = 35.6°$ observes that the satellite has a zenith angle of $z = 46.0°$ when it transits the local meridian. Calculate the distance of the satellite from the centre of the Earth (in Earth radius units). (I09 - T14 - B)

9. Assuming that Phobos moves around Mars on a perfectly circular orbit in the equatorial plane of the planet, give the length of time Phobos is above the horizon for a point on the Martian equator. (I11 - T04 - B)

10. Assume that you are living in the time of Copernicus and do not know anything about Kepler's laws. You might calculate the Mars–Sun distance in the same way as he did.

After accepting the revolutionary belief that all the planets are orbiting around the Sun, and not around the Earth, you find out that the orbital period of Mars is 687 days. Then you observe that 106 days after the opposition of Mars, the planet appears in quadrature. Calculate the Mars–Sun distance in astronomical units (AU). (I09 - T13 - C)

11. **Apparent magnitude of the Moon:** The apparent magnitude of the Moon as seen from the Sun is $M_m = 0.25$. Calculate the values of the apparent magnitudes of the Moon corresponding to full moon and first-quarter moon. (I14 - T11 - A)

For terrestrial observers, the following phase factor must be used to correct lunar brightness for the curvature of the lunar surface and phase angle of the moon (Ψ).

$$p(\Psi) = \frac{2}{3}\left[\left(1 - \frac{\Psi}{\pi}\right)\cos\Psi + \frac{1}{\pi}\sin\Psi\right] \qquad (3.1)$$

12. **The planet Taris:** The planet Taris is home to the Korribian civilisation. The Korribian species is a highly intelligent life form. They speak in Korribianese language. The Korribianese–English dictionary is shown in Table 3.1. Read it carefully. Korribian astronomers have been studying the heavens for thousands of years. Their knowledge can be summarised as follows: (I10 - T17 - C)

- Taris orbits its host star Sola in a circular orbit, at a distance of 1 Tarislength.
- Taris orbits Sola in 1 Tarisyear.
- The obliquity of Taris is 3° with respect **to the normal** to its orbit.
- There are exactly 10 Tarisdays in 1 Tarisyear.
- Taris has two moons, named Endor and Extor. Both have circular orbits.
- The sidereal orbital period of Endor (around Taris) is exactly 0.2 Tarisdays.
- The sidereal orbital period of Extor (around Taris) is exactly 1.6 Tarisdays.
- The distance between Taris and Endor is 1 Endorlength.

Table 3.1 *Korribianese–English dictionary*

Korribianese	English Translation
Corulus	A planet orbiting Sola
Endor	(i) Goddess of the night (ii) A moon of Taris
Endorlength	The distance between Taris and Endor
Extor	(i) God of peace (ii) A moon of Taris
Sola	(i) God of life (ii) The star which Taris and Corulus orbit
Solaptic	Apparent path of Sola and Corulus as viewed from Taris
Taris	A planet orbiting the star Sola, home of the Korribians
Tarisday	The time between successive midnights on the planet Taris
Tarislength	The distance between Sola and Taris
Tarisyear	Time taken by Taris to make one revolution around Sola

- Corulus, another planet, also orbits Sola in a circular orbit. Corulus has one moon.
- The distance between Sola and Corulus is 9 Tarislengths.
- The Tarisyear begins when the Solaptic longitude of Sola is zero.

(a) Draw the Sola System, and indicate all its planets and moons.

(b) How often does Taris rotate around its axis in 1 Tarisyear?

(c) What is the distance between Taris and Extor, in Endorlengths?

(d) What is the orbital period of Corulus, in Tarisyears?

(e) What is the distance between Taris and Corulus when Corulus is in opposition?

(f) If, at the beginning of a particular Tarisyear, Corulus and Taris were in opposition, what would the Solaptic longitude (as observed from Taris) of Corulus be 'n' Tarisdays from the start of that year?

(g) What would be the area of the triangle formed by Sola, Taris and Corulus exactly 1 Tarisday after the opposition?

13. An observer observed a transit of Venus near the North Pole of the Earth. The transit path of Venus is shown in Fig. 3.1. A, B, C and D are all on the path of transit and mark the centre of the Venus disk. At A and B, the centre of Venus is superposed on the limb of the Sun disk; C corresponds to the first contact while D to the fourth contact, $\Delta AOB = 90°$, MN is parallel to AB. The first contact occurred at 9:00 UT. Calculate the time of the fourth contact. (I10 - T14 - D)

14. On an average, the visual diameter of the Moon is slightly less than that of the Sun, so the frequency of annular solar eclipses is slightly higher than total solar eclipses. For an observer on the Earth, the duration of longest total solar eclipse is about 7.5 minutes, and the duration of longest annular eclipse is about 12.5 minutes. Here, the longest duration is the time interval from the second contact to the third contact. Suppose we count the occurrences of both types of solar eclipses for a very long time, estimate the ratio of the occurrences of annular solar eclipses and total solar eclipses. Assume the orbit of the Earth to be circular and the eccentricity of the Moon's orbit to be 0.0549. Count all hybrid eclipses as annular eclipses. (I10 - T15 - D)

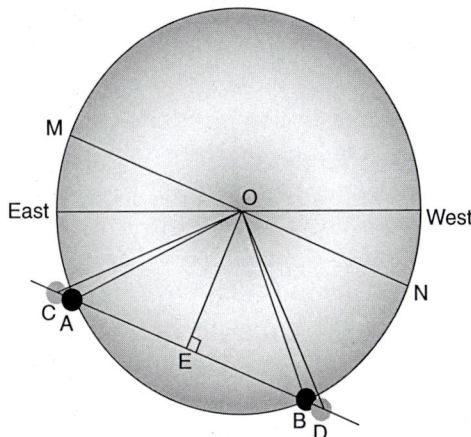

Fig. 3.1   *Transit of Venus*

3.2 Data Analysis

1. **The Moon's age:** The 60th anniversary celebrations of King Bhumibol Adulyadej's accession to the throne of Thailand (GMT + 07) were held from 8 to 13 June 2006. Photographs of the Moon taken at the same hour each night are shown below:

| 8th June, 2006 | 9th June, 2006 | 10th June, 2006 |

| 11th June, 2006 | 12th June, 2006 | 13th June, 2006 |

   Assuming that Albert Einstein's birth was at noon on 14 March 1879, use the data provided above to find the Moon's age (number of days since the new moon) on his birth date in Germany (GMT + 01). Estimate the errors in your calculation.   (I07 - D02 - B)

2. **Venus:** An observer in Deh-Namak, Iran (location of IOAA 2009 observational round) has observed Venus for seven months, from September 2008 till March 2009. During these observations, a good-quality CCD camera and image processing software were used to take high-resolution images and to extract high-precision data. Table 3.2 shows the data collected during the observation. In this table,

   Column 1 Date of observation

   Column 2 Earth–Sun distance in astronomical units (AU) for observation date and time. This value is taken from high-precision tables.

   Column 3 Observed phase of Venus, percentage of Venus's disk illuminated by the Sun as observed from the Earth.

   Column 4 Observed elongation of Venus, the angular distance between the centre of the Sun and the centre of Venus in degrees.

   (a) Using the data given in Table 3.2, calculate the Sun–Venus–Earth angle ($\angle SVE$) for all observing dates. This is the angular separation between the Sun and the Earth as seen from Venus.

   Note: Remember that the terminator line (line separating the bright and dark regions of Venus's surface) is always an arc of an ellipse.

Table 3.2   *Phase data for Venus*

Date	Earth–Sun Distance (AU)	Phase (%)	Elongation (SEV) (°)
20/9/2008	1.0043	88.4	27.56
10/10/2008	0.9986	84.0	32.29
20/10/2008	0.9957	81.6	34.53
30/10/2008	0.9931	79.0	36.69
9/11/2008	0.9905	76.3	38.71
19/11/2008	0.9883	73.4	40.62
29/11/2008	0.9864	70.2	42.38
18/1/2009	0.9838	49.5	47.09
7/2/2009	0.9863	37.2	44.79
17/2/2009	0.9881	29.6	41.59
27/2/2009	0.9904	20.9	36.16
19/3/2009	0.9956	3.8	16.08

(b) Calculate the Sun–Venus distance in AU for all observation dates.

(c) Plot the Sun–Venus distance versus observing date.

(d) Find the perihelion ($r_{v,min}$) and aphelion ($r_{v,max}$) distances of Venus from the Sun.

(e) Calculate the semi-major axis (a) of the Venus orbit.

(f) Calculate the eccentricity (e) of the Venus orbit.   (I09 - D02 - C)

4

Optics and Detectors

4.1 Theory

1. A crater on the surface of the Moon has a diameter of 80 km. Is it possible to resolve this crater with the naked eye? (I07 - T13 - A)

2. What would be the diameter of a radio telescope, working at a wavelength of $\lambda = 1$ cm, with the same resolution as an optical telescope of diameter $D = 10$ cm? (I11 - T05 - A)

3. Let us assume that we observe a Jupiter-like planet orbiting around a star at an average distance $d = 5$ AU. It has been found that the distance of this system from us is $r = 250$ pc. What is the minimum diameter, D, that a telescope should have to be able to resolve the two objects (star and planet)? We assume that the observation is carried out in the optical part of the electromagnetic spectrum ($\lambda \sim 500$ nm), outside the Earth's atmosphere and that the telescope optics are perfect (diffraction limited). (I13 - T2 - A)

4. The Galactic Centre is believed to contain a super-massive black hole with mass $M = 4 \times 10^6$ $M_\odot$. The astronomy community is trying to resolve its event horizon, which is a challenging task. For a non-rotating black hole, this event horizon is the same as the Schwarzschild radius, $R_\odot = 3(M/M_\odot)$ km. Assume that we have an Earth-sized telescope (using very long baseline interferometry). What wavelengths should we adopt in order to resolve the event horizon of the black hole? (I10 - T08 - B)

5. What is the minimum diameter of a telescope, observing in the visible and near ultraviolet bands and located at one of the Lagrangian points L_4 or L_5 of the Sun–Earth system, required to detect the Earth's wobbling relative to the ecliptic plane caused by the gravitational action of the Moon? (I12 - T12 - B)

6. The coordinates of the components of the visual binary star μ Sco as on 28 August 2008 are given in the table below.

Star	α (RA)	δ (Dec.)
μ Sco (primary)	$20^h17^m38.90^s$	$-12°30'30''$
μ Sco (secondary)	$20^h18^m03.30^s$	$-12°32'41''$

The stars are observed using a Zeiss refractor telescope, whose aperture and focal length are 600 mm and 10,780 mm, respectively, at the Bosscha Observatory. The telescope is equipped with a 765 × 510 pixel CCD camera. The pixel size of the chip is $9\mu m \times 9\mu m$. (I08 - T10 - B)

(a) Can both components of the binary be inside a single frame of the camera?

(b) What is the position angle of the secondary star, with respect to the North?

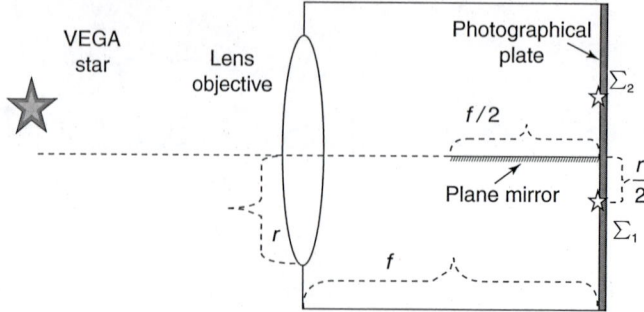

Fig. 4.1 *Camera with a mirror*

7. **The Vega star in the mirror:** Inside a camera, a plane mirror is placed along the optical axis of the objective (as shown in Fig. 4.1). The length of the mirror is half the focal distance of the objective. A photographic plate is placed at the focal plane of the camera. Two images of Vega at different brightness are captured on the photographic plate (see Fig. 4.1). The star Vega is not on the optical axis of the lens. The distance between the optical axis and the image Σ_1 is $\dfrac{r}{2}$ .Find the difference between the apparent photographical magnitudes of the two images of the star Vega.   (I14 - T9 - C)

8. Given below is a picture on a 35-mm film of an annular eclipse, which was observed from Dumai, North Sumatra on 22 August 1998. This picture was taken with a telescope having an effective diameter of 10 cm and f-ratio of 15. The diameter of the Sun's disk in the original picture on the film is 13.817 mm and the diameter of the Moon's disk is 13.235 mm. Estimate the distances of the Sun and the Moon (expressed in km) from the Earth and the percentage of the solar disk covered by the Moon during the annular eclipse.   (I08 - T11 - C)

9. On 2 April 2008, a telescope (10-cm diameter, f /10)at the Bosscha Observatory was used to observe the Sun and found an active region 0987 (based on the NOAA number) at 8° South and 40° West from the centre of the solar disk. The region was recorded with an SBIG ST-8

CCD camera (1600 × 1200 pixels, (9μm × 9μm) /pixel) and the size of the spot was 5 × 4 pixels. According to the Astronomical Almanac, the solar diameter on that day was 32'. How large is the corrected area of the active region in units of millionth of solar hemisphere (msh)?

(I08 - T02 - C)

Table 4.1 *Stars of Ursa Major*

Star Name	Bayer Name	Right Ascension	Declination	Apparant Magnitude	Absolute Magnitude
Dubhe	α UMa	11^{h}03^{m}43.84^s	61°45'4.0"	1.81	−1.08
Merak	β UMa	11^{h}01^{m}50.39^s	56°22'56.4"	2.34	0.41
Phecda	γ UMa	11^{h}53^{m}49.74^s	53°41'41.0"	2.41	0.36
Megrez	δ UMa	12^{h}15^{m}25.45^s	57°1'57.4"	3.32	1.33
Alioth	ε UMa	12^{h}54^{m}01.63^s	55°57'35.4"	1.76	−0.21
Mizar	ζ UMa	13^{h}23^{m}55.42^s	54°55'31.5"	2.23	0.33
Alcor		13^{h}25^{m}13.42^s	54°59'16.8"	3.99	2.01
Alkaid	η UMa	13^{h}47^{m}32.55^s	49°18'47.9"	1.85	−0.60

4.2 Data Analysis

1. In Fig. 4.2, part of the constellation of Ursa Major is shown. It was taken with a digital camera with a large CCD chip (17.0 mm × 22.0 mm). Find the focal length, f, of the optical system and estimate the error in your result. You may refer to Table 4.1 for the necessary data. (I13 - D01 - A)

2. **CCD image:**

   Fig. 4.3 presents a negative image of the sky taken by a CCD camera attached to a telescope whose parameters are presented in the accompanying table (which is part of the FITS data header file).

   Fig. 4.4 consists of two images: the one on the right (4.4B) is an enlarged view of part of Fig. 4.3 and the one on the left (4.4A) is an enlarged image of the same part of the sky taken some time earlier.

   Fig. 4.5 presents a sky map which includes the region shown in the CCD images.

   The stars in the images are far away and should ideally be seen as point sources. However, diffraction on the telescope aperture and the effects of atmospheric turbulence (known as 'seeing') blur the light from the stars. The brighter the star, the more of the spread-out light is visible above the level of the background sky. (I10 - D01 - B)

   (a) Identify any five bright stars (mark them in Roman numerals) from the image and mark them on both the image and the map.

   (b) Mark the field of view of the camera on the map.

   (c) Use this information to obtain the physical dimensions of the CCD chip in mm.

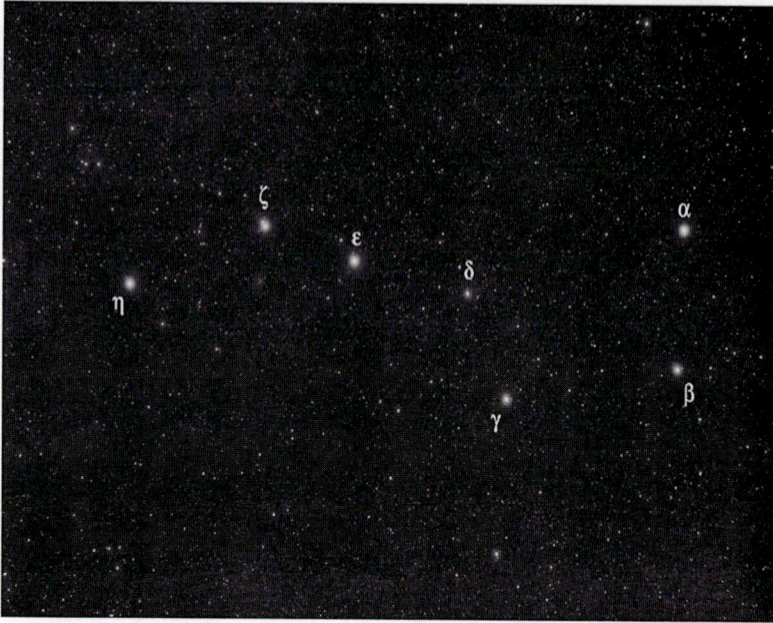

Fig. 4.2   *CCD photograph showing Ursa Major*

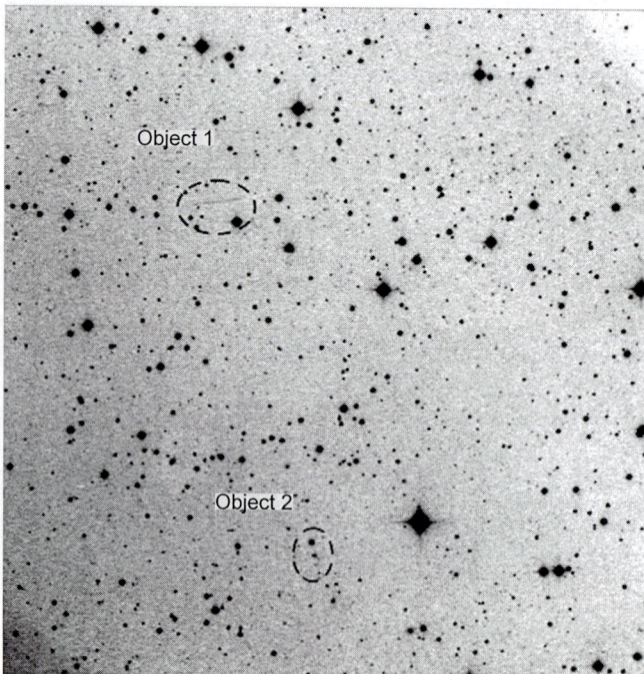

Fig. 4.3   *CCD photograph showing part of the sky*

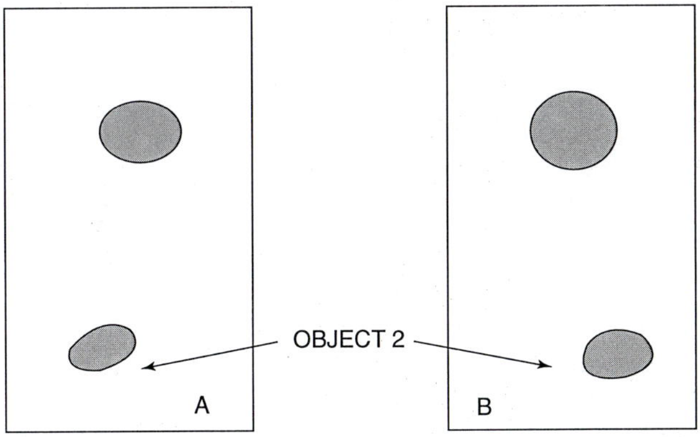

Fig. 4.4 *In this image, B is simply an enlargement of Fig. 4.3 around Object 2. On the other hand, A shows the same area observed some time earlier.*

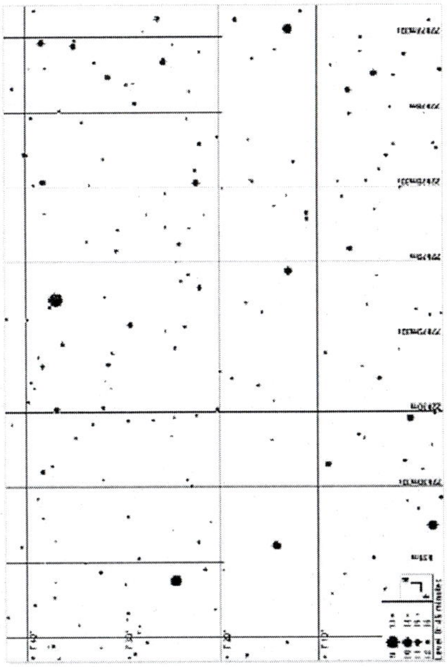

Fig. 4.5 *Sky map which contains the corresponding region*

(d) Estimate the size of the blurring effect in arcseconds by examining the image of the star in Fig. 4.4. (Note that due to changes in contrast necessary for printing, the diameter of the image appears to be about 3.5 times the full width at half maximum (FWHM) of the profile of the star.)

(e) Compare the result with the theoretical size of the diffraction disc of the telescope.

(f) Seeing of 1″ is often considered to indicate good conditions. Calculate the size of the star image in pixels if the atmospheric seeing was 1″ and compare it with the result from Question 2d.

(g) Two objects observed moving relative to the background stars have been marked on Fig. 4.3. The motion of one (Object 1) was fast enough that it left a clear trail on the image. The motion of the other (Object 2) is more easily seen on the enlarged image (Fig. 4.4B) and another image taken some time earlier (Fig. 4.4A). Using the above results, determine the angular velocity on the sky of both objects. Choose which of the statements in the list below are correct, assuming that the objects are moving on circular orbits.

The probable causes of the different angular velocities are:
• Different masses of the objects
• Different orbital velocities of the objects
• Different projections of the objects' velocities
For Fig. 4.3, the data header file is as follows:

BITPIX = 16	/ Number of bits per pixel
NAXIS = 2	/ Number of axes
NAXIS1 = 1024	/ Width of image (in pixels)
NAXIS2 = 1024	/ Height of image (in pixels)
DATE-OBS = 2010-09-07 05:00:40.4	/ Middle of exposure
TIMESYS = UT	/ Time scale
EXPTIME = 300.00	/ Exposure time (seconds)
OBJCTRA = 22 29 20. 031	/ RA of centre of the image
OBJCTDEC = +07 20 00. 793	/ Dec. of centre of the image
FOCALLEN = 3. 180m	/ Focal length of the telescope
TELESCOP = 0. 61m	/ Telescope aperture

In Fig. 4.4A, all the data above remains the same except
DATE-OBS= 2010-09-07 04:42:33.3 / Middle of exposure

3. **CCD image processing:** As an exercise in image processing, this problem involves the use of a simple calculator and tabular data (Tables 4.2 and 4.3) which contains the pixel values of an image during the given exposure time. This image, which is a part of a larger CCD image, was taken by a CCD camera installed on an amateur telescope and using a V band filter. Fig. 4.6 shows this 50×50 pixel image that contains five stars.

Tables 4.2 and 4.3 give the telescope and image specifications. The observer identified stars 1, 3 and 4 by comparing this image with standard star catalogues. True magnitudes (m_t) as given in the catalogue for stars 1, 3 and 4 are 9.03, 6.22 and 8.02, respectively.

(a) Using the available data, determine the instrumental magnitudes of the stars in the image. Assume the dark current is negligible and the image is flat fielded. For simplicity you can use a square aperture.

Note: The instrumental magnitude is calculated using the difference between the measured *flux* form the star in the aperture and the *flux* from an equivalent area of dark sky.

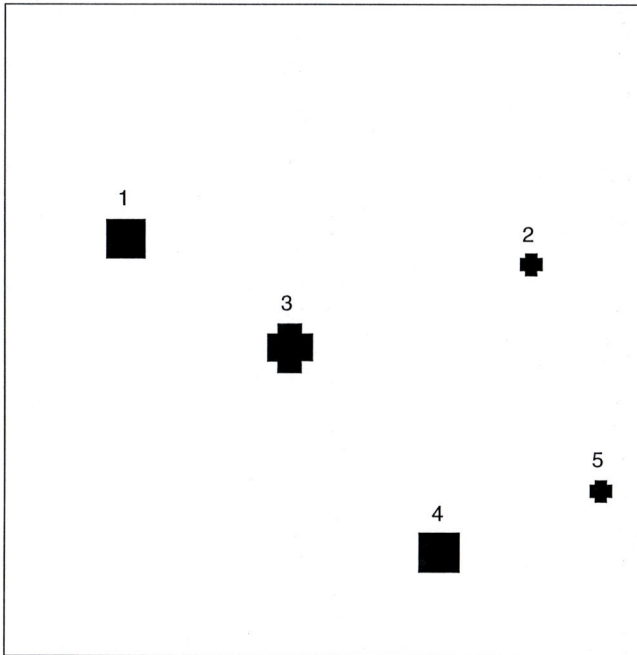

Telescope focal length	1.20 m
CCD pixel size	25 × 25 μm
Exposure time	450 s
Telescope zenith angle	25°
Average extinction coefficient in band	0.3 mag

Fig. 4.6 *CCD image*

(b) The instrumental magnitude of a star in a CCD image is related to true magnitude as

$$m_I = m_t + KX - Z_{mag} \qquad (4.1)$$

where K is extinction coefficient, X is the air mass, m_I and m_t are, respectively, the instrumental and true magnitude of the star and Z_{mag} is zero point constant. Calculate the zero point constant (Z_{mag}) for the identified stars and hence calculate the average zero point constant (Z_{mag}).

Note: Zero point constant is the constant difference between extinction-free instrumental magnitudes and the true magnitude.

(c) Calculate the true magnitudes of stars 2 and 5.

(d) Calculate the CCD pixel scale for the CCD camera in units of arcsec.

(e) Calculate average brightness of a dark sky in magnitude per square arcsec (m_{sky}).

(f) Use a suitable plot to estimate the astronomical seeing in arcsec. (I09 - D01 - C)

Table 4.2 Part I of the CCD readout table: Columns 1 to 25

9	9	4	1	8	2	1	8	1	2	1	6	9	3	7	2	0	6	5	10	4	10	11	42	170
1	0	6	6	6	3	8	4	9	0	8	3	3	3	2	8	3	4	7	9	10	5	40	2667	10780
3	7	1	8	7	4	6	4	4	7	9	7	6	6	3	2	6	8	2	7	5	10	165	10786	43705
6	9	3	3	6	8	7	2	9	7	1	9	6	5	3	7	3	2	2	1	2	8	43	2665	10785
5	5	7	9	0	2	9	1	4	3	2	4	3	1	1	5	5	3	6	3	8	9	3	40	165
8	9	3	1	4	7	4	8	6	0	1	6	9	1	6	4	8	6	10	7	2	1	1	10	10
3	2	6	6	8	2	2	7	3	7	1	5	4	2	3	0	3	2	4	3	5	9	3	4	4
5	8	3	2	3	1	3	5	1	6	5	0	7	7	6	8	0	3	4	9	6	4	4	7	1
5	8	9	9	4	9	7	2	8	2	8	4	3	1	3	8	3	2	10	7	1	5	1	4	6
2	4	4	8	9	8	0	9	6	9	9	8	2	5	6	5	5	7	0	1	0	8	6	4	9
5	3	6	2	2	8	1	5	3	0	9	1	5	7	4	9	6	10	6	2	4	2	1	8	1
4	8	1	8	6	4	1	10	1	8	2	10	8	1	9	9	5	0	1	10	5	9	1	3	9
1	3	7	6	1	4	9	8	3	4	7	0	4	1	5	4	10	7	6	8	8	9	3	2	9
1	2	2	5	3	10	0	8	7	7	4	5	4	5	18	6	3	6	7	5	1	6	5	10	3
3	9	2	3	8	4	9	6	5	7	3	10	7	206	804	206	8	1	6	6	7	8	8	2	6
5	1	3	4	5	7	0	7	7	2	9	1	13	798	3239	798	13	4	8	10	8	1	6	2	6
0	7	4	4	2	8	7	1	9	4	0	4	12	202	803	204	7	3	10	9	1	9	6	9	4
9	4	10	4	5	2	8	8	1	9	8	6	1	9	14	5	4	2	8	8	5	9	8	5	2
0	6	2	4	8	8	10	5	3	0	5	2	4	0	6	3	9	9	4	2	5	7	7	4	7
6	0	5	3	5	2	9	2	7	2	7	3	4	10	1	8	10	1	7	6	3	6	6	2	7
6	10	6	1	2	1	0	5	9	8	4	1	4	4	6	6	2	6	3	9	8	8	5	5	1
5	8	4	8	9	5	4	4	4	7	10	8	6	10	6	8	3	9	6	5	4	2	9	1	8
4	6	6	2	0	7	6	1	10	8	1	10	7	2	5	10	10	8	0	5	6	7	8	7	4
4	1	6	8	1	8	2	7	6	2	5	5	6	2	8	3	1	6	3	7	9	7	5	9	7
2	10	7	5	7	2	10	3	10	8	6	8	3	2	1	6	7	3	4	6	1	4	4	4	5

47	3	6	0	7	5	7	5	9	3	0	2	9	9	8	3	2	3	4	6	4	10	3	6	2
2658	42	1	6	5	9	2	7	10	8	6	6	5	7	4	3	5	5	10	1	2	2	8	3	6
10783	164	10	9	2	1	2	5	5	3	9	3	5	1	4	7	1	6	5	0	8	6	0	3	6
2663	44	2	4	10	3	1	5	7	3	1	9	7	1	6	2	9	10	5	3	4	0	4	6	9
45	4	7	3	2	8	4	7	5	1	6	5	7	3	7	9	0	7	7	9	2	8	8	8	1
9	8	6	1	8	5	4	9	3	2	0	2	8	1	9	4	2	3	1	2	3	6	6	3	1
3	6	5	5	2	9	8	9	5	6	5	7	3	1	9	2	8	4	4	9	3	8	8	5	3
6	6	7	10	5	3	6	7	4	9	1	0	3	3	7	9	7	5	10	2	6	6	7	6	3
9	8	6	7	10	2	3	1	1	6	5	9	2	1	3	2	2	0	10	2	4	1	4	7	1
0	2	4	2	7	3	5	1	8	9	0	4	6	3	9	1	9	6	7	2	7	10	8	5	5
1	2	5	9	3	4	8	5	1	3	1	3	7	6	1	0	2	5	2	8	7	0	5	1	2
0	10	5	9	6	7	9	8	6	8	7	3	5	7	5	7	7	8	6	5	6	8	6	1	3
3	2	4	1	0	0	6	3	5	6	2	1	9	7	7	6	5	4	1	4	8	2	5	8	5
2	1	0	2	2	4	9	2	6	6	4	1	9	7	7	3	9	7	2	2	7	1	1	9	3
1	8	3	8	9	10	1	8	7	5	3	3	9	10	10	6	2	2	9	3	2	8	4	8	2
9	4	9	7	1	1	9	3	8	9	5	5	7	3	7	9	8	7	7	6	6	4	6	1	2
4	9	9	5	3	3	5	1	0	9	1	2	7	3	9	7	1	7	7	9	9	3	5	1	1
6	1	10	8	4	5	3	0	8	8	7	0	6	6	0	10	9	8	7	5	0	8	2	5	3
2	3	6	7	5	4	9	3	1	2	0	8	7	1	1	8	4	4	8	8	4	4	2	3	5
3	9	7	5	4	8	3	9	5	7	3	4	5	2	5	4	7	10	4	10	5	2	5	0	7
3	7	3	1	6	5	1	7	3	9	8	5	4	8	2	7	3	2	3	4	9	8	5	1	6
0	1	1	9	8	5	8	6	9	8	8	2	6	1	9	7	2	6	0	8	0	8	2	7	4
4	1	4	2	8	2	4	3	0	6	2	7	0	2	5	6	5	1	1	8	3	2	2	2	8
5	6	9	0	1	1	5	8	7	6	10	9	1	2	8	0	7	7	3	10	6	4	8	4	2
1	4	1	4	2	3	3	3	5	7	1	7	6	3	1	6	1	1	8	5	1	7	1	8	6

Table 4.3   *Part II of the table: Columns 26 to 50*

26	27	28	29	30	31	32	33	34	35	36	37	38	39	40	41	42	43	44	45	46	47	48	49	50
1	5	2	2	2	9	2	3	9	2	10	4	10	2	6	6	6	2	3	8	7	1	3	7	6
6	0	4	3	1	1	1	1	5	5	7	3	1	4	0	3	5	8	8	6	2	10	3	1	6
8	9	3	2	9	3	9	3	7	7	10	9	2	7	10	9	5	3	0	1	9	3	3	4	3
9	7	5	8	3	9	8	9	9	4	1	9	0	7	9	8	4	8	1	5	8	8	6	0	0
8	8	4	1	9	3	1	9	9	9	0	1	7	1	5	0	5	9	8	5	3	9	4	2	7
3	2	2	2	2	6	10	1	4	5	7	4	1	7	6	8	5	2	1	5	9	5	5	8	4
7	5	1	8	5	5	8	3	6	4	2	9	2	9	3	6	7	8	8	4	8	7	9	9	4
1	4	9	2	2	5	1	9	6	5	4	1	3	6	8	1	10	9	3	8	2	10	0	3	1
7	2	5	0	5	3	7	5	3	5	3	9	2	1	3	7	7	7	2	3	8	4	4	1	9
3	1	3	2	3	0	8	2	4	6	4	9	6	3	2	5	7	4	3	5	5	8	1	6	3
10	6	4	4	4	6	3	8	3	5	8	3	1	5	4	5	6	5	0	3	4	7	2	2	0
4	6	3	7	4	10	6	3	5	5	2	0	3	8	1	2	4	6	2	10	1	2	2	5	9
6	7	5	4	7	6	1	9	3	6	1	10	5	10	6	8	4	8	10	5	2	0	5	8	7
7	8	4	3	3	5	1	5	8	7	8	6	0	5	3	8	5	9	1	5	0	1	3	0	4
3	5	6	5	1	5	2	5	1	6	12	4	5	5	1	3	4	3	2	1	5	5	8	10	7
1	4	3	0	4	2	2	1	5	94	353	92	5	6	7	3	6	4	2	4	9	4	8	4	1
9	3	8	1	3	6	9	1	9	355	1426	356	11	8	9	8	9	8	7	2	5	2	6	5	2
3	9	0	4	4	7	4	8	6	96	351	89	8	8	9	6	7	6	9	0	0	8	3	7	8
8	7	7	8	2	3	7	9	2	8	12	6	1	2	3	4	7	0	9	2	6	6	0	3	2
5	3	9	6	8	7	7	5	8	5	10	9	8	2	9	9	6	3	1	4	7	10	8	4	8
2	9	10	6	1	6	3	5	9	8	7	10	1	6	4	10	1	5	1	2	6	5	7	8	2
4	7	8	7	3	5	8	1	9	4	10	9	1	5	6	7	5	9	0	7	5	4	0	7	3
1	9	7	5	3	1	9	1	5	0	8	1	10	8	2	5	4	7	4	2	1	8	3	7	10
1	6	5	6	9	10	3	2	10	9	2	2	6	6	10	1	3	10	7	9	1	10	8	6	4
6	3	3	10	5	1	4	4	2	9	0	10	3	3	10	10	9	4	10	8	9	3	5	6	10
0	5	1	1	1	1	8	9	6	9	5	4	10	5	2	5	8	6	4	5	5	4	0	2	10
1	9	6	8	8	0	0	6	5	6	10	3	4	3	8	7	1	3	7	4	6	9	3	9	3
2	0	9	7	7	10	1	1	2	2	6	6	3	1	0	0	2	2	5	9	5	8	5	1	9

6	6	4	1	1	5	3	3	3	3	3	3	3	9	9	0	6	6	0	7	5	3	3	3	9	3	8	6	3	2	4	10	7
5	8	3	8	3	6	8	3	1	6	1	1	6	4	6	7	7	7	9	5	1	5	6	9	9	1	2	5	9	10	0	9	5
4	2	2	3	9	0	6	7	10	6	2	5	9	5	5	5	7	6	9	5	7	0	8	2	4	8	2	7	8	8	5	7	7
1	3	1	7	4	9	2	8	3	5	2	6	2	4	2	2	7	6	0	6	6	2	1	4	8	8	6	0	8	7	8	8	2
9	2	9	4	2	24	95	11	1	4	2	2	9	6	2	7	4	4	7	3	2	10	8	5	0	2	2	7	6	6	8	9	10
10	5	2	2	5	96	355	10	8	7	8	3	8	4	5	3	5	6	0	8	8	9	5	8	10	8	7	6	9	5	9	4	8
8	8	7	7	8	25	96	8	3	2	3	8	9	7	2	5	2	5	5	2	6	8	2	3	8	8	6	0	2	8	4	7	9
8	0	7	8	6	1	25	6	8	9	8	2	6	2	2	8	6	6	5	6	5	6	6	4	8	8	0	9	5	8	1	4	1
2	10	2	6	6	1	1	9	9	6	2	2	4	2	2	7	4	10	4	9	7	3	4	3	5	5	2	1	3	8	5	3	5
0	3	7	6	6	8	9	2	6	4	2	7	0	7	7	6	0	1	5	1	0	6	1	1	6	5	4	1	1	2	5	5	5
2	6	8	2	2	4	3	2	9	0	7	7	6	8	4	9	6	8	6	6	7	14	38	12	35	7	0	6	0	4	2	6	1
4	3	4	5	5	8	5	2	6	0	8	6	3	9	2	3	8	9	7	5	3	505	2041	510	8	7	4	2	4	2	1	4	5
1	1	8	2	4	4	9	7	9	0	3	7	0	4	7	4	0	9	7	0	6	2040	8236	2031	2040	6	2	4	2	8	8	8	6
8	7	4	5	0	1	6	8	6	0	4	8	2	8	0	2	6	3	7	6	3	508	2040	504	16	3	1	2	8	8	7	0	2
7	1	2	5	5	6	2	3	4	9	2	3	8	3	10	8	2	3	4	1	10	8	40	10	2	10	4	8	0	8	6	10	8
1	7	8	6	4	3	3	9	3	6	8	4	6	4	8	6	3	8	3	4	7	2	3	2	8	7	5	2	8	6	2	8	3
1	0	8	2	3	1	5	8	9	3	9	6	4	3	4	8	9	9	8	3	5	8	10	2	6	6	1	7	8	5	6	6	2
0	5	4	5	9	7	3	9	1	5	4	8	3	5	3	9	9	9	9	4	1	9	5	1	3	7	6	6	8	8	5	9	4
5	1	2	6	6	8	5	3	6	3	4	9	9	4	9	5	3	3	3	4	6	3	2	3	6	4	9	0	9	2	8	3	10
1	0	3	2	6	4	1	9	3	6	2	4	9	1	9	9	9	9	8	4	6	6	2	6	8	8	0	10	8	3	4	9	3
8	7	2	2	3	0	7	8	8	3	5	4	4	8	3	9	9	9	3	2	2	8	2	6	2	2	2	3	6	4	10	5	7
6	1	0	7	7	5	5	4	9	3	4	4	2	5	3	3	3	9	7	5	5	9	5	2	5	7	3	4	2	3	7	7	7

EA: In IOAA 2009, this table was printed on a single A3 sheet as a 50 × 50 grid. Here, this table is divided into two (Tables 4.2 and 4.3) to fit the size of the book. Table 4.3 should be placed to the right of Table 4.2 to complete the grid.

5

Physics of Stars and Planets

5.1 Theory

1. At what wavelength does a star with a surface temperature of 4000 K emit most intensely?
   (I07 - T08 - A)

2. Estimate the effective temperature of the photosphere of the Sun using the naked eye colour of the Sun. (I10 - T13 - A)

3. Calculate the total luminosity of a star whose surface temperature is 7500 K and whose radius is 2.5 times that of our Sun. Give your answer in units of solar luminosity.
   (I07 - T09 - A)

4. The difference in brightness between two main-sequence stars in an open cluster is 2 magnitudes. Their effective temperatures are 6000 K and 5000 K, respectively. Estimate the ratio of their radii. (I10 - T12 - A)

5. Luminous blue variable (LBV) stars vary greatly in visual brightness; however, their bolometric magnitude remains constant. Imagine an LBV star with a black-body temperature of 5000 K at its maximum visual brightness and 30,000 K at its minimum visual brightness. Calculate the ratio of the star radius between the two situations above.
   (I12 - T07 - A)

6. If the escape velocity from a solar mass object's surface exceeds the speed of light, what would be its radius? (I10 - T02 - A)

7. If the Sun were to collapse gravitationally to form a non-rotating black hole, what would be the radius of its event horizon (its Schwarzschild radius)? (I07 - T14 - A)

8. Calculate the mean mass density for the region inside event horizon of a super-massive black hole with total mass $1 \times 10^8 \, M_\odot$ inside the Schwarzschild radius. (I09 - T01 - A)

9. Most of the energy emitted by the Sun is generated in its core via the so-called proton–proton (p–p) nuclear chain reaction, which has three different branches. The most energetic branch transforms $2He^3$ into $He^4 + 2H^1$. Calculate the energy released (in MeV) and the fractional reduction of the mass of the particles involved in this reaction. (I12 - T06 - A)

10. A star emits radiation with wavelength values in a narrow range $\Delta\lambda \ll \lambda$, i.e., the wavelength has values between λ and $\lambda + \Delta\lambda$. According to Planck's relationship (for an absolute black body), the energy emitted by star per unit time through unit of area of its surface, per unit wavelength is given by

$$I(\lambda) = \frac{2\pi h c^2}{\lambda^5 \left(e^{\frac{hc}{\lambda kT}} - 1 \right)}$$
(5.1)

Find the relation between two wavelengths λ_1 and λ_2, both in the range $\Delta\lambda$, if we know $I(\lambda_1) = 1.1 I(\lambda_2)$ and $hc = \lambda kT$.   (I14 - T6 - B)

11. What would be the effective temperature on the Earth's surface if we ignore the greenhouse effect but take into account the Earth's non-vanishing albedo? Assume that the Earth's orbit around the Sun is circular.   (I13 - T1 - B)

12. **Spaceship orbiting the Sun:** A spherical spaceship orbits (radius $= R_N$) the Sun on a circular orbit, and spins around an axis of rotation that is perpendicular to the orbital plane of the spaceship. The temperature on the exterior surface of the ship is T_N. Assume that the spaceship is a perfect black body and there is no activity inside it. Find the apparent magnitude of the Sun and the angular diameter of the Sun as seen by an astronaut onboard the spaceship.   (I14 - T8 - B)

13. The radiation coming to the Earth from the Sun must penetrate the Earth's atmosphere before reaching the Earth's surface. The Earth also releases radiation into its environment and this radiation must penetrate the Earth's atmosphere before going to outer space. In general, the transmittance (t_1) of solar radiation during its penetration towards the Earth's surface (t_1) is higher than that of the radiation from the Earth (t_2). Let $T_\odot$ be the effective temperature of the Sun, $R_\odot$ the radius of the Sun, $R_\oplus$ the radius of the Earth, and $d_{\oplus-\odot}$ the distance between the Sun and the Earth. Derive the temperature of the Earth's surface as a function of the aforementioned parameters.   (I08 - T09 - B)

14. Suppose a star has a mass of $20\,M_\odot$. If 20% of the star's mass is now in the form of helium, calculate the helium burning lifetime of this star. Assume that the luminosity of the star is $100 L_\odot$, of which 30% is contributed by helium burning. Assume no additional helium is being produced at this time and all the helium is available for burning. The fusion of helium into carbon by the triple-α process is given by $3\,^4He \rightarrow\,^{12}C + \gamma$.   (I08 - T04 - B)

15. A main-sequence star at a distance of 20 pc is barely visible through a certain space-based telescope which can record all wavelengths. The star will eventually move up along the giant branch, during which time its temperature will drop by a factor of 3 and its radius will increase 100-fold. What is the new maximum distance at which the star can still be (barely) seen using the same telescope?   (I08 - T07 - B)

16. Estimate the number of solar neutrinos which should pass through a 1 m² area of the Earth's surface perpendicular to the Sun every second. Use the fact that each fusion reaction in the Sun produces 26.8 MeV of energy and 2 neutrinos.   (I11 - T14 - B)

17. If 0.8% of the initial total solar mass could be transformed into energy during the lifetime of the Sun, estimate the maximum possible lifetime for the Sun. Assume that solar luminosity remains constant.   (I10 - T05 - B)

18. Estimate the minimum energy a proton would need to penetrate the Earth's magnetosphere. Assume that the initial penetration is perpendicular to a belt of constant magnetic field $30\,\mu T$ and thickness 1.0×10^4 km. Prepare a sketch of the particle trajectory. (Note that at such high energies, the momentum can be replaced by the expression E/c. Ignore any radiative effects).   (I11 - T10 - B)

19. A main-sequence star with radius and mass $R = 4R_\odot$ and $M = 6M_\odot$ has an average magnetic field of 10^{-4}T. Calculate the strength of the magnetic field of the star when it evolves to a neutron star with a radius of 20 km.   (I09 - T10 - B)

20. **Cosmic radiation:** During studies on cosmic radiation, a neutral unstable particle, called π^0 meson, was identified. The rest-mass of π^0 meson was much larger than the rest-mass of the electron. Studies revealed that during its flight, the π^0 meson disintegrates into two

photons. Find an expression for the initial velocity of the π^0 meson, if after its disintegration, one of the photons has the maximum possible energy E_{max} and consequently, the other photon has the minimum possible energy E_{min}. Note that the expression for the relativistic energy of any particle is $E^2 = P^2C^2 + m_0^2c^4$. (I14 - T3 - B)

21. **A planet and its surface temperature:** A fast-rotating planet of radius R with surface albedo α is orbiting a star of luminosity L. The orbital radius is d. It is assumed that at equilibrium all of the energy absorbed by the planet is re-emitted as black-body radiation. (I07 - T16 - B)

    (a) What is the radiation flux from the star at the planet's surface?
    (b) What is the total energy absorbed by the planet per unit time?
    (c) What is the reflected luminosity of the planet?
    (d) What is the average black-body temperature of the planet's surface?
    (e) If we were to assume that one side of the planet is always facing the star, what would be the average surface temperature of that side?
    (f) For the planet in Question 21d, if $\alpha = 0.25$, $d = 1.523$ AU and $L = L_\odot$, calculate the surface temperature of the planet in Kelvins.

22. It is estimated that the Sun will have spent a total of about $t_1 = 10$ billion years on the main sequence before evolving away from it. Using the graph given in Fig. 5.1 estimate the corresponding amount of time, t_2, if the Sun were five times more massive.   (I13 - T3 - B)

    EA: In reality, the Mass–Luminosity relation for low-mass stars and intermediate-mass stars is as follows.

    $$L \propto M^4 (0.43M_\odot \le M \le 2M_\odot)$$

    $$\propto M^{3.5} (2M_\odot \le M \le 20M_\odot) \qquad (5.2)$$

    Obtain a better estimate for the main-sequence lifetime of a five-solar-mass star.

23. The graph in Fig. 5.1 gives the Mass–Luminosity relation for main-sequence stars. Find an expression for the main-sequence lifetime of each star as a function of the corresponding main-sequence lifetime of the Sun. Assume that the total mass fraction of any star converted to energy η_{star} is known and the luminosity of each star remains constant during its entire main-sequence life. (I14 - T5 - B)

24. An astronaut with mass $M = 100$ kg steps out of the spaceship for a repair mission. He has to repair a satellite at rest relative to the spaceship, about $d = 90$ m away from it. After he finishes his job, he realizes that the systems designed to ensure his return to the spaceship are broken. He also observes that he has air only for 3 minutes. He notices that he has a vacuum-sealed cylindrical can (base section $S = 30$ cm²) firmly attached to his glove, with some ice ($m = 200$ g, $T = 272$ K) inside. The can is not completely filled with ice.

    Determine if the astronaut will be able to return safely to the shuttle, before his air reserve empties, if he manages to open the can in the correct direction. Note that he cannot throw away any of his equipment or touch the satellite. You can assume that the pressure of the saturated water vapour at 272 K is $p_s = 550$ Pa and the molar mass of water is 18 g mol⁻¹. (I14 - T4 - C)

25. Calculate how much the radius of the Earth's orbit increases as a result of the Sun losing mass due to thermo-nuclear reactions at its centre in 100 years. Assume that the Earth's orbit remains circular during this period. (I09 - T12 – C)

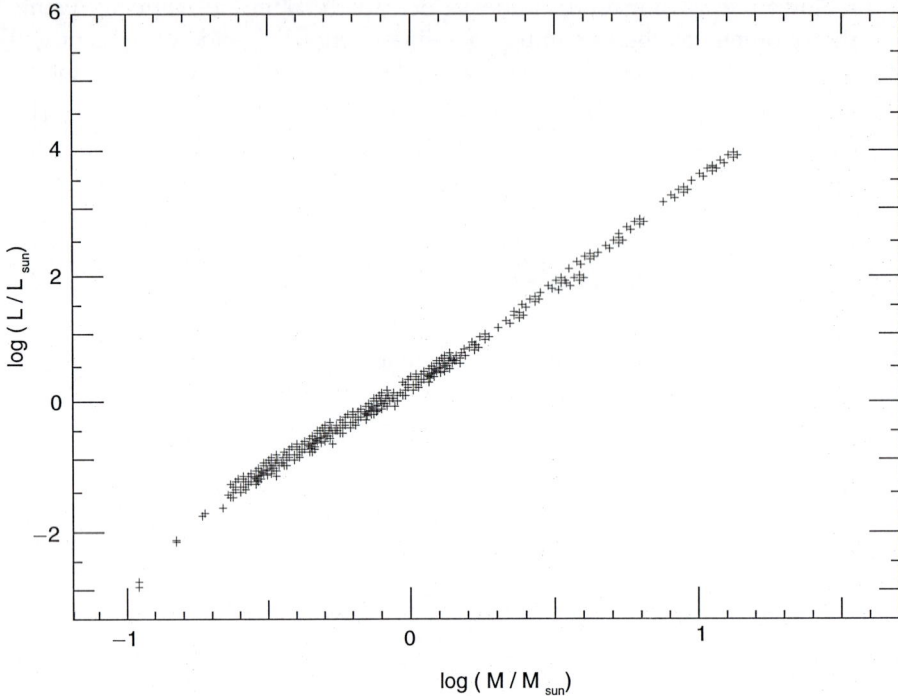

Fig. 5.1 *Mass–Luminosity relation for low- and intermediate-mass stars*

26. A pulsar, located 1000 pc from the Earth and 10,000 times more luminous than our Sun, emits radiation only from its two opposite poles, creating a homogeneous emission beam shaped like a double cone with an opening angle $\alpha = 4°$. Assuming the angle between the rotation axis and the emission axis is 30°, and random orientation of the pulsar beams in relation to an observer on Earth, what is the probability of detecting the pulses? In case we can see it, what is the apparent bolometric magnitude of the pulsar?   (I12 - T08 - C)

5.2 Data Analysis

1. A few facts about the photometry of asteroids:

   - Asteroids are small, irregularly shaped solar system objects that orbit the Sun in approximately elliptical orbits.
   - Their brightness, observed at a given instant from the Earth, depends on the surface area illuminated by the Sun and the part of the asteroid which is visible to the observer. Both vary as the asteroid moves.
   - The way sunlight is reflected by the surface of the asteroid depends on its texture and on the angle between the Sun, the asteroid and the observer (phase angle), which varies as the Earth and the asteroid move along their orbits. In particular, asteroids with surfaces covered by fine dust (called regoliths) exhibit a sharp increase in brightness at phase angles φ close to zero (i.e., when they are close to opposition).

Table 5.1 *Geometric configuration of the asteroid on different nights*

Night	D	R	φ	M_{star}
A	0.36	1.35	0.0	8.2
B	1.15	2.13	8.6	8.0
C	2.70	1.89	15.6	8.1

- Since the observed flux of any source decreases with the square of the distance, the observed magnitude of an asteroid also depends on its distance from the Sun and from the observer at the time of the observation. Their apparent magnitude (m) outside the atmosphere is then

$$M(t) = m_r(t) + 5\log(RD) \tag{5.3}$$

where m_r is usually called reduced magnitude (the magnitude the asteroid would have if its distance from the Sun and the Earth were reduced to 1 AU) and depends only on the visible illuminated surface area and on phase angle effects. R and D are the heliocentric and geocentric distances, respectively.

Consider now the following scenario. Light curves of a given asteroid were obtained at three different nights at different points of its orbit, and at each time a photometric standard star was observed in the same frame of the asteroid. Table 5.1 shows the geometric configuration of the asteroid each night (phase angle φ in degrees, R and D in AUs), and the catalogued calibrated magnitude of the same standard star. Consider this calibrated magnitude as the final apparent magnitude after correcting for all the extinction effects.

Table 5.2 contains the time of each observation (in hours) as an offset from the first observation of that night, the air mass and the uncalibrated magnitude of the asteroid and the uncalibrated magnitude of the star for each night.

Air mass is the dimensionless thickness of the atmosphere along the line of sight, and is equal to 1 when the observer is looking towards zenith.

(a) Plot the star's uncalibrated magnitude versus air mass for each set.

(b) Calculate the extinction coeffcient for each night. Note that the magnitude outside the atmosphere is given by

$$M = m - \beta X + A \tag{5.4}$$

where β is the extinction coeffcient, A is the zero point coeffcient for the night, X is the air mass of the observation and m is the magnitude measured from the ground.

You are also given that in the method of least squares estimation of angular coeffcients, for a straight line described by

$$yi = \alpha + \beta x_i \tag{5.5}$$

$$\beta = \frac{\sum_{i=1}^{n} x_i y_i - \frac{1}{n}\sum_{i=1}^{n} x_i \sum_{i=1}^{n} y_i}{\sum_{i=1}^{n} (x_i)^2 - \frac{1}{n}\left(\sum_{i=1}^{n} x^i\right)^2} \tag{5.6}$$

Table 5.2 *Magnitudes of the asteroid and reference star for three nights (A, B and C) at different times*

Δt (hr)	Air Mass	Night A		Night B		Night C	
		m_{ast}	m_{star}	m_{ast}	m_{star}	m_{ast}	m_{star}
0	1.28	7.44	8.67	11.64	8.58	13.24	8.38
0.44	1.18	7.38	8.62	11.53	8.54	13.21	8.36
0.89	1.11	7.34	8.59	11.56	8.6	13.13	8.34
1.33	1.06	7.28	8.58	11.49	8.52	13.11	8.33
1.77	1.02	7.32	8.58	11.58	8.48	13.11	8.32
2.21	1	7.33	8.56	11.79	8.63	13.15	8.32
2.66	1	7.33	8.56	11.67	8.53	13.17	8.32
3.1	1.01	7.3	8.56	11.53	8.46	13.17	8.32
3.54	1.03	7.27	8.58	11.47	8.48	13.13	8.33
3.99	1.07	7.27	8.58	11.63	8.67	13.15	8.34
4.43	1.13	7.31	8.61	11.51	8.51	13.14	8.34
4.87	1.21	7.37	8.63	11.65	8.55	13.14	8.37
5.31	1.32	7.42	8.67	11.77	8.61	13.21	8.38
5.76	1.48	7.49	8.73	11.88	8.75	13.3	8.43
6.2	1.71	7.59	8.81	11.86	8.78	13.34	8.47
6.64	2.06	7.69	8.92	12.03	9.03	13.39	8.54
7.09	2.62	7.87	9.14	12.14	9.19	13.44	8.65
7.53	3.67	8.2	9.49	12.63	9.65	13.67	8.87

(c) Were the observations affected by clouds in one night?

(d) Plot the corrected magnitude of the asteroid against time for each set of observations. If the standard star is in the same frame as the object, the corrected magnitude of the object can be obtained by

$$M_{ast} = m_{ast} - m_{star} + M_{star} \qquad (5.7)$$

where capital letters denote the corrected and small letters denote the uncorrected magnitudes.

(e) Determine the rotation period of the asteroid for each night. Consider that the light curve for this asteroid has two minima and two maxima, and that the semi-period is the average of intervals between the two maxima and the two minima.

(f) Determine the amplitude (difference between maximum and minimum) of the light curve for each night.

(g) Plot the corrected reduced magnitude m_r (use the mean value of each light curve) versus phase angle φ.

(h) Calculate the angular coeffcient (slope) of the phase curve (the plot in the previous part) considering only the points away from the opposition.

(i) Is there any reason to assume a surface covered by fine dust (regolith)?   (I12 - D01 - B)

2. **The age of the meteorites:** The basic equation of radioactive decay can be written as $N(t) = N_0 e^{-\lambda t}$, where $N(t)$ and N_0 are the number of remaining atoms of the radioactive isotope (or parent isotope) at time t and its initial number at $t = 0$, respectively, while λ is the decay constant. The decay of the parent produces daughter nuclides $D(t)$, or radiogenics, which is defined as $D(t) = N_0 - N(t)$.

A group of astronomers investigated a number of meteorite samples to determine their ages. They took samples from two meteorites, one containing Allende chondrites (A) and the other one containing basaltic achondrite (B). By examining these samples, they measured the abundance of ^{87}Rb and ^{87}Sr, assuming that ^{87}Sr was entirely produced by the decay of ^{87}Rb. The value of λ is 1.42×10^{-11} per year for this isotopic decay of ^{87}Rb. In addition, quantities of non-radiogenic element ^{86}Sr were also measured. The results of measurement are given in the table below, expressed in ppm (parts per million).   (I08 - D03 - C)

Sample	Type	^{86}Sr (ppm)	^{87}Rb (ppm)	^{87}Sr (ppm)
1	A	29.6	0.3	20.7
2	B	58.7	68.5	44.7
3	B	74.2	14.4	52.9
4	A	40.2	7.0	28.6
5	A	19.7	0.4	13.8
6	B	37.9	31.6	28.4
7	A	33.4	4.0	23.6
8	B	29.8	105.0	26.4
9	A	9.8	0.8	6.9
10	B	18.5	44.0	15.4

(a) Express the time t in term of $\dfrac{D(t)}{N(t)}$.

(b) Determine the half-life $T_{1/2}$, i.e., the time required to obtain a half number of parents after decay.

(c) Knowledge of the ratio between the two isotopes is more valuable than only the absolute abundance of each isotope. It is quite likely that there was some strontium present initially. By taking $\dfrac{^{87}Rb}{^{86}Sr}$ as an independent variable and $\dfrac{^{87}Sr}{^{86}Sr}$ as a dependent variable, establish a simple linear regression model that describes the data.

(d) Plot $\dfrac{^{87}Rb}{^{86}Sr}$ versus $\dfrac{^{87}Sr}{^{86}Sr}$ and also the regression line for each type of meteorite.

(e) Subsequently, help the astronomers determine the age of each type of meteorite and error in its estimation. Which type is older?

(f) Determine the initial value of $\left(\dfrac{^{87}Sr}{^{86}Sr}\right)_0$ for each type of meteorite along with errors.

Notes:

- Due to the unique nature of this problem, you may have to use a minimum of 7 decimal digits for intermediate calculations. This requirement is not consistant with the regular practice of deciding the number of decimal digits as per the significant figures. Nonetheless, it is essential. If one uses lower precision, then values of regression coeffcients will change significantly.

If we fit a straight line $Y = a + bX$ to a set of points (X_i, Y_i) via simple linear regression, then

$$b = \frac{S_{xy}}{S_{xx}} \tag{5.8}$$

$$a = \bar{y} - b\bar{x} \tag{5.9}$$

$$S_a = \sqrt{\frac{S_{yy} - \dfrac{S^2xy}{S_{xx}}}{(n-2)S_{xx}} \times \sum x_i^2} \tag{5.10}$$

$$S_b = \sqrt{\frac{S_{yy} - \dfrac{S^2xy}{S_{xx}}}{(n-2)S_{xx}}} \tag{5.11}$$

where S_a and S_b are standard deviations in the estimation of a and b

$$S_{xx} = \sum_{i=1}^{n} X_i^2 - \frac{1}{n}\left(\sum_{i=1}^{n} X_i\right)^2 \tag{5.12}$$

$$S_{yy} = \sum_{i=1}^{n} Y_i^2 - \frac{1}{n}\left(\sum_{i=1}^{n} Y_i\right)^2 \tag{5.13}$$

$$S_{xy} = \sum_{i=1}^{n} X_iY_i - \frac{1}{n}\left(\sum_{i=1}^{n} X_i\right)\left(\sum_{i=1}^{n} Y_i\right) \tag{5.14}$$

3. **Thermodynamic test:** A hypothetical shuttle is launched to investigate the atmosphere (100% CO_2) of two planets P_1 and P_2. The atmosphere is in static thermodynamic equilibrium. When the shuttle is near each planet, a radio probe is launched towards that planet, in the vertical direction (in the direction of the planet's radius). When the radio probe reaches terminal velocity, it starts sending values of the pressure of the atmosphere. The atmospheric pressure (conventional units) of planet P_1 as a function of the time of descent is plotted in Fig. 5.2 (left). When the probe touches the surface of planet P_1, it sends the value of the temperature $T_0 = 700$ K and the value of gravitational acceleration $g_1 = 10$ ms^{-2}.

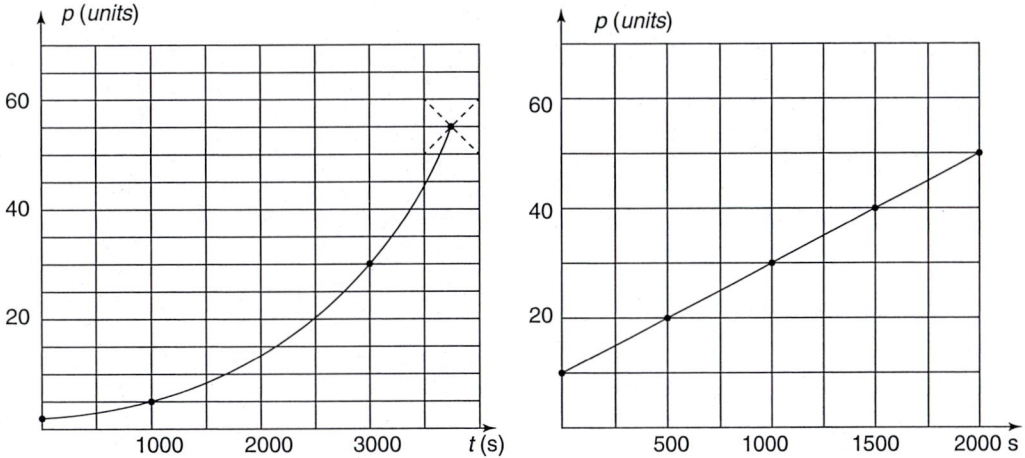

Fig. 5.2   *Atmospheric pressure on planet P_1 (left) and P_2 (right)*

The gravitational acceleration on both the planets is assumed to be constant during uniform descent of the radio probes.   (I14 - D02 - B)

(a) Find the altitude h_1 from where the radio probe R_1 starts the uniform descent and thus starts transmitting information. The molar mass of CO_2 is $\mu = 44$ g mol^{-1}.

(b) Find the temperature of planet P_1 at altitude $h = 39.6$ km.

(c) The atmospheric pressure (conventional units) of planet P_2 as a function of the time of descent is plotted in Fig. 5.2 (right). When the probe touches the surface of planet P_2, it sends the value of the temperature $T_0 = 750$ K and the value of gravitational acceleration $g_2 = 8$ ms^{-2}.

Draw the dependency graphs for $p = f(h)$ and $T = f(h)$ in the CO_2 atmosphere of planet P_2.

6

Stellar Observations

6.1 Theory

1. In a binary system, the apparent magnitude of the primary star is 1.0 and that of the secondary star is 2.0. Find the maximum combined magnitude of this system.(I10 - T01 - A)

2. A supernova shines with a luminosity 10^{10} times that of the Sun. If such a supernova appears in our sky as bright as the mid-day Sun, how far away (in parsec) from us must it be located? (I07 - T11 - A)

3. The magnitude of the faintest star you can see with the naked eye is $m = 6$, whereas that of the brightest star in the sky is $m = -1.5$. What is the energy–flux ratio of the faintest to that of the brightest star? (I07 - T15 - A)

4. What would be a full moon's visual magnitude if the Moon's albedo was equal to 1? (I12 - T04 - A)

5. A K-type star in the main sequence has a luminosity of 0.40 $L_\odot$. This star is observed to have a flux of 6.23×10^{-14} W/m^2. What is the distance (in parsec) to this star? You may ignore the atmospheric effect. (I07 - T10 - A)

6. Estimate the number of photons per second that arrive on our eye at $\lambda = 550$ nm (V-band) from a G2 main-sequence star with apparent magnitude $m = 6$ (the threshold of naked eye visibility). Assume all the radiation from this star is in $\lambda = 550$ nm. (I09 - T02 - A)

7. **Pressure of light**: For an observer on Earth, the pressure of the radiation emitted by the Sun is $p_{rad'\odot}$ and the pressure of the radiation emitted by a star Σ is $p_{rad'}\Sigma$. Calculate the apparent visual magnitude of star Σ, if the apparent visual magnitude of the Sun is $m_\odot$. (I14 - T7 - B)

8. We are interested in finding habitable exoplanets. One way to achieve this is through the dimming of the star, when the exoplanet transits across the stellar disk and blocks a fraction of the light. Estimate the maximum luminosity ratio for an Earth-like planet orbiting a star similar to the Sun. (I10 - T07 - B)

9. Recently in London, because of a very thick layer of fog, the visual magnitude of the Sun became equal to the (usual – as observed during cloudless nights) magnitude of the full moon. Assuming that the reduction in the intensity of light due to the fog is given by an exponential equation, calculate the exponential coefficient, τ, which is usually called optical depth. (I13 - T13 - B)

10. A star has a measured I-band magnitude of 22.0. How many photons per second are detected from this star by the Gemini telescope (8-m diameter)? Assume that the overall quantum efficiency is 40% and the filter passband is flat. (I10 - T09 - B)

Filter	λ_0 (nm)	$\Delta\lambda$ (nm)	F_{Vega} $(Wm^{-2}nm^{-1})$
I	8.00×10^2	24.0	8.30×10^{-12}

11. What is the angular amplitude of the oscillatory motion of the Sun, due to the existence of Jupiter, as measured by an observer located at Barnard's Star? What is the period of this oscillation?   (I11 - T11 - B)

12. A star has an effective temperature $T_{eff} = 8700$ K, absolute magnitude $M = 1.6$ mag and apparent magnitude $m = 7.2$ mag. Find (a) the star's distance d, (b) its luminosity L and (c) its radius R. (Ignore extinction).   (I13 - T6 - B)

13. A star has visual apparent magnitude $m_v = 12.2$ mag, parallax $p = 0.001''$ and effective temperature $T_{eff} = 4000$ K. Its bolometric correction is BC $= -0.6$ mag.
(a) Find its luminosity as a function of solar luminosity.
(b) Is the star a red giant, a blue giant or a red dwarf?   (I13 - T7 - B)

14. An old planetary nebula with a white dwarf (WD) in its centre, is located 50 pc away from Earth. In the exact same direction, but behind the nebula, lies another WD, identical to the first, but located 150 pc from the Earth. Consider that the two WDs have the same absolute bolometric magnitude of +14.2 and intrinsic colour indices $(B - V)_0 = 0.300$ and $(U - V)_0 = 0.330$. Extinction occurs in the interstellar medium and in the planetary nebula.

When we measure the colour indices for the closer WD (the one that lies at the centre of the nebula), we find the values $(B - V)_1 = 0.327$ and $(U - B)_1 = 0.038$. In this part of the galaxy, the interstellar extinction rates are 1.50, 1.23 and 1.00 magnitudes per kiloparsec for the filters U, B and V, respectively. Calculate the colour indices for the second star as they would be measured by us.   (I12 - T09 - C)

15. An astronomer on the Earth observes a globular cluster, which has an angular diameter α and contains N stars, each one with the same absolute magnitude M_0 and is at a distance D from the Earth. A biologist is sitting at the centre of that cluster.   (I12 - T16 – C)

(a) What is the difference between the combined visual magnitudes of all stars observed by the astronomer and the biologist? Consider that the spatial distribution of stars in the cluster is perfectly homogeneous and the biologist is measuring the combined magnitude of the entire cluster.

(b) What is the diameter of the astronomer's telescope, considering that he wants to visualise the cluster with the same brightness as the biologist?

(c) What would be the difference between the visual magnitudes observed by the two scientists if the diameter of the field of view of the biologist is also α.

16. A UBV photometric (UBV Johnson's) observation of a star gives $U = 8.15$, $B = 8.50$ and $V = 8.14$. Based on the spectral class, one obtains the intrinsic colour $(U - B)_0 = -0.45$. If the star is known to have a radius of $2.3R_\odot$, absolute bolometric magnitude of -0.25 and bolometric correction (BC) of -0.15, determine:

(a) The intrinsic magnitudes U_0, B_0 and V_0 of the star
(b) The effective temperature of the star
(c) The distance to the star

Note: For typical interstellar matter, take the ratio of total extinction to selective extinction $R_V = 3.2$ and the colour excess (i.e., selective extinction) in $(B - V)$ to be about 72% of the colour excess in $(U - B)$.   (I08 - T17 - D)

6.2 Data Analysis

1. Fig. 6.1 shows a photograph of the sky in the vicinity of the Hyades open cluster. The V-filter in Johnson's photometric system was used. Fig. 6.2 is a chart of the region with known V-magnitudes (m_V) of several stars (note that in order to avoid confusion with the stars, no decimal point is used; i.e., a magnitude $m_V = 8.1$ is noted as 81).   (I13 - D03 - A)

   Hint: Some of the stars may not be in the chart.

   (a) Identify as many of the stars shown with a number and an arrow in Fig. 6.2 and mark them on Fig. 6.1.

   (b) Comparing the V-magnitudes of the known stars in Fig. 6.1, estimate the V-magnitudes of the stars shown with a number and an arrow in Fig. 6.2.

2. **Light curves of stars:** A pulsating variable star KZ Hydrae was observed with a telescope equipped with a CCD camera. Fig. 6.3 shows a CCD image of KZ Hyd marked together with the comparison star and the check star. Table 6.1 lists the observation time in heliocentric Julian dates ($HJD* = HJD - 2453800$), the magnitude differences of KZ Hyd and the check star relative to the comparison star in the V and R bands.

   (a) Draw the light curves of KZ Hyd relative to the comparison star in the V and R bands.

   (b) What are the average magnitude differences of KZ Hyd relative to the comparison star in the V and R bands?

   (c) What are the photometric precisions in V and R?

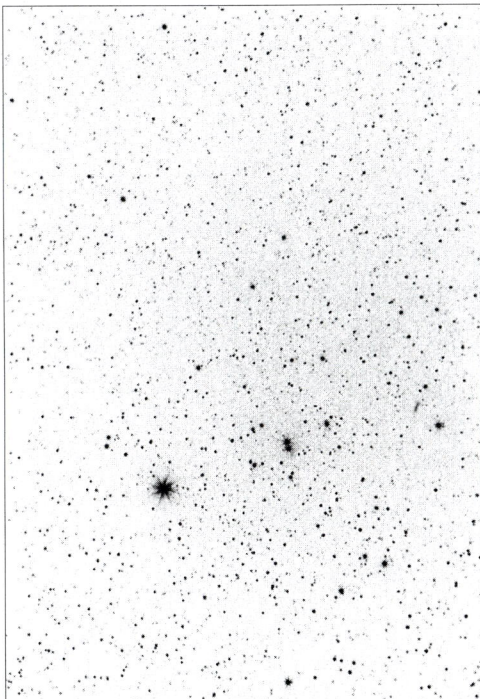

Fig. 6.1 *Photograph of the Hyades cluster*

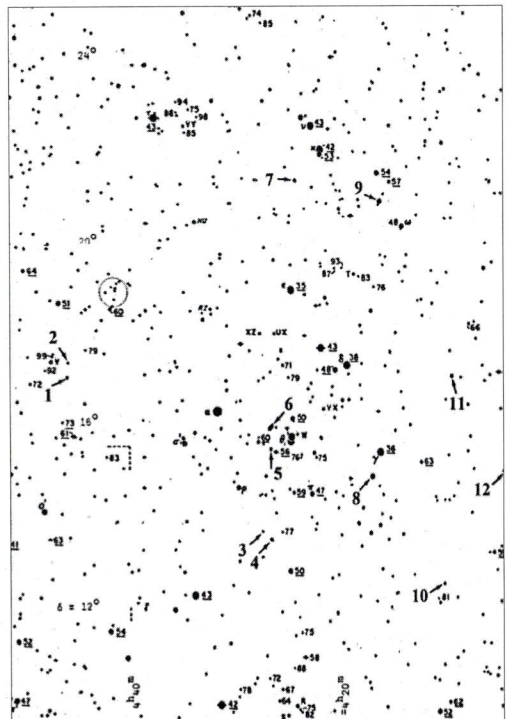

Fig. 6.2 *Astronomical chart of the Hyades cluster region*

Table 6.1 *Data for the light curves of KZ Hyd in V and R. δV and δR are magnitude differences in the V and R bands for KZ Hyd relative to the comparison star in V and R. $δV_{chk}$ and $δR_{chk}$ are the same for the check star.*

HJD*	δV	$δV_{chk}$	HJD*	δR	$δR_{chk}$
3.162	0.068	4.434	3.1679	0.260	2.789
3.1643	0.029	4.445	3.1702	0.185	2.802
3.1667	−0.011	4.287	3.1725	−0.010	2.789
3.1691	−0.100	4.437	3.1749	−0.147	2.809
3.1714	−0.310	4.468	3.1772	−0.152	2.809
3.1737	−0.641	4.501	3.1796	−0.110	2.789
3.1761	−0.736	4.457	3.1820	−0.044	2.803
3.1784	−0.698	4.378	3.1866	0.075	2.805
3.1808	−0.588	4.462	3.1890	0.122	2.793
3.1831	−0.499	4.326	3.1914	0.151	2.793
3.1855	−0.390	4.431	3.1938	0.177	2.782
3.1878	−0.297	4.522	3.1962	0.211	2.795
3.1902	−0.230	4.258	3.1986	0.235	2.796
3.1926	−0.177	4.389	3.2011	0.253	2.788
3.195	−0.129	4.449	3.2035	0.277	2.796
3.1974	−0.072	4.394	3.2059	0.288	2.783
3.1998	−0.036	4.362	3.2083	0.296	2.796
3.2023	−0.001	4.394	3.2108	0.302	2.791
3.2047	0.016	4.363	3.2132	0.292	2.806
3.2071	0.024	4.439	3.2157	0.285	2.779
3.2096	0.036	4.078	3.2181	0.298	2.779
3.2120	0.020	4.377	3.2206	0.312	2.787
3.2145	0.001	4.360	3.2231	0.313	2.804
3.2169	0.001	4.325	3.2255	0.281	2.796
3.2194	0.005	4.355	3.2280	0.239	2.795
3.2219	0.041	4.474	3.2306	0.115	2.792
3.2243	0.009	4.369	3.2330	−0.111	2.788
3.2267	−0.043	4.330	3.2354	−0.165	2.793
3.2293	−0.183	4.321	3.2378	−0.152	2.781
3.2318	−0.508	4.370	3.2403	−0.088	2.787
3.2342	−0.757	4.423	3.2428	−0.014	2.780
3.2366	−0.762	4.373	3.2452	0.044	2.766
3.2390	−0.691	4.427	3.2476	0.100	2.806
3.2415	−0.591	4.483	3.2500	0.119	2.791
3.2440	−0.445	4.452	3.2524	0.140	2.797
3.2463	−0.295	4.262	3.2548	0.190	2.825

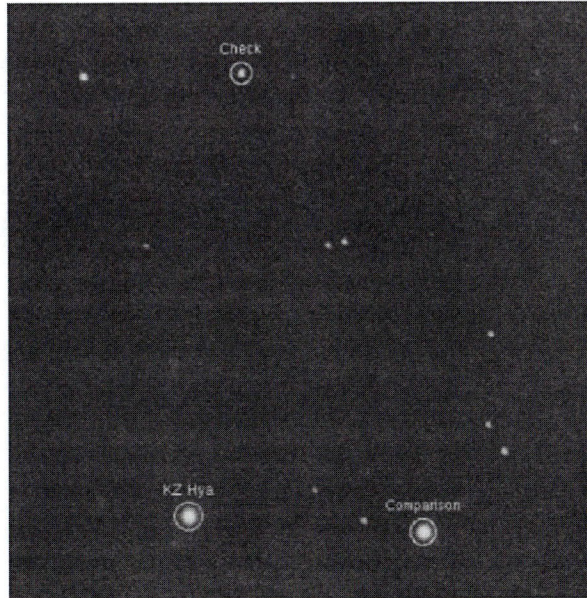

Fig. 6.3 *Image showing star KZ Hydrae*

(d) Estimate the pulsation periods of KZ Hyd in V and R.

(e) Give the estimation of the peak-to-peak pulsation amplitudes of KZ Hyd in V and R.

(f) What is the phase delay between the V and R bands, in terms of the pulsation period?

(I10 - D02 - A)

3. You are given five recent photographs of the solar photosphere (adapted from www.spaceweather.com) shot at exactly the same time every two days (1 May 2013–9 May 2013) in equatorial coordinates (Figs 6.4, 6.5, 6.6, 6.7 and 6.8). You are also given two transparent Stonyhurst grids (Figs 6.10 and 6.9) on transparent sheets, which display heliocentric coordinates (heliocentric longitude $\lambda_\odot$ and heliocentric latitude $\beta_\odot$). They cover the interval between 28 April and 15 May. As the ecliptic plane is slightly inclined to the solar equator, the solar equator seems to move up and down a little more than 7 degrees from the centre of the solar disc over the course of a year. This angle, B_0, varies sinusoidally through the year. Furthermore, the axis of rotation of the Sun, as seen from the Earth, does not coincide with the axis of rotation of the Earth. The angle on the plane of the sky between the two axes P_0 also varies through the year. The numerical value of these angles (B_0 and P_0) are indicated on each of the five images of the Sun.   (I13 - D02 - A)

(a) Mark the axis of rotation of the Sun on each photograph.

(b) Choose three prominent sunspots that can be followed in all (or most) photographs and mark them as S1, S2 and S3 on the photos. Using the appropriate Stonyhurst grids, find their coordinates ($\lambda_\odot$, $\beta_\odot$) for each day (1 May to 9 May).

(c) Plot the graphs $\Delta\lambda_\odot/\Delta t$ for each sunspot, where $\Delta\lambda_\odot$ is measured with respect to the first reading.

(d) Calculate its synodic period (P) of rotation in days for each sunspot.

(e) Estimate the average synodic period ($P_\odot$) of rotation of the Sun in days.

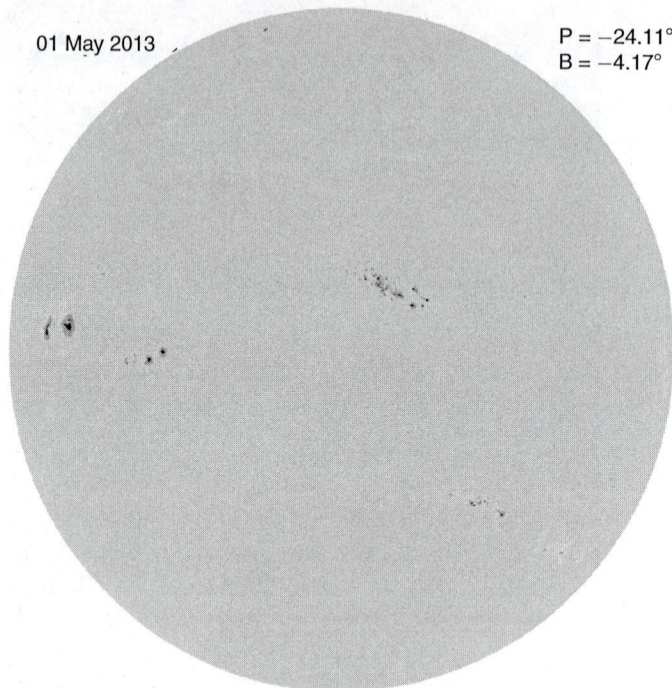

Fig. 6.4 *Image of the Sun for 1 May 2013*

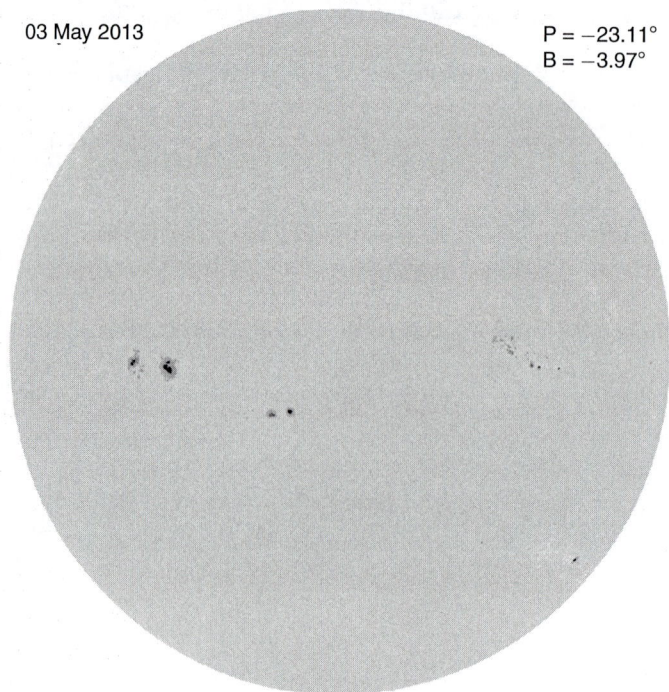

Fig. 6.5 *Image of the Sun for 3 May 2013*

05 May 2013

P = −23.34°
B = −3.76°

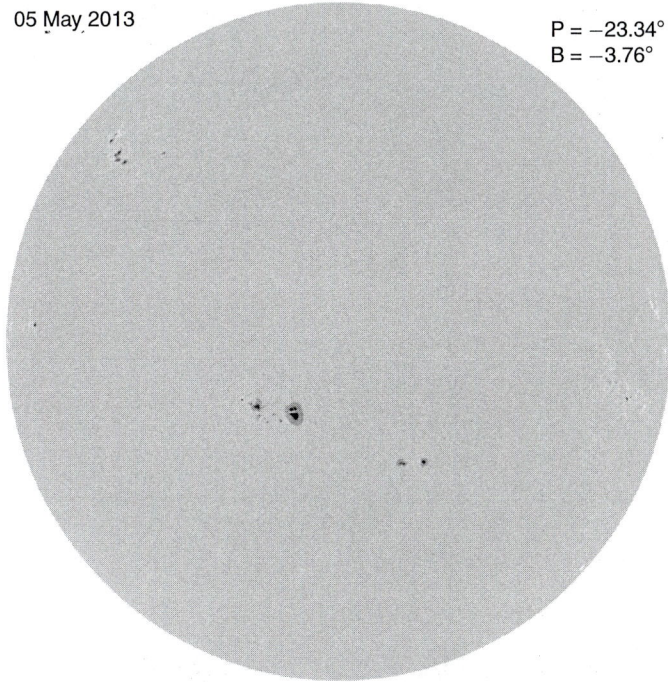

Fig. 6.6   *Image of the Sun for 5 May 2013*

07 May 2013

P = −22.92°
B = −3.55°

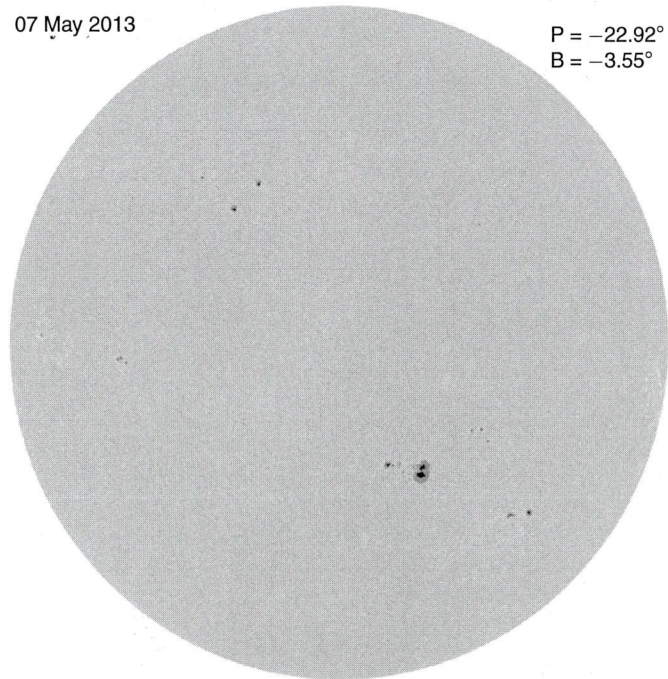

Fig. 6.7   *Image of the Sun for 7 May 2013*

09 May 2013

P = −22.46°
B = −3.33°

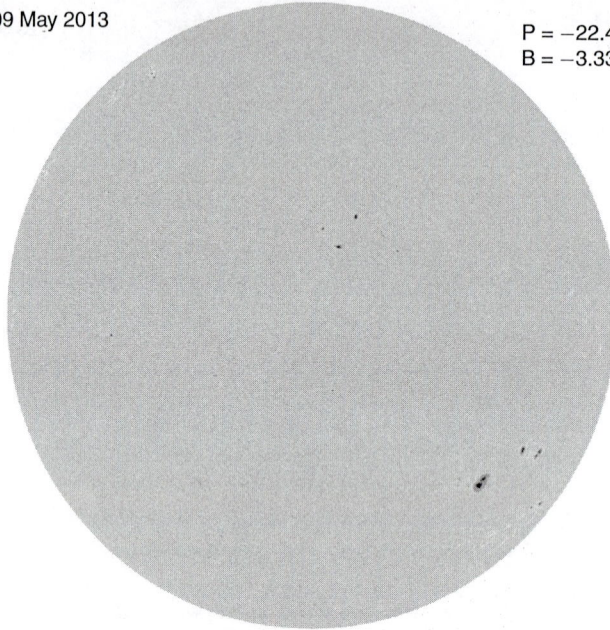

Fig. 6.8   *Image of the Sun for 9 May 2013*

−4°

APRIL 28 TO MAY 6

40

30

20

10

80 70 60 50 40 30 20 10 0 10 20 30 40 50 60 70 80

10

20

30

40

+4°

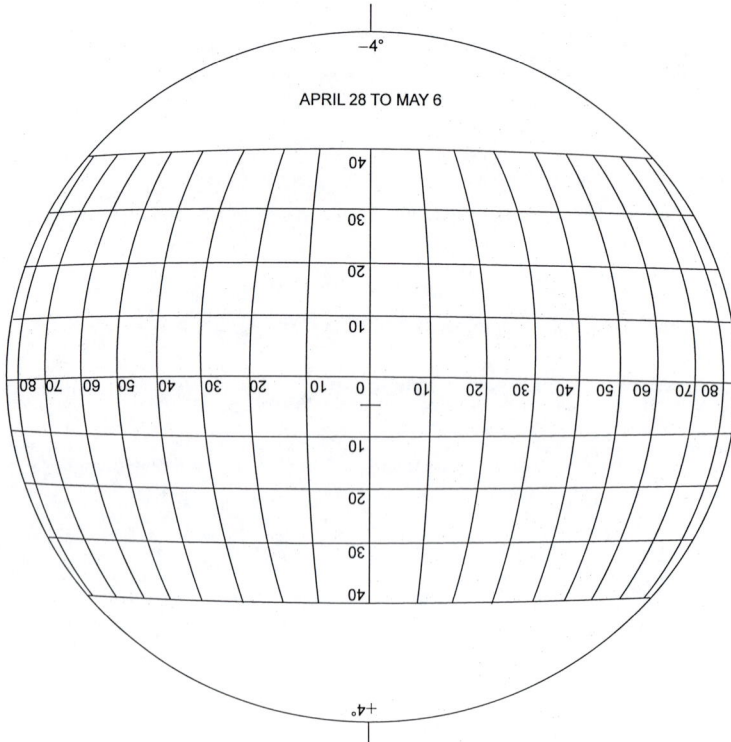

Fig. 6.9   *Stonyhurst grid 1*

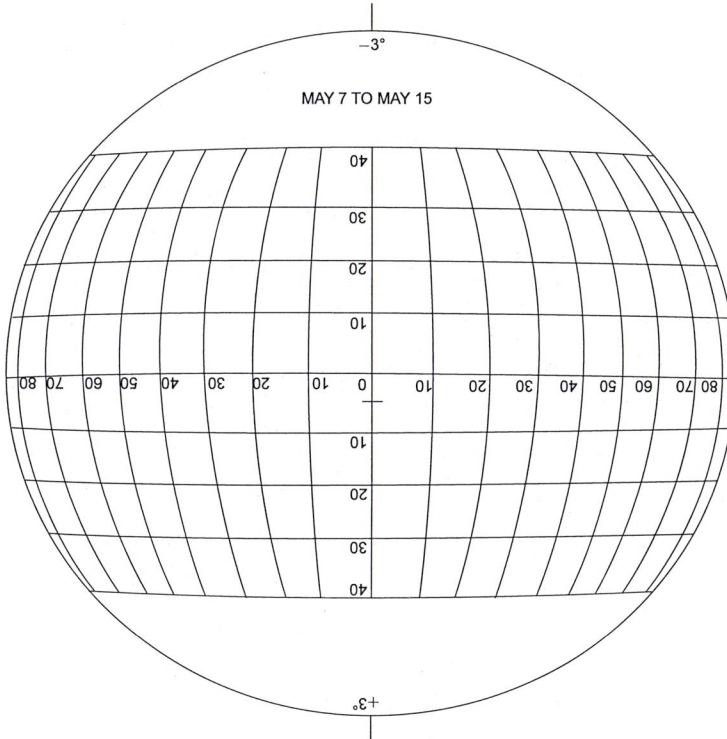

Fig. 6.10 *Stonyhurst grid 2*

4. **Observer on an extrasolar star:** The Sirius star, located in the constellation Canis Majoris, is the brightest star in the night sky of Earth ($m_0 = -1.46$). What the observer's eye sees as a single star is actually a binary star system. The high brightness of Sirius is the combined effect of its intrinsic luminosity and its proximity to the Earth ($d_0 = 2.64$ pc).

The Mizar multiple star system in the constellation Ursa Major consists of four stars seen along the same line of sight from the Earth. Some of these stars form a gravitationally bound system. Let us assume that an observer (observer A) is located on one of the planets of the Sirius system ($a_{pl} = 10$ AU). Determine:

(a) The magnitude of the Sun as seen by observer A ($m_\odot$).

(b) The magnitude of the Sirius star system as seen by observer A (m_{Sr}).

(c) The combined intrinsic luminosity in the direction of the Mizar system L_{Mz}.

(d) The average distance between the gravitationally bound stars of the Mizar system and the Earth.

(e) The geocentric angular distance between the Mizar system and Sirius ($\Delta\theta$).

(f) The physical distance between the gravitationally bound stars of the Mizar system and observer A (d_{Mz}).

(g) The magnitude of the entire Mizar system as seen by observer A (m_{Mz}).

Also estimate errors in all your answers. In the table below, information for the stars from the Mizar system as measured from the Earth is given.   (I14 - D03 - B)

Star Number	Name of the Star	Apparent Magnitude m	Parallax p (milliarcseconds)
1	Alcor	3.99 ± 0.01	39.91 ± 0.13
2	Mizar A	2.23 ± 0.01	38.01 ± 1.71
3	Mizar B	3.86 ± 0.01	38.01 ± 1.71
4	Sidus Ludoviciana	7.56 ± 0.01	8 ± 0.4

The equatorial coordinates of the Mizar system and those of Sirius, located on the geocentric map, are:

$\alpha_{Mz} = 13^h23^m55.5^s$; $\delta_{Mz} = 54°55'31"$.

$\alpha_{Sr} = 6^h45^m$; $\delta_{Sr} = -16°43'$.

5. **Moving cluster method:** You are given a list of 35 stars from the field of the Hyades open cluster, observed by the Hipparcos space telescope (see Table 6.2). The information listed in the columns of the text file for each of the 35 stars is:

- The Hipparcos catalogue number (HIP)
- Their right ascension (alpha - α) [h m s]
- Their declination (delta - δ) [° ' "]
- Their trigonometric parallax (p) [" $\times 10^3$]
- Their proper motion in RA multiplied by cos δ (mu_a x cosd - $\mu_\alpha \times \cos \delta$) [" $\times 10^3$ /yr]
- Their proper motion in declination (mu_d - $\mu\delta$) [" $\times 10^3$ /yr]
- Their radial velocity (v_r - v_r) [km/s]

All calculations should be performed in a spreadsheet programme (e.g., MS Excel).

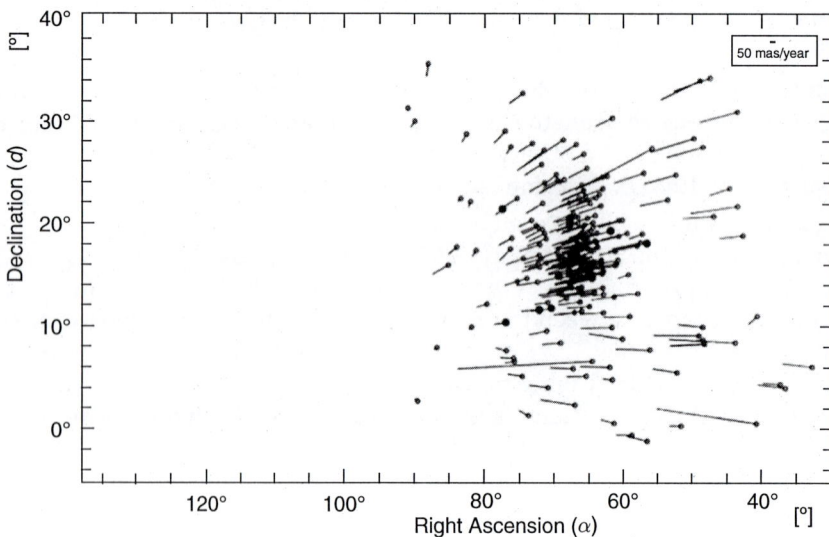

Fig. 6.11   *Distance of the Hyades cluster using the moving cluster method*

Table 6.2 *Stars in the direction of the Hyades cluster*

HIP	alpha			delta			p	mu_ax cosd	mu_d	v_r
13834	2	58	5.08	20	40	7.7	31.41	234.79	−31.64	28.1
14838	3	11	37.67	19	43	36.1	19.44	154.61	−8.39	24.7
18170	3	53	9.96	17	19	37.8	24.14	143.97	−29.93	35
18735	4	0	48.69	18	11	38.6	21.99	129.49	−28.27	31.7
19554	4	11	20.2	5	31	22.9	25.89	146.86	5	36.6
20205	4	19	47.53	15	37	39.7	21.17	115.29	−23.86	39.28
20261	4	20	36.24	15	5	43.8	21.2	108.79	−20.67	36.2
20400	4	22	3.45	14	4	38.1	21.87	114.04	−21.4	37.8
20455	4	22	56.03	17	32	33.3	21.29	107.75	−28.84	39.65
20542	4	24	5.69	17	26	39.2	22.36	109.99	−33.47	39.2
20635	4	25	22.1	22	17	38.3	21.27	105.49	−44.14	38.6
20711	4	26	18.39	22	48	49.3	21.07	108.66	−45.83	35.6
20713	4	26	20.67	15	37	6	20.86	114.66	−33.3	40.8
20842	4	28	0.72	21	37	12	20.85	98.82	−40.59	37.5
20885	4	28	34.43	15	57	44	20.66	104.76	−15.01	40.17
20889	4	28	36.93	19	10	49.9	21.04	107.23	−36.77	39.37
20894	4	28	39.67	15	52	15.4	21.89	108.66	−26.39	38.9
20901	4	28	50.1	13	2	51.5	20.33	105.17	−15.08	39.9
21029	4	30	33.57	16	11	38.7	22.54	104.98	−25.14	41
21036	4	30	37.3	13	43	28	21.84	108.06	−19.71	38.8
21039	4	30	38.83	15	41	31	22.55	104.17	−24.29	39.56
21137	4	31	51.69	15	51	5.9	22.25	107.59	−32.38	36
21152	4	32	4.74	5	24	36.1	23.13	114.15	6.17	39.8
21459	4	36	29.07	23	20	27.5	22.6	109.97	−53.86	43.3
21589	4	38	9.4	12	30	39.1	21.79	101.73	−14.9	44.7
21683	4	39	16.45	15	55	4.9	20.51	82.4	−19.53	35.6
22044	4	44	25.77	11	8	46.2	20.73	98.87	−13.47	39.6
22157	4	46	1.7	11	42	20.2	12.24	67.48	−7.09	43
22176	4	46	16.78	18	44	5.5	10.81	73.03	−69.79	44.11
22203	4	46	30.33	15	28	19.6	19.42	91.37	−24.72	42.42
22565	4	51	22.41	18	50	23.8	17.27	79.66	−32.76	36.8
22850	4	54	58.32	19	29	7.6	14.67	63.32	−28.41	38.4
23497	5	3	5.7	21	35	24.2	20.01	68.94	−40.85	38
23983	5	9	19.6	9	49	46.6	18.54	63.54	−7.87	44.16
24019	5	9	45.06	28	1	50.2	18.28	55.86	−60.57	44.9

(a) Calculate the angular distance (φ) between each of the stars and the point of convergence, which is at ($\alpha_c = 6^h7^m$, $\delta_c = 6°56'$).

(b) Calculate the proper motion (μ) of each star.

(c) Use the above data to calculate the distance (r_μ) for each star using the following equation:

$$r_\mu = \frac{v_r \tan \varphi}{4.74047\,\mu} \tag{6.1}$$

(d) Do all stars belong to the Hyades cluster? You can assume that any star whose distance from the centre of the cluster ($r_\mu = 46.34$ pc) is larger than 10 pc, is not part of the cluster. Omit these stars from the following calculations.

(e) Independently calculate the distance r_π of each star in the list using the trigonometric parallax angle π.

(f) Find the average distance of the Hyades cluster r_μ and r_π, and its standard deviation σ_μ and σ_π, for each method (moving cluster and trigonometric parallax methods).

(g) Which method is more accurate?   (I13 - D04 - B)

6. **Determination of stellar mass in a visual binary system**: The star α-Centauri (Rigel Kentaurus) is a triple star consisting of two main-sequence stars α-Centauri A and α-Centauri B, representing a visual binary system. The third star, called Proxima Centauri, is smaller, fainter and farther away than the other two stars. The angular distance between α-Centauri A and α-Centauri B is 17.59". The binary system has an orbital period of 79.24 years. The visual magnitudes of α-Centauri A and α-Centauri B are −0.01 and 1.34, respectively. Their colour indices are 0.65 and 0.85, respectively. Use the data below to answer the following questions.   (I08 - D02 - C)

(a) Plot the curve BC versus $(B - V)_0$.

(b) Determine the apparent bolometric magnitudes of α-Centauri A and α-Centauri B using the corresponding curve.

(c) Calculate the mass of each star.

Notes:

- Bolometric correction (BC) is a correction that must be made to the apparent magnitude of an object in order to convert an object's visible band magnitudes to its bolometric magnitudes, i.e.,

$$BC = M_v - M_{bol} = m_v - m_{bol} \tag{6.2}$$

- Mass–Luminosity relation:

$$M_{bol} = -10.2\left(\frac{M}{M_\odot}\right) + 4.9 \tag{6.3}$$

where M and $M_\odot$ are the mass of the star and the Sun, respectively.

- Data giving colour versus bolometric correction:

$(B - V)_0$	T_{eff}	BC
−0.25	24500	2.30
−0.23	21000	2.15

$(B - V)_0$	T_{eff}	BC
−0.20	17700	1.80
−0.15	14000	1.20
−0.10	11800	0.61
−0.05	10500	0.33
0.00	9480	0.15
0.10	8530	0.04
0.20	7910	0
0.30	7450	0
0.40	6800	0
0.50	6310	0.03
0.60	5910	0.07
0.70	5540	0.12
0.80	5330	019
0.90	5090	0.28
1.00	4840	0.40
1.20	4350	0.75

where BC stands for bolometric correction and $(B - V)_0$ for the intrinsic colour of the star.

Binaries and Variables

7.1 Theory

1. A binary system is 10 pc away, the largest angular separation between the components is 7.0" and the smallest is 1.0". Assume that the orbital period is 100 years and that the orbital plane is perpendicular to the line of sight. If the semi-major axis of the orbit of one component corresponds to 3.0", that is, $a_1 = 3.0"$, estimate the mass of each component of the binary system, in terms of solar mass. (I10 - T04 - A)

2. Figure 7.1 shows the relation between absolute magnitude and period for classical Cepheids in the first panel and the light curve (apparent magnitude versus time in days) of a classical Cepheid in the Small Magellanic Cloud in the second panel. (I13 - T4 - A)

   (a) Estimate the distance of the Cepheid from us.

   (b) Revise your estimate assuming that the interstellar extinction towards the Cepheid is $A = 0.25$ mag.

3. A binary system of stars consists of star A and star B with brightness ratio 2. The binary system is difficult to resolve and is observed from the Earth as one star of fifth magnitude. Find the apparent magnitude of each of the two stars (m_A, m_B). (I13 - T8 - A)

4. Sirius A, with visual magnitude $m_V = -1.47$ (the brighter star in the sky) and stellar radius $R_A = 1.7 R_\odot$, is the primary star of a binary system. The existence of its companion, Sirius B, was deduced using astrometry in 1844 by the well-known mathematician and astronomer Friedrich Bessel, before it was directly observed. Assuming that both stars were of the same spectral type and that Sirius B is fainter by 10 mags ($\Delta m = 10$), calculate the radius of Sirius B. (I13 - T12 - A)

5. An eclipsing binary system consists of two giant stars of the same size in close orbits. As a result of mutual gravitational force, the stars are deformed from a perfect sphere to an oblate spheroid with $a = 2b$, where a and b are the semi-major and semi-minor axes, respectively (the major axes are always co-linear). The inclination of the orbital plane to the plane of the sky is 90°. Calculate the amplitude of light variation in magnitude (Δm) as a result of the orbital motion of the two stars. Ignore temperature variation due to tidal deformation and limb darkening on the surface of the stars. *Note:* An oblate spheroid is a geometrical shape made by the rotation of an ellipse around its major axis, like a rugby ball or melon. (I09 - T15 - B)

6. **Orbital motion:** Figure 7.2 represents the relative orbit of a binary star. A star of mass m moves around a star of mass M in the indicated direction, where $m = M$. The major axis of the ellipse is aligned with the direction to the observer, and the motion of the star is in the plane of the diagram. (I11 - G02 - B)

Cepheid Period -Luminosity Relation

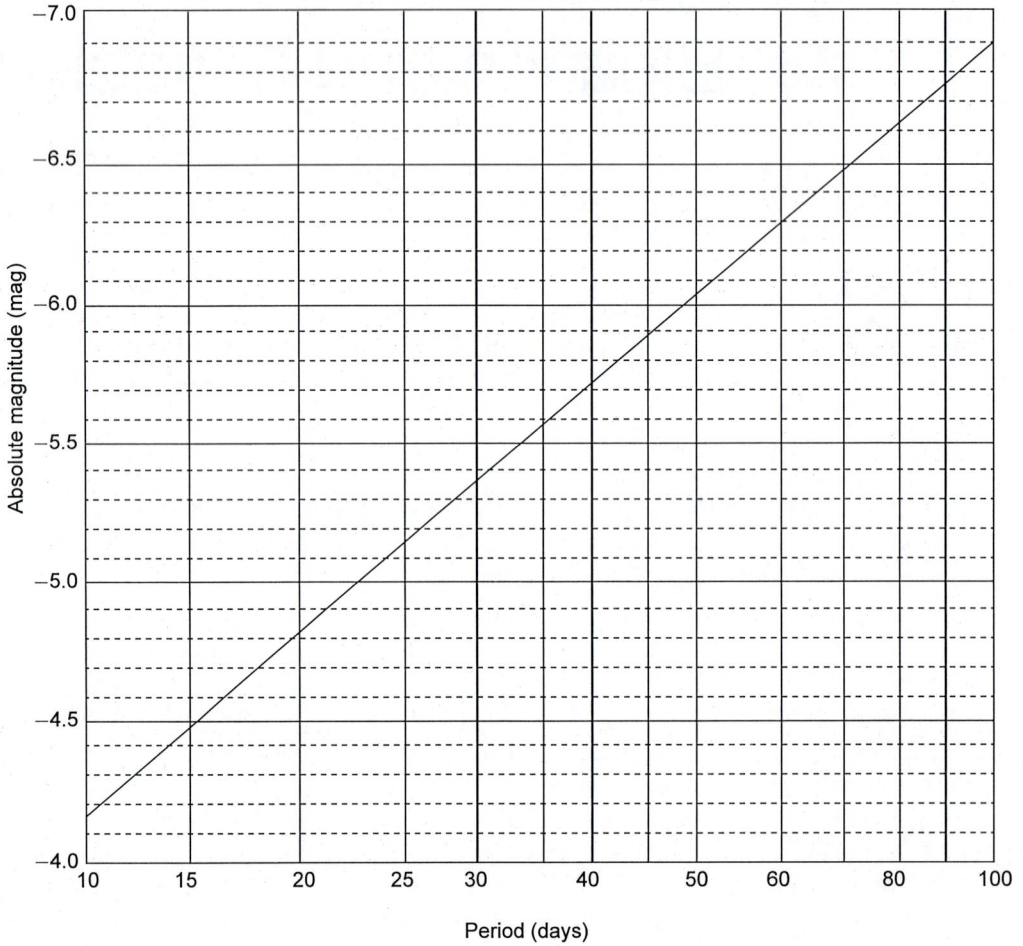

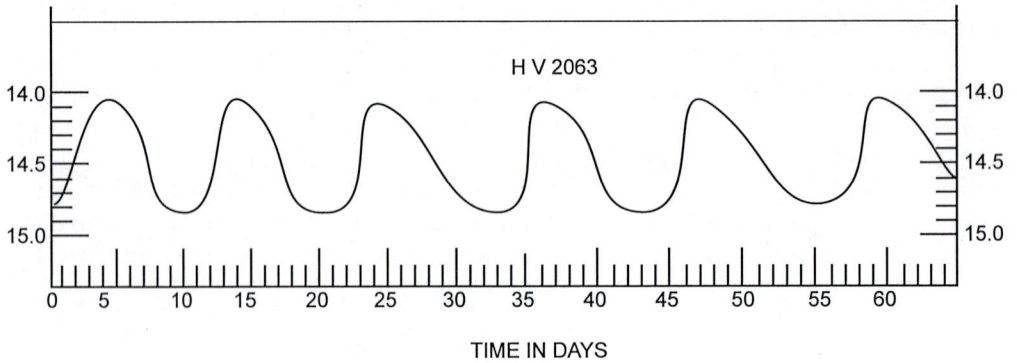

Fig. 7.1 *Mass–Luminosity relation for low and intermediate mass stars*

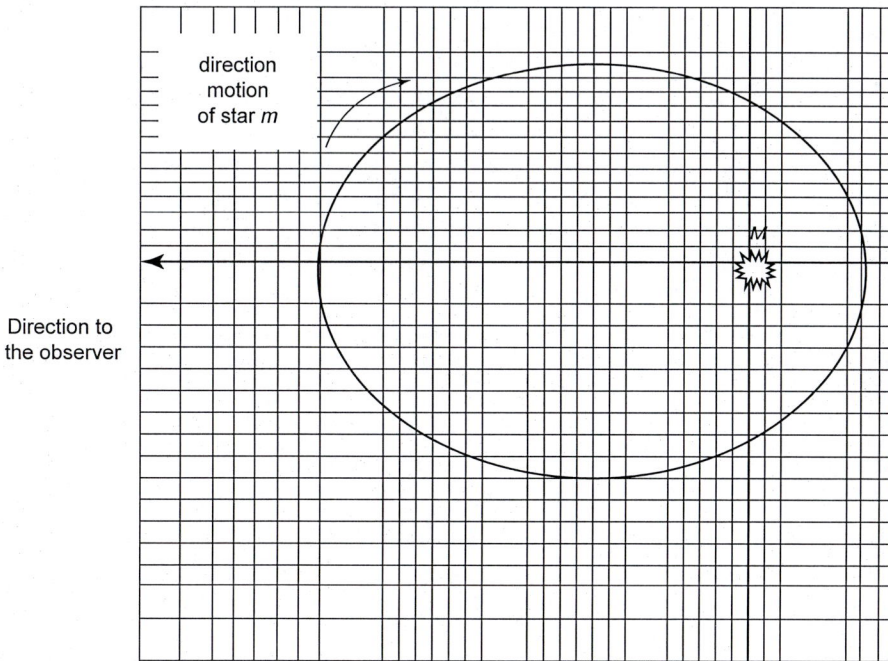

Fig. 7.2 *Direction of orbit of the double star*

(a) Find the part of the ellipse where the angular velocity ω of m is less than its mean angular velocity $\langle\omega\rangle$, and indicate this as accurately as possible on the scale diagram on the answer sheet.

Note: The instantaneous angular velocity ω of m is equal to the mean angular velocity $\langle\omega\rangle$ when the distance between stars $r = \sqrt{ab}$, where a and b are the semi-axes of the orbit.

Also mark those places on the ellipse for which the observer will see:

(b) Extreme tangential (perpendicular to the line of sight) velocity: $v_{t_{max}}$ and $v_{t_{min}}$

(c) Extreme radial (parallel to the line of sight) velocity: $v_{r_{max}}$ and $v_{r_{min}}$

7. **Absolute magnitude of a Cepheid:** Cepheids are variable stars, whose luminosities vary due to stellar pulsations. The period of the oscillations of a Cepheid star of radius R and mass M is given by

$$P = 2\pi R\sqrt{\frac{R}{GM}} \tag{7.1}$$

You can assume that the temperature of the star remains constant during the pulsation. Express the mean bolometric magnitude of the Cepheid M_{cep} in the following form.

(I14 - T12 - B)

$$M_{cep} = -2.5\log k - (\frac{10}{3})\log P \tag{7.2}$$

8. **Minimum of an eclipsing binary:** Figure 7.3 shows the secondary (shallower) minimum of the bolometrically corrected light curve of an eclipsing binary star. The difference between magnitudes $m_{1,Bol} - m_{0,Bol} = 0.33$ magnitude. We also know from simultaneous spectroscopy that the star with the smaller radius was totally eclipsed by the larger star during the secondary minimum (as only one spectrum was observable during the minimum).

   Determine the change in brightness of this binary during the primary minimum and draw the shape of the primary minimum using the same scale as the secondary minimum. Label the graph with the appropriate parameters. You may assume that the eclipses are central, that the stars are spheres of constant surface brightness, and that the distance between the stars does not change.   (I11 - G04 - B)

9. A binary star system consists of two stars with mass M_1 and M_2 separated by a distance D. M_1 and M_2 are revolving with an angular velocity ω in circular orbits about their common centre of mass. Mass is continuously being transferred from one star to the other. This transfer of mass causes their orbital period and their separation to change slowly with time.

   In order to simplify the analysis, we will assume that the stars are like point particles and that the effects of the rotation about their own axes are negligible.   (I07 - T17 - B)

   (a) What is the total angular momentum and kinetic energy of the system?

   (b) Find the relation between the angular velocity ω and the distance D between the stars.

   (c) In time duration Δt, a mass transfer between the two stars results in a change in mass ΔM_1 in star M_1, find the quantity $\Delta \omega$ in terms of ω, M_1, M_2 and ΔM_1.

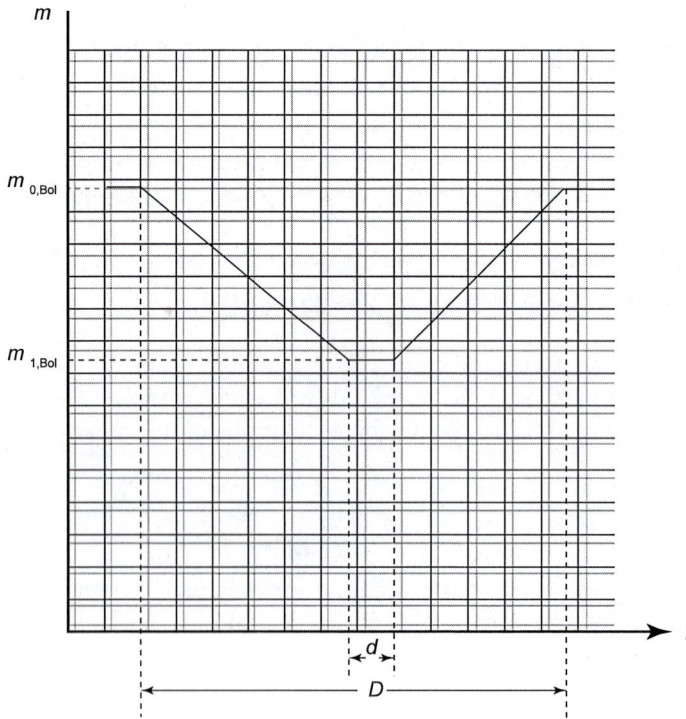

Fig. 7.3   *Light curve of an eclipsing binary*

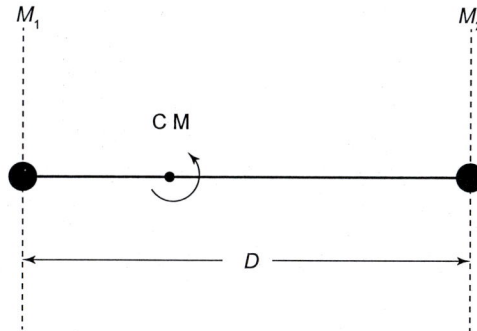

Fig. 7.4 *Mass transfer binaries*

(d) In a certain binary system, $M_1 = 2.9M_\odot$, M2 $= 1.4M_\odot$ and the orbital period $T = 2.49$ days. After 100 years, the period T has increased by 20 s. Find the value of $\dfrac{\Delta M_1}{M_1 \Delta t}$ (in the unit per year).

(e) In which direction is mass flowing, from M_1 to M_2, or M_2 to M_1?

(f) Find also the value of $\dfrac{\Delta D}{D\delta t}$ (in per year units).

You may use these approximations:

$$(1 + x)^n \sim 1 + nx, \quad \text{when } x = 1;$$

$$(1 + x)(1 + y) \sim 1 + x + y, \quad \text{when } x, y = 1.$$

10. The planetarium program 'Guide' gives the following data for two main-sequence, one-solar-mass stars:

Star	1	2
Right Ascension	$14^h 29^m 44.95^s$	$14^h 39^m 39.39^s$
Declination	$-62°40'46.14''$	$-60°50'22.10''$
Distance	1.2953 pc	1.3475 pc
Proper motion in RA	$-3.776''$ / year	$-3.600''$ / year
Proper motion in Declination.	$0.95''$ / year	$0.77''$ / year

Based on this data, determine whether these stars form a gravitationally bound system.

Note: The proper motion in R.A. has been corrected for the declination of the stars.

(I11 - T18 - C)

11. A transit of duration 180 minutes was observed for a planet which orbits the star HD209458 with a period of 84 hours. The Doppler shift of absorption lines arising in the planet's atmosphere was also measured, corresponding to a difference in radial velocity of 30 km/s (relative to the Earth) between the beginning and the end of the transit. Assuming a

circular orbit exactly edge-on to the observer, find the approximate radius and mass of the star and the radius of the orbit of the planet.   (I11 - T16 - C)

12. An eclipsing binary star system has a period of 30 days. The light curve in the figure below shows that the secondary star eclipses the primary star (from point A to point D) in eight hours (measured from the time of first contact to final contact), whereas from point B to point C, the total eclipse period is one hour and eighteen minutes. Spectral analysis yields the radial velocity of the primary star to be 30 km/s and that of the secondary star to be 40 km/s. If we assume that the orbits are circular and have an inclination of $i = 90°$, determine the radii and mass of both stars in units of solar radius and solar mass.
                                                                                (I08 - T16 - D)

Table 7.1   *Cepheid period–magnitudes data*

Cepheid	P_0 (days)	$\langle M_v \rangle$
SU Cas	1.95	−1.99
V1726 Cyg	4.24	−3.04
SZ Tau	4.48	−3.09
CV Mon	5.38	−3.37
QZ Nor	5.46	−3.32
α UMi	5.75	−3.42
V367 Sct	6.30	−3.58
U Sgr	6.75	−3.64
DL Cas	8.00	−3.80
S Nor	9.75	−3.95
ζ Gem	10.14	−4.10
X Cyg	16.41	−4.69
WZ Sgr	21.83	−5.06
SW Vel	23.44	−5.09
SV Vul	44.98	−6.04

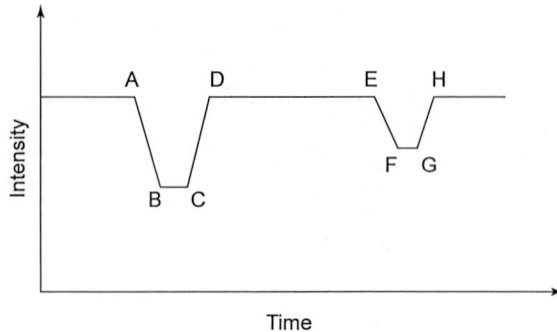

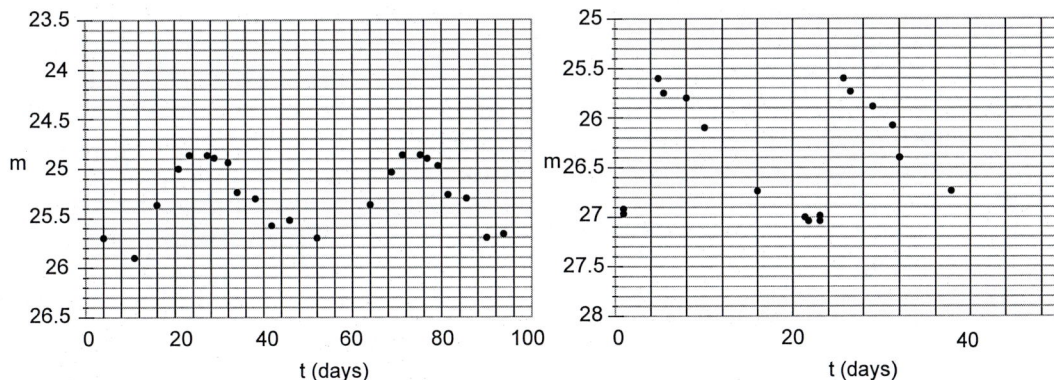

Fig. 7.5   *Light curves of two Cepheids*

7.2 Data Analysis

1. Cepheids are very bright variable stars whose mean absolute magnitudes are functions of their pulsation periods. This allows astrophysicists to easily determine their intrinsic luminosities from the variation in their observed apparent magnitudes. In Table 7.1, P_0 is the pulsation period in days and $\langle M_V \rangle$ is the mean absolute visual magnitude.

   (a) Plot all Cepheids in a scatter diagram. $\log_{10}(P_0)$ should be the abscissa and $\langle M_V \rangle$ should be the ordinate.

   (b) Fit, using the least squares method, a straight line to the $\langle M_V \rangle$ vs $\log_{10}(P_0)$ plot. This equation enables you to obtain the absolute magnitude from the pulsation period for any Cepheid.

   (c) Two panels in Figure 7.5 show the light curves of two Cepheids. Use the available data to estimate the distances to each of these Cepheids. Also estimate the uncertainty in the distance determination (only rough estimate is expected).

   (d) Comparing the difference between the distances of the two stars with the typical size of a galaxy, would it be likely for these two stars to be in the same galaxy?

   (I12 - D02 - A)

2. **Analysis of times of minima:** Figure 7.6 shows the light curve of the eclipsing binary V1107 Cas, classified as a W Ursae Major is type. Table 7.2 contains a list of observed minima of light variation. The columns contain: the serial number of the minimum, the date on which the minimum was observed, the heliocentric time of minimum expressed in Julian days and an error (in fractions of a day). Using these:

   (a) Determine an initial period of V1107 Cas, assuming that the period of the star is constant during the interval of observations. Assume that observations during one night are continuous. Duration of transit is negligible.

   (b) Draw what is known as an (O–C) diagram (for observed–calculated) of the times of minima, as follows:

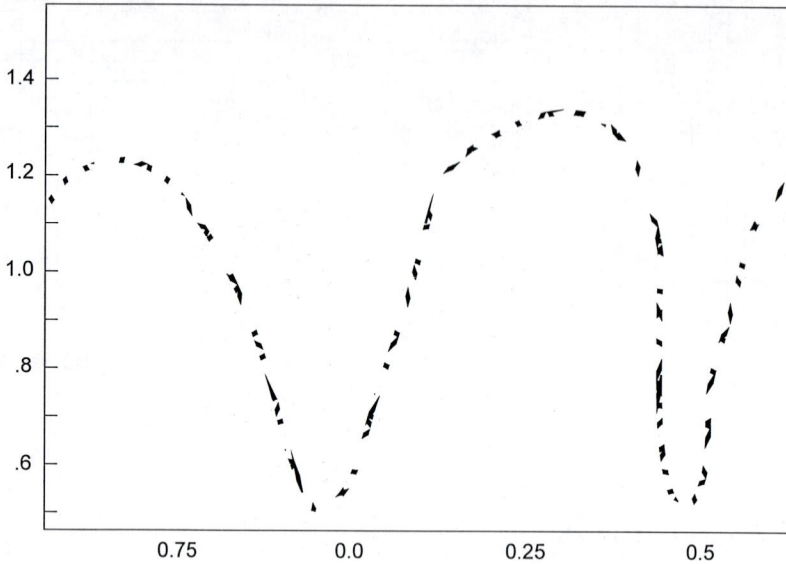

Fig. 7.6   *Light curve of V1107 Cas*

On the *x*-axis, put the number of periods elapsed (the epoch) from a chosen initial moment M_0; on the *y*-axis, the difference between the observed moment of minimum M_{obs} and the moment of minimum calculated using the formula ("ephemeris"):

$$M_{calc} = M_0 + P \times E \tag{7.3}$$

where E, the epoch, is exactly an integer or half-integer, and P is the period in days.

(c) Using this (O–C) diagram, improve the determination of the initial moment M_0 and the period P. Also estimate the errors in their values.

(d) Calculate the predicted times of minima of V1107 Cas, in heliocentric JD, occurring between 19^h, 1 September 2011 UT and 02^h, 2 September 2011 UT.   (I11 - D01 - C)

Table 7.2   *Observed times of minima for V1107 Cassiopeae*

No.	Date of Minimum (UT)	Time of Minimum (Heliocentric JD)	Error
1	22 December 2006	2 454 092.4111	0.0004
2	23 December 2006	2 454 092.5478	0.0002
3	23 September 2007	2 454 367.3284	0.0005
4	23 September 2007	2 454 367.4656	0.0005
5	15 October 2007	2 454 388.5175	0.0009
6	15 October 2007	2 454 388.6539	0.0011
7	26 August 2008	2 454 704.8561	0.0002

(Cont'd)

Table 7.2 (Contd)

No.	Date of Minimum (UT)	Time of Minimum (Heliocentric JD)	Error
8	5 November 2008	2 454 776.4901	0.0007
9	3 January 2009	2 454 835.2734	0.0007
10	15 January 2009	2 454 847.3039	0.0004
11	15 January 2009	2 454 847.4412	0.0001
12	16 January 2009	2 454 847.5771	0.0004

8

Galactic Astrophysics

8.1 Theory

1. The spin–flip transition of atomic hydrogen at rest generates an electromagnetic wave of the frequency $\nu_0 = 1420.406$ MHz. Such an emission from a gas cloud near the galactic centre is observed to have a frequency $\nu = 1421.65$ MHz. Calculate the velocity of the gas cloud. Is it moving towards or away from the Earth? (I07 - T12 - A)

2. Radio wavelength observations of a gas cloud swirling around a black hole in the centre of our galaxy show that radiation from the hydrogen spin–flip transition is detected at a frequency of 1421.23 MHz. If this gas cloud is located at a distance of 0.2 pc from the black hole and is orbiting in a circle, determine the speed of this cloud and whether it is moving towards or away from us and calculate the mass of the black hole. (I08 - T06 - A)

3. In the centre of our galaxy, in the intense radio source Sgr A*, there is a black hole with large mass. A team of astronomers measured the angular distance of a star from Sgr A* and its orbital period around it. The angular distance was 0.12" and the period was 15 years. Calculate the mass of the black hole in solar mass. (I13 - T10 - A)

4. Assuming that G-type main-sequence stars (such as the Sun) in the disc of the Milky Way obey a vertical exponential density profile with a scale height of 300 pc, by what factor does the density of these stars change at 0.5 and 1.5 kpc from the mid-plane relative to the density in the mid-plane? (I10 - T10 - B)

5. Galaxy NGC 2639 is morphologically identified as an Sa galaxy with measured maximum rotational velocity $v_{max} = 324$ km/s. After corrections for any extinction, its apparent magnitude in B is $m_B = 12.22$. It is customary to measure the radius of galaxy to a distance known as R_{25} (in units of kpc). R_{25} is the distance at which the galaxy's surface brightness falls to 25 $mag_B/arcsec^2$.

   Spiral galaxies tend to follow a typical relation:

   $$logR_{25} = -0.249M_B - 4.00 \tag{8.1}$$

   where M_B is the absolute magnitude in B.
   Apply the B-band Tully–Fisher relation for Sa spirals

   $$M_B = -9.95log(v_{max}) + 3.15 \tag{8.2}$$

   where v_{max} is in km/s, to calculate the mass of NGC 2639 out to R_{25}. If the colour index of the Sun is $(B_\odot - V_\odot) = 0.64$, write the mass in units of solar mass $M_\odot$ and its luminosity B-band in units of $L_\odot$. (I08 - T15 - B)

6. The galactic longitude of a star is $l = 15°$. Its radial velocity with respect to the Sun is $V_r = 100$ km/s. Assume that the stars in the disk of the galaxy are orbiting around the galactic centre in circular orbits, in the same sense in the galactic plane as the Sun, and have constant velocity of $V_0 = 250$ km/s. Calculate the distance of the star from the centre of the galaxy.
 (I09 - T09 - C)

7. **Apparent number density of stars in the galaxy:** Let us model the number density of stars in the disk of Milky Way Galaxy with a simple exponential function of

$$n(r) = n_0 e^{-(\frac{r-R_0}{R_d})} \tag{8.3}$$

where r represents the distance from the centre of the galaxy, R_0 is the distance of the Sun from the centre of the galaxy, R_d is the typical size of the disk and n_0 is the stellar density of the disk at the position of the Sun. All distances are expressed in kpc. An astronomer observes the centre of the galaxy within a small field of view. We take a particular type of red giant star as the standard candle for the observation, with approximately constant absolute magnitude of $M = -0.2$:

(a) A telescope has a limiting magnitude of $m = 18$. Calculate the maximum distance to which this telescope can detect these red giant stars. For simplicity, we ignore the presence of interstellar medium so there is no extinction.

(b) Assume an extinction of 0.7 mag/kpc for the interstellar medium. Repeat the calculation as carried out in Question 7a and obtain a rough number for the maximum distance that these red giant stars can be observed.

(c) Give an expression for the number of these red giant stars per magnitude within a solid angle of Ω that we can observe with apparent magnitude in the range of m and $m + \Delta m$, (i.e., $\dfrac{\Delta N}{\Delta m}$). Red giant stars contribute fraction f of overall stars. In this part, assume no extinction in the interstellar medium, as in Question 7a. Assume the size of the disk is infinite.
 (I09 - T17 - C)

Hint: The Taylor series expansion for $x = 1$

$$\log_{10}(1+x) = \frac{1}{\ln(10)}(x - \frac{x^2}{2} + \frac{x^3}{3} - \frac{x^4}{4} + ...) \tag{8.4}$$

8. Astronomers studied a spiral galaxy with an inclination angle of 90° from the plane of the sky (edge-on) and apparent magnitude 8.5. They measured the rotational velocity and radial distance from the galactic centre and plotted its rotation curve.
 (I12 - T17 - C)

(a) Approximate the rotation curve in Fig. 8.1 with a continuous function V(D) composed of two straight lines.

(b) Using the same observations, they estimated that the rotation period of the pressure wave in the galactic disk is half of the rotation period of the mass of the disk. Estimate the time it takes for a spiral arm to take another turn around the galactic centre (use the function constructed in the previous question).

(c) Calculate the distance to the galaxy using the Tully–Fisher relation.

(d) Calculate the maximum and minimum values of the observed wavelengths of the hydrogen lines corresponding to 656.28 nm in the spectrum of this galaxy.

Hint: Also take into account the cosmological expansion.

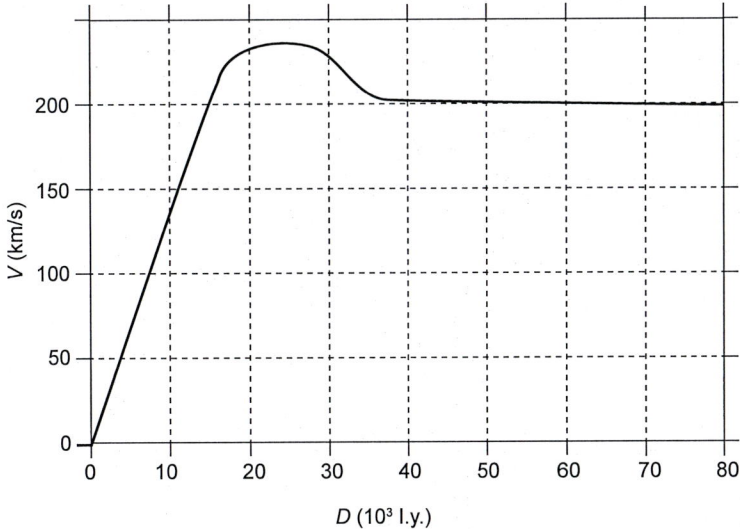

Fig. 8.1 *Rotation curve of the spiral galaxy*

(e) Using Fig. 8.1, estimate the mass of the galaxy up to a radius of 3×10^4 light years.

(f) Estimate the number of stars in the galaxy, assuming:

- The mean mass of the stars is equal to one solar mass and one-third of the baryonic mass of the galaxy is in the form of stars.
- The fraction of baryonic to dark matter in the galaxy is the same as the fraction for the whole Universe.

Notes:

- *Tully–Fisher relation:* The luminosity of a galaxy is proportional to the fourth power of the velocity variation ($\Delta V = V_2 - V_1$), which is the largest difference of rotational velocities in the galaxy. The proportionality constant of this relation is $\kappa = 0.317 \, L_\odot$ (km/s)$^{-4}$, where $L_\odot$ is the bolometric solar luminosity.
- *Approximate composition of the Universe:*
  - 4% baryons
  - 22% dark matter
  - 74% dark energy

9. Interstellar distances are large compared to the size of stars. Thus, stellar clusters and galaxies which do not contain diffuse matter essentially do not obscure objects behind them. Estimate what proportion of the sky is obscured by stars when we look in the direction of a galaxy of surface brightness $\mu = 18.0$ mag arcsec^{-2} in V-band. Assume that the galaxy consists of stars similar to the Sun.   (I11 - T09 - D)

10. (a) Using the virial theorem for an isolated, spherical system, i.e., that $-2\langle K \rangle = \langle U \rangle$, where K is the kinetic energy and U is the potential energy of the system, explain how we can measure the total mass of a cluster of galaxies if we know the radial velocity dispersion of the cluster's galaxy members and the cluster's radius. Assume that the cluster is isolated, spherical, has homogeneous density and that it consists of N galaxies of mass m each.

(b) Find the virial mass, i.e., the mass calculated from the virial theorem, of the Coma cluster, which lies at a distance of 90 Mpc from us, if you know that the radial velocity dispersion of its member galaxies is $\sigma_{v_r} = 1000$ km s^{-1} and that its angular diameter (on the sky) is about 4°.

(c) From observations, the total luminosity of the galaxies comprising the cluster is approximately $L = 5 \times 10^{12} L_\odot$. If the mass to luminosity ratio of the cluster, $M/L \sim 1$ (all the mass of the cluster is visible mass), this should correspond to total mass $M \approx 5 \times 10^{12} M_\odot$ for the mass of the cluster. Compare this value to the total mass of the cluster you derived in the previous question.

(I13 - T18 - D)

8.2 Data Analysis

1. **Weighing a galaxy:** Fig. 8.2 is a photograph of the spiral galaxy NGC 7083, which lies at a distance of 40 Mpc, and Fig. 8.3 is a fragment of its spectrum. The slit of the spectrograph was aligned with the major axis of the image of the galaxy. The x-axis of the spectrum represents wavelength, and the y-axis represents the angular distance of the emitting region from the core of the galaxy, where 1 pixel corresponds to 0.82 arcsec. Two bright emission lines are visible with rest wavelengths of $\lambda_1 = 656.4$ nm and $\lambda_2 = 658.4$ nm. Use the spectrum to plot the rotation curve of the galaxy and estimate the mass of the central bulge.

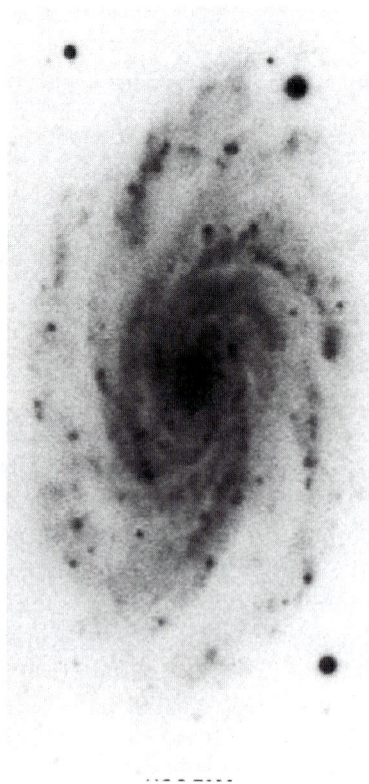

Fig. 8.2 *Spiral galaxy NGC 7083*

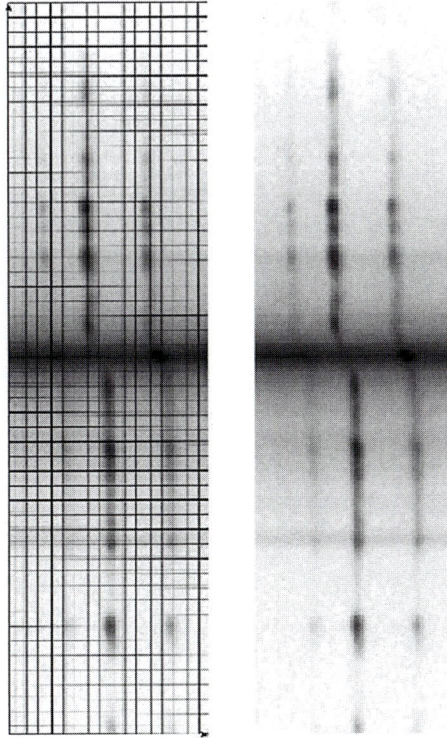

Fig. 8.3 *Spectrum of spiral galaxy NGC 7083. In the image on the left, the grid drawn is along pixels of CCD*

Assumption: The central bulge is spherical. The photograph of the galaxy has the correct proportions.   (I11 - D02 - B)

2. **Black hole in Milky Way:** By observational facts, scientists admit the presence of a black hole at the centre of Milky Way. At the centre of Milky Way, a hypothetical black hole (Sagittarius A*) is located. A star S* is orbiting the black hole SA*.

   Table 8.1 presents the epoch of observations and the angular position coordinates (α, β) of the star S* at those epochs. The coordinates represent the angular distances of the projection or the star S* in the coordinates system (U, W), centred on Sagittarius A* (see Fig. 8.4).

   An angular distance $\phi = 1''$ corresponds to a linear distance in the sky-plane $d_0 = 41$ light days, and therefore to a scale $S_0 = \dfrac{d}{\phi} = 41 \dfrac{\text{lightdays}}{\text{arc sec}}$.

Table 8.1 *Position of S* with respect to Sagittarius A**

	Date (year)	α arcsec	β arcsec
1	1995.222	0.117	−0.166
2	1997.526	0.097	−0.189
3	1998.326	0.087	−0.192

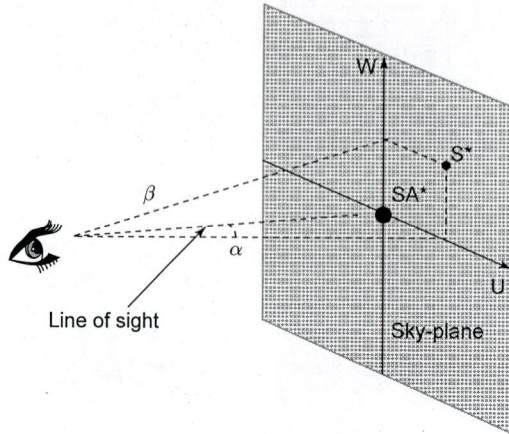

Fig. 8.4   *U–W coordinate system for S* and Sagittarius A**

	Date (year)	α arcsec	β arcsec
4	1999.041	0.077	−0.193
5	2000.414	0.052	−0.183
6	2001.169	0.036	−0.167
7	2002.831	−0.000	−0.120
8	2003.584	−0.016	−0.083
9	2004.165	−0.026	−0.041
10	2004.585	−0.017	0.008
11	2004.655	−0.004	0.014
12	2004.734	0.008	0.017
13	2004.839	0.021	0.012
14	2004.936	0.037	0.009
15	2005.503	0.072	−0.024
16	2006.041	0.088	−0.050
17	2007.060	0.108	−0.091

(a) Plot the projection of the trajectory of the star S* in the plane P (see Fig. 8.5) on a graph paper. This plane is closer to the observer. In this plane, $\phi = 1''$ would correspond to a linear distance $d = 1200$ mm so the scale is $S = \dfrac{d_0}{\phi} = 1200\,\dfrac{\text{mm}}{\text{arcsec}}$. To draw an accurate ellipse, you can trace the ellipse (drawn to correct scale) provided to you, by keeping a carbon paper on the graph.

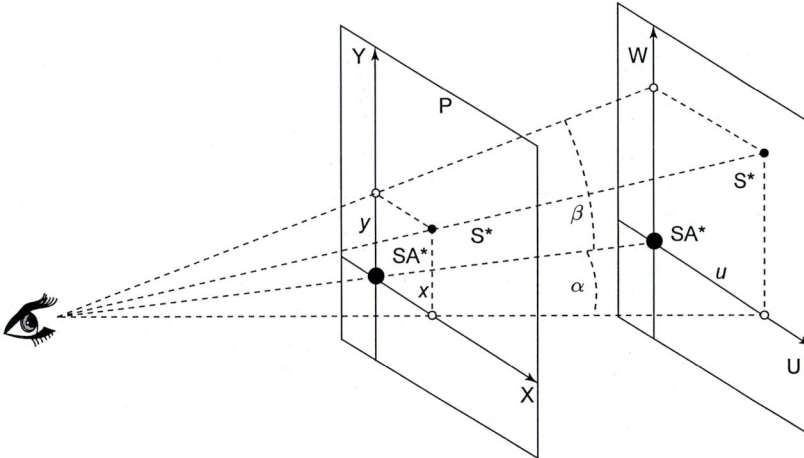

Fig. 8.5 *Projection of the U–W system in plane P*

(b) By using the plot, prove that the line of sight is normal to the actual plane of orbit.

(c) Estimate the following orbital elements of star S* around the black hole Sagittarius A*:

   (i) *a* - semi-major axis (in light day units); *b* - semi-minor axis (in light day units); *e* - eccentricity

   (ii) r_{min} - the minimum distance between S* and SA* (in light day units); r_{max} - the maximum distance between S* and SA* (in light days)

   (iii) The distance from the observer to S*

   (iv) The orbiting period of star S* around Sagittarius A* (obtain the best possible result by taking as many measurements as possible and by taking their arithmetic mean)

   (v) The total mass of the system Sagittarius A* - Star S*.   (I14 - D01 - D)

Extragalactic Astrophysics

9.1 Theory

1. Given that cosmic background radiation has the spectrum of a black body throughout the evolution of the Universe, determine how its temperature changes with redshift z. In particular, give the temperature of the background radiation at the epoch $z \approx 10$ (that of the farthest currently observed objects). The current temperature of cosmic background radiation is 2.73 K. (I11 - T15 - A)

2. The observed redshift of a QSO is $z = 0.20$. Estimate its distance. (I10 - T03 - A)

3. The Doppler shift of three remote galaxies has been measured with the help of spectral observations: (I13 - T15 - A)

Galaxy	Redshift, z
3C 279	0.536
3C 245	1.029
4C41.17	3.8

   (a) Calculate their recession velocity using classical as well as relativistic relation.

   (b) At what percentage of the speed of light do they recede?

   (c) What is the present distance of each galaxy?

4. The average temperature of the cosmic microwave background (CMB) is currently $T = 2.73$ K. It yields the origin of CMB to be at redshift $z_{CMB} = 1100$. The current densities of the dark energy, dark matter and normal matter components of the Universe as a whole are: $\rho_{DE} = 7.1 \times 10^{-30}$ g/cm^3, $\rho_{DE} = 2.4 \times 10^{-30}$ g/cm^3 and $\rho_{NM} = 0.5 \times 10^{-30}$ g/cm^3, respectively. What is the ratio between the density of dark matter to the density of dark energy at the time CMB was emitted, if we assume that dark energy is the energy of empty space? (I08 - T05 - B)

5. The optical spectrum of a galaxy, whose distance has been measured to be 41.67 Mpc, shows the Balmer Hα line redshifted to $\lambda = 662.9$ nm. (I13 - T5 - B)

   (a) Use this to calculate the value of the Hubble constant H_0.

   (b) Using your results, estimate the age of the Universe.

6. Consider a type Ia supernova in a distant galaxy which has a luminosity of $5.8 \times 10^9 \, L_\odot$ at its maximum light. Suppose you observe this supernova using your telescope and find that its brightness is 1.6×10^{-7} times the brightness of Vega. The redshift of its host galaxy is known to be $z = 0.05$. Calculate the distance of this galaxy (in pc) and also the Hubble time. (I08 - T12 - B)

7. Assume the mass of neutrinos to be $m_v = 10^{-5} m_e$. Calculate the number density of neutrinos required to compensate the dark matter of the universe. Assume the universe is flat and 25% of its mass is dark matter.

   Hint: Take classical total energy equal to zero.   (I09 - T11 - C)

8. In a homogeneous and isotropic universe, the matter (baryonic matter + dark matter) density parameter $\Omega_m = \dfrac{\rho_m}{\rho_c} = 32\%$, where ρ_m is the matter density and ρ_c is the critical density of the Universe. Assume that the Earth is located at the centre of our local cluster.

   (a) Calculate the average matter density in our local neighbourhood.

   (b) Calculate the escape velocity of a galaxy 100 Mpc away from us. Note that the recession velocity of galaxies in Hubble's law equals the corresponding escape velocity at that distance for the critical density of the Universe that we observe.

   (c) The particular galaxy is orbiting around the centre of our cluster of galaxies on a circular orbit. What is the angular velocity of this galaxy in the sky?

   (d) Will we ever discriminate two such galaxies that are initially at the same line of sight, if they are both moving in circular orbits but at different radii?   (I13 - T16 - C)

9. Based on the spectrum of a galaxy with redshift $z = 6.03$, it was determined that the age of the stars in the galaxy is 560 to 600 million years. At what z did the epoch of star formation occur in this galaxy?

   Assume that the rate of expansion of the Universe is given by a flat cosmological model with cosmological constant $\Lambda = 0$. (In such a model the scale factor $a \alpha t^{\frac{2}{3}}$, where t is time since the Big Bang).   (I11 - T11 - C)

10. Assume that the Universe is currently well described by a density parameter $\Omega_0 = 1$, there is no dark energy, and the current temperature of the Universe is 2.73 K. Knowing that the temperature of the Universe is inversely proportional to its radius (the scale factor), compute how long, starting from present time, it will take for the Universe to cool down by 0.1 K.   (I12 - T10 – C)

11. The deflection of light by a gravitational field was first predicted by Einstein in 1912, a few years before the publication of General Relativity Theory in 1916. A massive object that causes a light deflection behaves like a classical lens (Fig. 9.1). This prediction was confirmed by Sir Arthur Stanley Eddington in 1919. Consider a spherically symmetric object with mass M. This object will act like a lens, with an impact parameter ξ measured from the centre of the object. The deflection equation in this case is given by

$$\phi = \frac{4GM}{\xi c^2} \tag{9.1}$$

In a simpified model, the impact parameter may be seen as the shortest separation between the centre of the lens and the path of a particular light ray. In Fig. 9.2, the massive object which behaves like a lens is at L. Light rays emitted from the source S being deflected by the lens are observed by observer O as images S_1 and S_2. Here, ϕ, β and θ are very very small angles.   (I07 - T18 - C)

   (a) For a special case in which the source is perfectly aligned with the lens such that $\beta = 0$, show that a ring-like image will occur with the angular radius, called Einstein radius θ_E, given by

Fig. 9.1 *Image of the Abel cluster showing gravitational lensing. Image credit: HST*

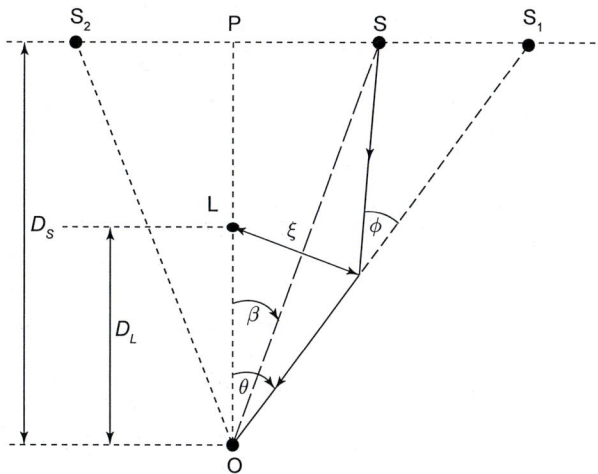

Fig. 9.2 *Geometric model of gravitational lensing*

$$\theta_E = \sqrt{\left(\frac{4GM}{c^2}\right)\left(\frac{D_S - D_L}{D_L D_S}\right)} \qquad (9.2)$$

(b) The distance (from the Earth) of a source star is about 50 kpc. A solar-mass lens, along the line of sight, is about 10 kpc from the star. Calculate the angular radius of the Einstein ring formed by this solar-mass lens with the perfect alignment.

(c) What is the resolution of the Hubble space telescope with a 2.4-m diameter mirror? Can the Hubble telescope resolve the Einstein ring in Question 11b?

(d) In Fig. 9.2, for an isolated point source S, there will be two images (S_1 and S_2) formed by the gravitational lens. Find the positions (θ_1 and θ_2) of the two images. The answer should be given in terms of β and θ_E.

(e) Find the ratio $\dfrac{\theta_{1,2}}{\beta}$ ($\dfrac{\theta_1}{\beta}$ or $\dfrac{\theta_2}{\beta}$) in terms of η. Here $\theta_{1,2}$ represents each of the image positions in Question 11d and η stands for the ratio $\dfrac{\beta}{\theta_E}$.

(f) Find also the values of magnification $\dfrac{\Delta\theta}{\Delta\beta}$ in terms of η for $\theta = \theta_{1,2}$ ($\theta = \theta_1$ or $\theta = \theta_2$), when $\Delta\beta = \beta$ and $\Delta\theta = \theta$.

12. Within the field of a galaxy cluster at a redshift of $z = 0.500$, a galaxy which looks like a normal elliptical is observed, with an apparent magnitude in the B filter $m_B = 20.40$ mag. The luminosity distance corresponding to a redshift of $z = 0.500$ is $d_L = 2754$ Mpc. The spectral energy distribution (SED) of elliptical galaxies in the wavelength range 250 nm to 500 nm is adequately approximated by the formula

$$L\lambda(\lambda) \propto \lambda^4 \qquad (9.3)$$

(i.e., the spectral density of the object's luminosity, also known as the monochromatic luminosity, is proportional to λ^4).

(a) What is the absolute magnitude of this galaxy in the B filter?

(b) Can it be a member of this cluster?

Hints:

Try to establish a relation that describes the dependence of the spectral density of flux on distance for a small wavelength interval.

Normal elliptical galaxies have maximum absolute magnitude equal to -22 mag.

For B band, the effective midpoint wavelength is 445 nm and FWHM is 94 nm.

(I11 - T17 - D)

13. Measurement of the cosmic microwave background (CMD) radiation shows that its temperature is practically the same at every point in the sky to a very high degree of accuracy. Let us assume that light emitted at the moment of recombination ($T_r \approx 3000$ K, $t_r \approx 300000$ years) is only reaching us now ($T_0 \approx 3$ K, $t_0 \approx 1.5 \times 10^{10}$ years). Scale factor (a) is defined as such $a_0 = a$ ($t = t_0$) = 1and $a_t = a(t < t_0)$ <1. Note that the time from the end of inflation ($t = 10^{-32}$ seconds) to the time of recombination was the radiation-dominated period and the matter-dominated period started at the recombination. During the radiation-dominated period, a is proportional to $t^{1/2}$, while during the matter-dominated period, a is proportional to $t^{2/3}$. (I08 - T18 - D)

(a) Estimate the horizon distances when recombination took place. Assume that temperature T is proportional to $1/a$.

(b) Consider two points in the CMB imprint, which are currently observed at a separation angle $\alpha = 5°$. At the recombination epoch, would it have been possible for observers at these two points to communicate with each other using photons?

(c) Estimate the size of our Universe at the end of the inflation period.

Note: Horizon distance is the present day angular separation between two points, such that an observer at one of the points would be just able to receive photons from the other point.

9.2 Data Analysis

1. **Virgo cluster:** The Virgo cluster of galaxies is the nearest large cluster which extends over nearly 10 degrees across the sky and contains a number of bright galaxies. It will

be interesting to find the distance to the Virgo cluster and to deduce certain cosmological information from it. The table below provides the distance estimates using various distance indicators (listed in the left column). The right column lists the mean distance $(d_i)\pm$ the standard deviation (s_i).   (I08 - D01 - B)

	Distance Indicator	Virgo Distance (Mpc)
1	Cepheids	14.9 ± 1.2
2	Novae	21.1 ± 3.9
3	Planetary Nebulae	15.2 ± 1.1
4	Globular Cluster	18.8 ± 3.8
5	Surface Brightness Fluctuations	15.9 ± 0.9
6	Tully–Fisher relation	15.8 ± 1.5
7	Faber–Jackson relation	16.8 ± 2.4
8	Type Ia Supernovae	19.4 ± 5.0

(a) As different methods give slightly different distances, we need to compute the average distance. This average, calculated by applying the weighted mean, can be taken as an estimate to the distance to the Virgo cluster.

$$d_{avg} = \frac{\sum_{i=1}^{n} \frac{d_i}{s_i^2}}{\sum_{i=1}^{n} \frac{1}{s_i^2}} \tag{9.4}$$

EA: Here weights are simply the inverse of variance. The lower the standard deviation, the higher the confidence and hence the higher the weight.

(b) What is the rms uncertainty (in units of Mpc) in that estimate?

(c) The spectra of the galaxies in Virgo indicate an average recession velocity of 1136 km/sec for the cluster. Can you estimate the Hubble constant H_0 and error in its estimation?

(d) What is Hubble time (age of the Universe) using the value of the Hubble constant you found and the uncertainty in its value?

10

Night Sky Observation

10.1 General Night Sky

1. Move the pointer along the celestial equator. (I07 - O01 - A)
2. Aim the pointer at the vernal equinox. (I07 - O02 - A)
3. Aim the pointer at the star named alpha-Arietis (α-Ari). (I07 - O04 - A)
4. In the constellation of Pegasus and its vicinity, there is an obvious square of bright stars (Great Square of Pegasus). Aim the pointer at the brightest star of the square.
    (I07 - O03 - A)
5. Aim the pointer at the stars Antares (αSco), Vega (αLyr), Altair (α-Aql) and Peacock (α-Pav). Also point to the constellation Corona Australis. (I12 - O01 - A)
6. Aim the pointer at three zodiacal constellations of your choice. (I12 - O11 - A)
7. The planetarium is projecting the sky of Beijing at 21:00 local time in mid-August. The staff will point to five constellations in the sky with a laser pointer, one minute for each. Identify the constellations (IAU names) in the order in which the five constellations have been shown. (I10 - O01 - B)
8. The planetarium is projecting the sky of Beijing, at 21:00 local time in mid-August. Identify any five constellations (IAU names) you can see that are crossed by the celestial equator.
    (I10 - O02 - B)
9. Fig. 10.1 (frame size $\cong 100° \times 70°$) shows a part of the sky for 22 October 2009 at 21:00 local time. Four bright stars in the Perseus and Andromeda constellations are missing in this chart. Find these missing stars by looking at the sky. Then, draw a cross on the location of each missing bright star in these two constellations on the chart. Use numbers in Table 10.1 to indicate these crosses.

    Note: Polaris is indicted by the N symbol in the figure. (I09 - O01 - C)
10. **Equal area star chart:** You are given an equal area sky map, as shown in Fig. 10.3. The map represents the sky in Suceava (latitude 47°39' North, longitude 26°15' East) at 19:00 UT on the day of the test. The observer who made the sky map was at very high altitude above Suceava; the zenith point is in the centre of the chart.

    (a) Draw on the map the horizon for an observer located on the ground in Suceava.

    (b) Draw on the map the celestial equator, the ecliptic, the galactic equator and the local meridian.

    (c) Mark the cardinal points (as N for north, E for east, S for south and W for west). Mark all the visible planets (except Uranus and Neptune) of the Solar System on the map and number them as P1, P2, ..., P6 in the order of increasing orbital radius (skip number 3 for the Earth). Note that planets are not currently shown on the map.

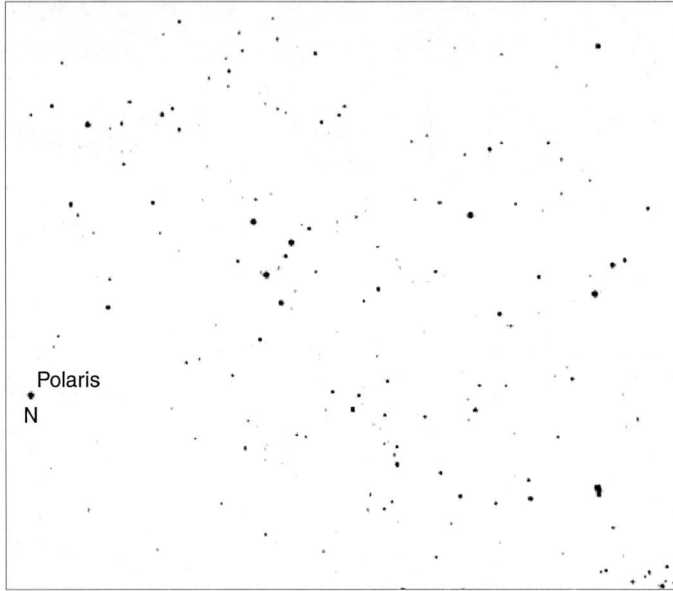

Fig. 10.1 *Photograph of the northern sky*

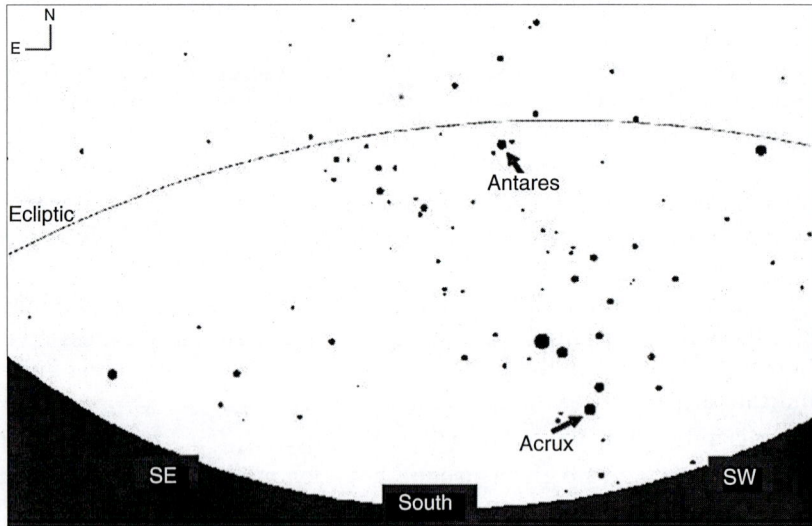

Fig. 10.2 *Sky map for Scorpio and surrounding regions*

(d) Identify and mark the four brightest stars in the visual band above the horizon line. Number the stars starting from 1 - the brightest, and continue with the fainter ones till number 4 for the faintest and give either the Bayer names or proper names.

(e) Draw on the map approximate figures of any 15 constellations which lie completely above the horizon. Each constellation you mark should be identified on the map with the IAU abbreviation.

Table 10.1 *The Bayer and common names of some stars around Perseus*

Number	Bayer Name	Number	Bayer Name
1	α-Per (Mirfak)	7	γ-And (Almach)
2	α-And (Alpheratz)	8	δ-And
3	ε-Per	9	51-And
4	ξ-Per (Menkib)	10	β-And(Mirach)
5	γ-Per	11	ζ-Per (Atik)
6	β-Per(Algol)		

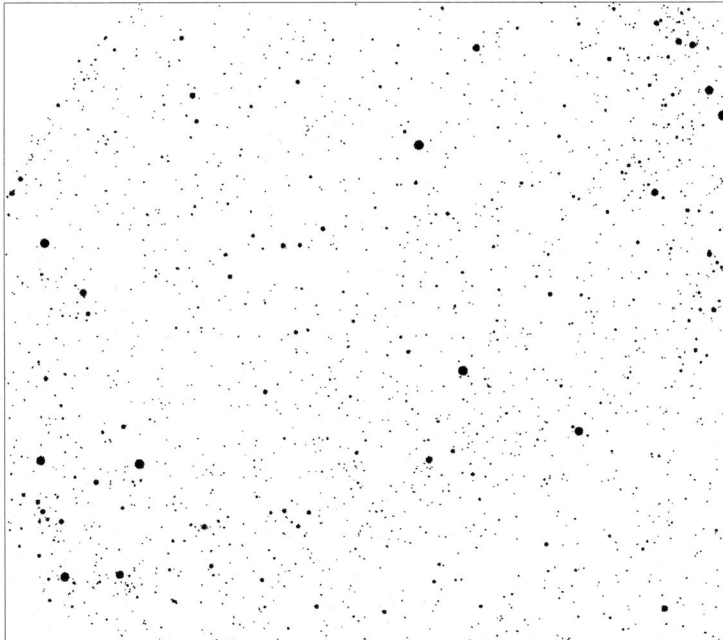

Fig. 10.3 *Equal area star chart*

(f) Mark on the map the positions of M31, M27, M13, β Cygni and δ Ursa Minoris.

(g) Estimate the sidereal time of the map.

(h) Estimate the equatorial coordinates (right ascension and declination) of the star Altair (α Aquilae).   (I14 - O01 - D)

11. Fig. 10.2 shows a part of the southern sky chart for 21 August 2008 at 19:00 local time. Unfortunately, a number of bright stars in the Capricorn and Scorpio constellations are missing. Now, you have to find those missing bright stars in both constellations by looking at the sky directly.   (I08 - O01 - D)

(a) Draw small circles on the locations of the missing bright stars in the Capricorn and Scorpio constellations.

Table 10.2   *The Bayer and common names of some stars around Scorpio*

Number	Common Names	Number	Common Names
1	Rukbat (α Sgr)	18	Albali (ε Aqr)
2	Graffias (β Sco)	19	Altair (α Aql)
3	Nunki (σ Sgr)	20	Shaula (λ Sco)
4	Deneb (α Cyg)	21	Vrischika (π Sco)
5	Zaniah (η Vir)	22	Arich (γ Vir)
6	Tarazed (γAql)	23	Deneb Algedi (δ Cap)
7	Dabih (β Cap)	24	Heze (ζ Vir)
8	Girtab (κ Sco)	25	Nusakan (β CrB)
9	Spica (α Vir)	26	Wei (ε Sco)
10	Sabik (η Oph)	27	Syrma (ι Vir)
11	Dschubba(δ Sco)	28	Nashira (γ Cap)
12	KausAustralis (ε Sgr)	29	Lesath(ν Sco)
13	Algiedi(α Cap)	30	Zavijava(β Vir)
14	Sadr (γ Cyg)	31	Arcturus(α Boo)
15	Vindemiatrix (ε Vir)	32	Megrez(δ UMa)
16	Antares(α Sco)	33	Chara(β CVn)
17	Yen(ζ Cap)	34	Sargas(θ Sco)

(b) Identify them by putting the numbers on the sky chart, as many as possible based on Table 10.2.

(c) Afterwards, draw on the sky chart the borders of the Scorpio and Capricorn constellations.

12. **Constellations:** Jan Hevelius (1611–1687) introduced 11 new constellations in the sky. The International Astronomical Union confirmed seven of those, as listed in Table 10.3, in 1928:

(a) Mark each of the above constellations on Fig. 10.4 by a point lying anywhere within the constellation. Label the marks using the appropriate serial number or IAU name.

(b) Mark on the same map the positions of any 13 objects from the Messier Catalogue (not necessarily from the constellations above), giving the Messier number (M xx) for each.

The map is prepared for epoch J 2000.0 and uses a polar projection with a linear scale in declination. It includes stars brighter than about the fifth magnitude.   (I11 - G01 - D)

Table 10.3   *Constellations of Jan Hevelius*

No.	IAU Abbr.	Latin Name	Translation	Coordinates of the Centre	
				RA α	Dec. δ
1	CVn	Canes Venatici	Hunting dogs	13h 00m	+40°
2	Lac	Lacerta	Lizard	22h 30m	+46°
3	LMi	Leo Minor	Smaller Lion	10h 10m	+32°
4	Lyn	Lynx	Lynx	8h 00m	+48°
5	Sct	Scutum	Shield	18h 40m	-10°
6	Sex	Sextans	Sextant	10h 15m	-3°
7	Vul	Vulpecula	(Little) Fox	20h 15m	+24°

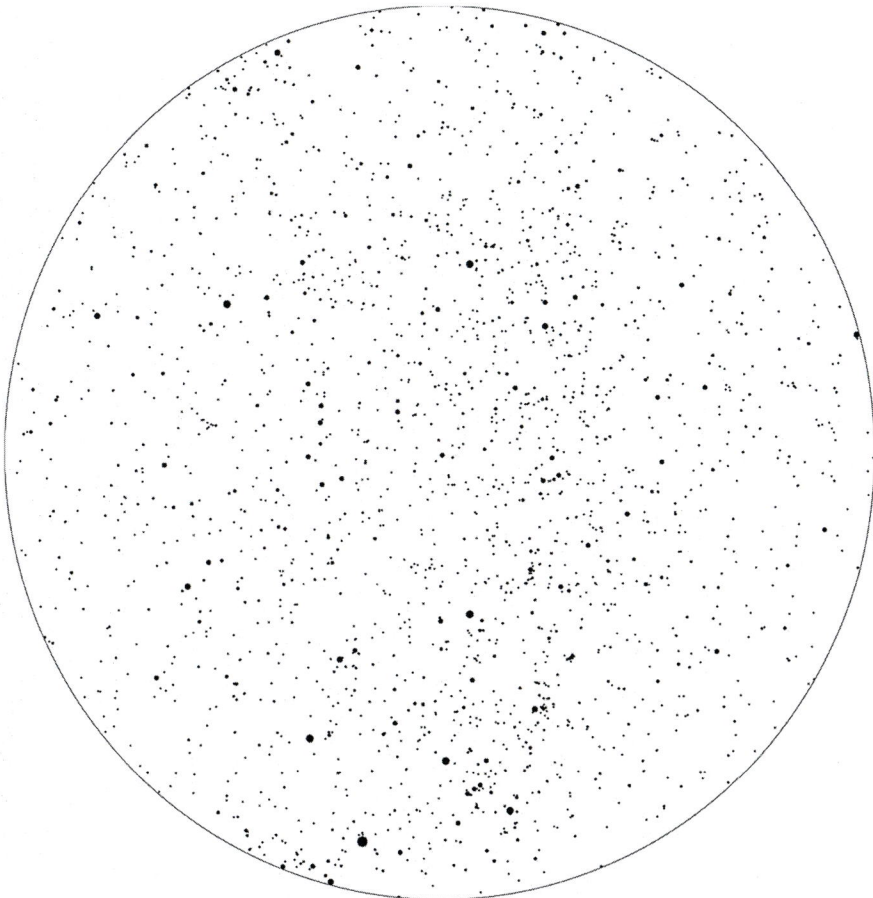

Fig. 10.4   *Map of sky used in IOAA 2011*

10.2 Magnitude and Angular Size

1. Start with the star named Aldebaran (α-Tau) in the constellation Taurus, turn the pointer 35 degrees north followed by 6 degrees west (in equatorial coordinate). Then, aim the pointer at the brightest star in close vicinity.   (I07 - O05 - A)

2. The open star cluster Hyades in constellation Taurus is one of the clusters nearest to us, being only 151 light years away. Fig. 10.5 lists the brightness of some stars indicated by the apparent magnitude in parentheses. Please estimate the apparent magnitude of the star Gamma-Tauri (γ-Tau) to the nearest first decimal digit.   (I07 - O06 - B)

3. (a) Fig. 10.6 shows a part of the sky which contains the Cepheus constellation, for 22 October 2009 at 22:00 local time. Five bright stars in the Cepheus constellation are identified by numbers (1, 2, 3, 4, 5) and common names. Estimate the angular distance (in units of degrees) between two pairs of stars shown in Table 10.4.   (I09 - O02 - B)

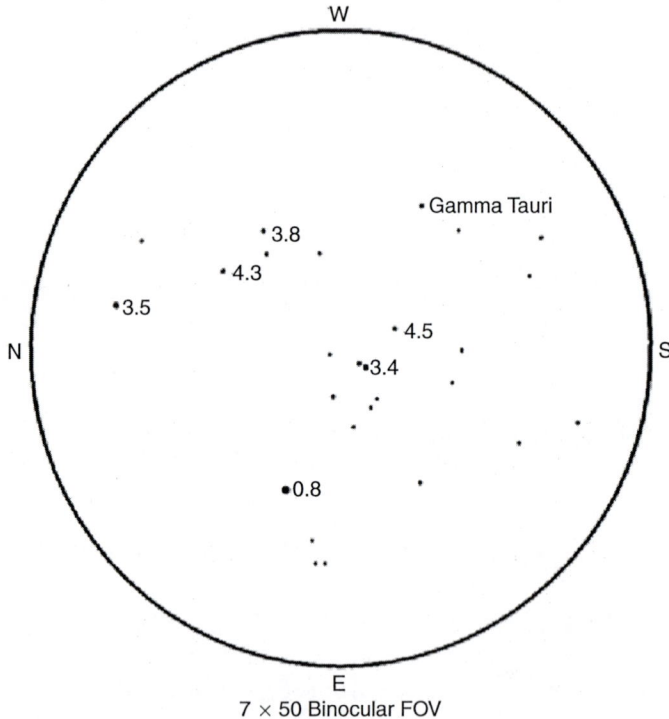

Fig. 10.5 *Sky map for Taurus region*

Table 10.4 *Angular distance*

Pairs of Stars	Angular Distance (degrees)
1 (Errai) and 2 (Alfirk)	
1 (Errai) and 3 (Alderamin)	

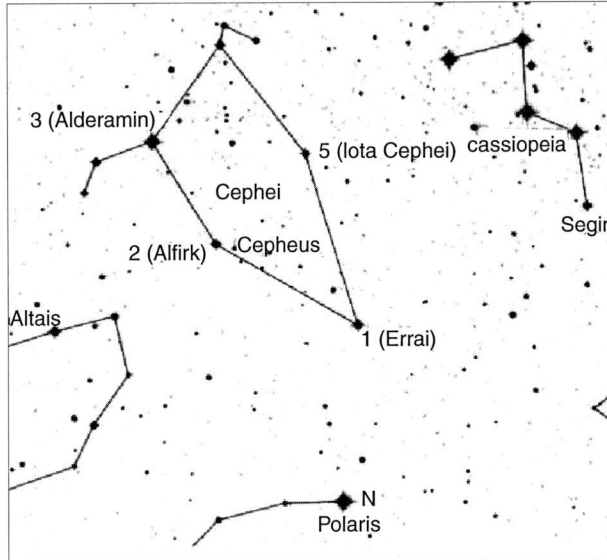

Fig. 10.6 *Sky map for Cepheus region*

Table 10.5 *Star magnitudes*

Star Name	mv
Polaris	1.95
Altais	3.05
Segin	3.34
2 (Alfirk)	
3 (Alderamin)	

(b) Use Table 10.5 and Fig. 10.6 to estimate the apparent visual magnitude of stars 2 (Alfirak) and 3 (Alderamin) in Table 10.5.

10.3 Instrument Aided Observations

1. Identifying telescope components: (I11 - G03 - A)

   (a) Look at the pictures of the telescope in Fig. 10.7 and match the names of the items with the corresponding letters in Table 10.6.

   (b) Select and circle the correct answer for each of the questions below:

   21. Mount design:

      a. Fork   b. Transit
      c. Dobsonian Alt–Azimuth   d. German Equatorial

Fig. 10.7   *Parts of a telescope*

22. Optical type:
    a. Newtonian b. Cassegrain   c. Keplerian   d. Galilean
23. Objective aperture:
    a. 60 mm   b. 80 mm   c. 90 mm   d. 100 mm
    and objective lens focal length:
    a. 400 mm   b. 500 mm   c. 600 mm   d. 800 mm
24. Eyepiece focal length:
    a. 4 mm   b. 6 mm   c. 12.5 mm   d.25 mm
25. Used for visual observations of the sky, the finder scope gives a picture which is:
    a. normal   b. rotated by 180°
    c. reflected in one axis   d. rotated by 90°
26. Used for visual observations with the diagonal mirror, the instrument gives a picture which is:
    a. normal   b. rotated by 180°
    c. reflected in one axis   d. rotated by 90°
(c) Determine the following theoretical instrument parameters:
    27. Magnification:
    28. Focal ratio:
    29. Resolution (in arcseconds):
    30. Limiting magnitude: (I11 - G03 - A)
2. Assemble a telescope indoors with an equatorial mount. Your team will be given a maximum of 10 minutes to assemble it. The direction of North will be indicated to you. At the end of the round, the students should take the telescope apart again.
   The coordinates of Beijing: longitude: 116°48'E, latitude: 40°32'N.   (I10 - G01 - A)

Table 10.6   *Parts of a telescope*

Item Name	Letter
(example) Tripod	**M**
1. Counterweight	
2.Right Ascension Setting Circle (RA Scale)	
3. Declination Setting Circle (Declination Scale)	
4. Right Ascension locking knob	
5. Declination locking knob	
6. Geographical latitude scale	
7. Finder scope	
8. Focuser tube	
9. Focuser knob	
10. Eyepiece	
11. Declination Axis	
12. Right Ascension Axis (Polar Axis)	
13. Right Ascension slow motion adjustment	
14. Declination flexible slow motion adjustment	
15. 90° diagonal mirror	
16. Azimuth adjustment knobs	
17. Altitude adjustment screws	
18. Lock screw	
19. Spirit level bubble	
20. Eyepiece reticle light switch and brightness control	

3. Point your telescope to the binary star ε - Trianguli Australis using Fig. 10.8 as a guide. If you are not able to point at the star, the instructor will do it for you, but you will lose 50% of the points. The components of this pair have magnitudes 4.1 and 9.3 and are separated by 82". Indicate the colour of each star: (I12 - O04 - A)
   Brighter: White / blue ()   Yellow ()   Red()
   Dimmer: White / blue ()   Yellow ()   Red()

4. Point your telescope to the binary ystar Albireo (β-Cygni) using Fig. 10.9 as a guide. If you are not able to point at the star, the examiner will do it for you but you will lose 50% of the points. The components of that pair are of magnitude 3.2 and 4.7, separated by 34.8". Indicate the colour of each star: (I12 - O14 - A)

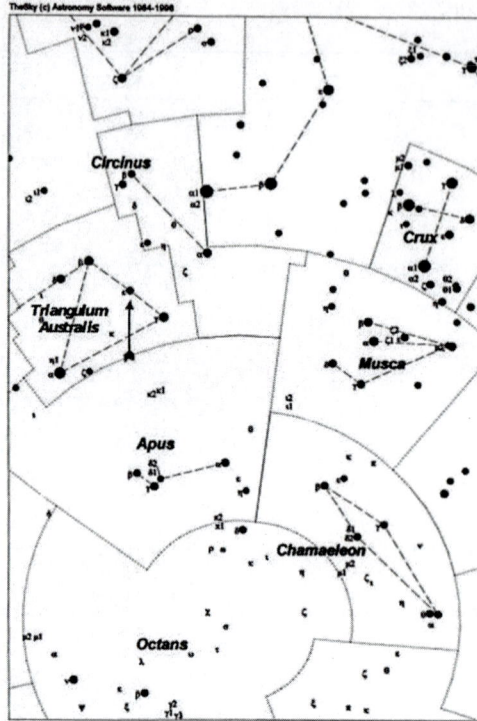

Fig. 10.8 *Sky map of Southern Pole region*

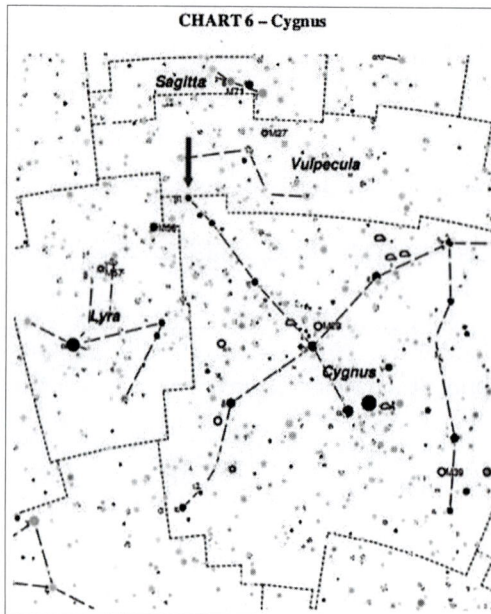

Fig. 10.9 *Sky map of Cygnus region*

Brighter: White ()   Blue ()   Yellow ()   Red ()

Dimmer: White ()   Blue ()   Yellow ()   Red ()

5. For this task, four telescopes have been pointed to four specific objects. Identify which one corresponds to: Open Cluster (OC), Globular Cluster (GC), Emission Nebulae (EN) and Planetary Nebulae (PN). (I12 - O05 - A)

   Object 1 ()   Object 2 ()   Object 3 ()   Object 4 ()

6. Without using the setting circles (coordinate dials) of the equatorially mounted telescope, complete the following tasks:

   (a) Bring the bright star ($m = 3.51$ mag) γ Sagitta ($\alpha = 19^h58^m45.39^s$, $\delta = +19°29'31.5''$) to the centre of view of the telescope.

   (b) Bring the famous Dumbell Nebula, i.e., M27 ($\alpha = 19^h59^m36.34^s$, $\delta + 22°43'16.09''$) to the centre of the field of view. (I13 - O02 - B)

7. Use Fig. 10.10 to point to ν-Scorpii. If you are not able to point at the star, you can ask the examiner to do it for you but you will not get marks for pointing. *Note:* Use a 2x Barlow + 10 mm eyepiece to draw what you see through the eyepiece. It is not necessary to mark the North. (I12 - O12 - B)

8. Point your telescope to the star SAO 209318 using Fig. 10.10. Notice a small nebulous patch close to that star. Use your 10 mm or 10 mm + 2x Barlow to estimate the distance between the star and the nebulous patch, in arcminutes (coordinates to SAO 209318 are α: 17h 50m 51s and δ: $-37°2'$). Express your answer using 0.5' precision. Note that the field of view of the 10-mm eyepiece on this telescope is 24 arcmin or 0.4°. If you are not able to point at the star, the examiner will do it for you but you will lose 50% of the points. (I12 - O13 - B)

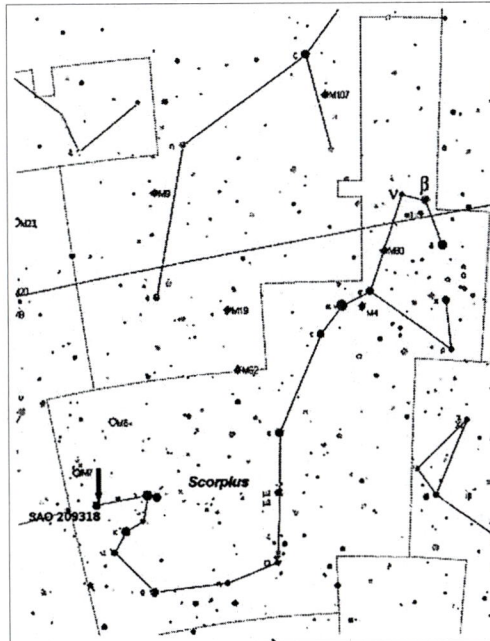

Fig. 10.10 *Map of Scorpio region marked with SAO 209318 and ν-Sco*

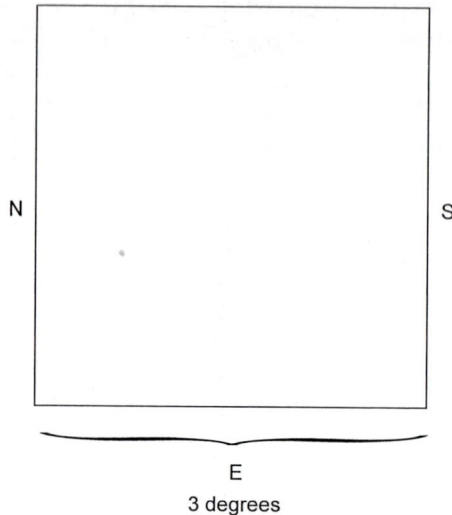

Fig. 10.11   *Field for drawing of Andromeda Galaxy*

9. Observe the Andromeda Galaxy (M31) and then draw the approximate shape and size of the galaxy that you see through the binoculars in Fig. 10.11 with correct orientation (in equatorial coordinates). The field of view of the binoculars is 6.8°.   (I07 - O07 - B)

10. You are given a properly aligned telescope with two eyepieces (10 mm and 25 mm) and a digital timer. Chose one of the two eyepieces and using a suitable, bright object measure the field of view of the telescope. You may refer to the catalogue of bright stars to obtain their equatorial coordinates. You should complete the task in 10 minutes or less.

          (I13 - O01 - C)

11. The telescope is pointing to Caph in Cassiopeia constellation (RA: $0^h9.7^m$; Dec: 59°12'). Using the clock beside the telescope, write down the local time (in the format of HH:MM:SS). Note down readings from dials on the telescope mount.   (I09 - O03 - C)

    (a) Point your telescope to any one of the following stars. Write down the name of the selected star and notify the examiner to check it. Deneb (Alpha Cygni) / Alfirk (Beta Cephei) / Algol (Beta Persei) / Capella (Alpha Aurigae).

    (b) Note down readings from the dials on the telescope mount again. Estimate the declination and the hour angle of the star you have chosen.

12. The telescope for this task is aimed at open cluster NGC 6231. Ensure that the 10-mm Plössl eyepiece is fixed on the telescope. Estimate the diameter of the field of view of this telescope using the two angular distances shown in Fig. 10.12 as reference. Express your answer in arcminutes.   (I12 - O02 - C)

13. Use Fig. 10.13 to estimate the magnitude of the missing star, shown as a cross, inside NGC 6231. Use the magnitude of other stars as reference.   (I12 - O03 - C)

    Note: To avoid confusion between decimal point and real stars, decimal points are not shown. So, magnitude 60 corresponds to magnitude 6.0. Give your answer with a precision of 0.1 magnitude. Also note that 8.0 star in the chart is a variable.

14. On the day of vernal equinox, a rare transit of Mercury is going to take place at 14:00 local time. A team of astronomers reaches a mountaintop, early in the morning, in order to align

The sky (D) Astronomy software 1964–1998

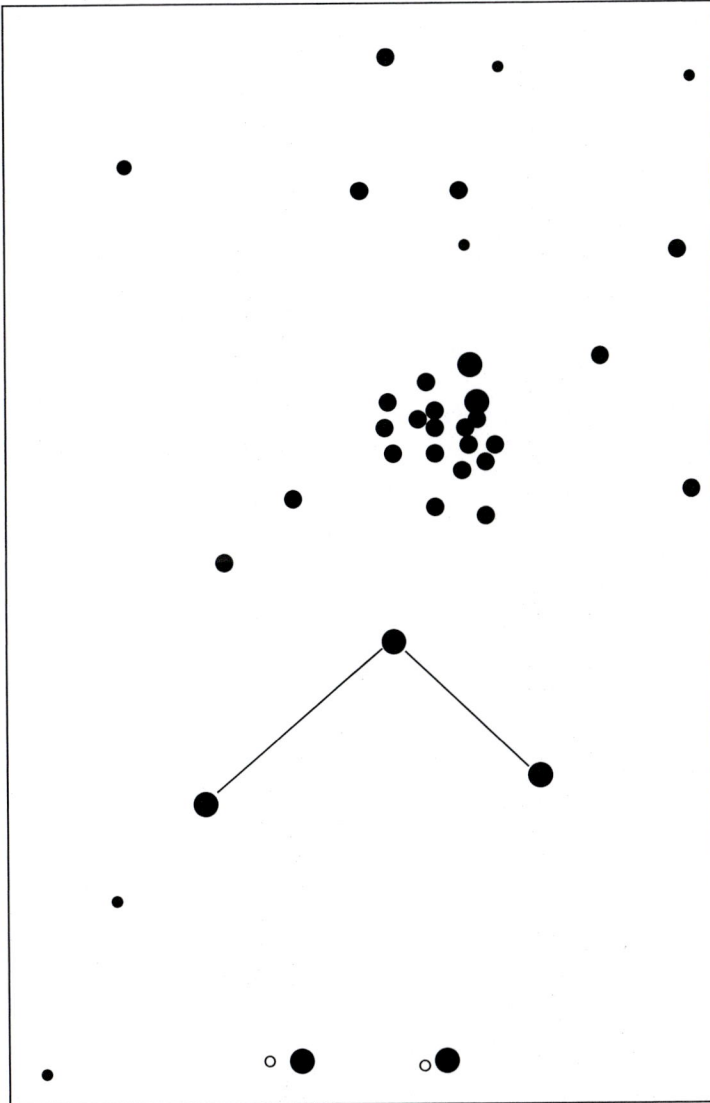

Fig. 10.12 *Image of NGC 6231 with angular separation*

their equatorially mounted telescope for transit observations. The site is new and they do not know the geographical coordinates. Unfortunately the sky is covered with clouds. No celestial objects are visible. Suddenly, at around local noon, the Sun is seen through the clouds. An experienced astronomer manages to roughly align the telescope in less than two minutes, using just the position of the Sun, date and time of the event and a spirit level. Can you guess his method and execute it step by step?   (I13 - O03 - C)

15. You have to identify as many stars as possible in the field of a celestial photograph using the telescope and CCD provided. You can choose one of the five recommended regions in

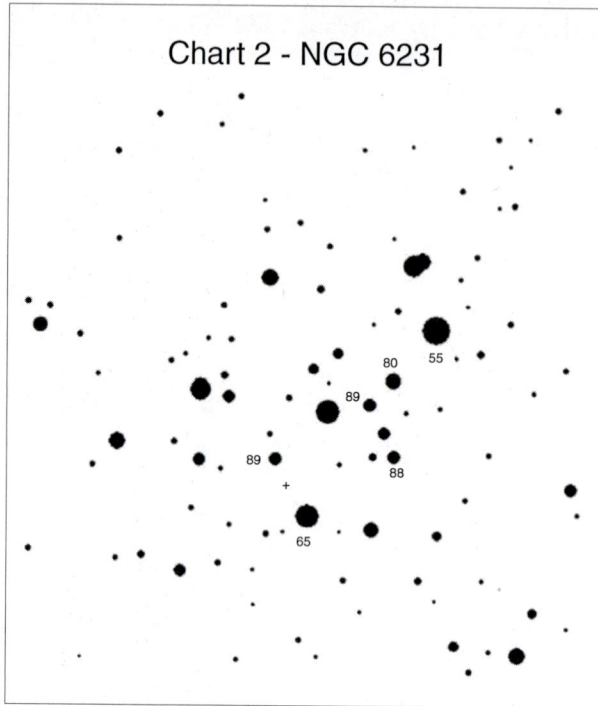

Fig. 10.13   *Image of NGC 6231 with magnitudes*

the sky listed below. Then, point the telescope in the direction of the selected sky region. Take three photographs with different exposure times and record images of the sky using the CCD camera. Save the observational data. Transfer the data to printing facilities to print out the result. Ask the technical assistant for help. Choose the best prints-out and use the image to identify the stars in the field of observations. The step by step process for this is given below.   (I08 - O02 - D)

(a) Choose only one out of the following five recommended regions to the directions of (marked by the following bright clusters):

- M7: $(\alpha = 17^h53^m.3, \delta = -34°46.2')$
- M8: $(\alpha = 18^h04^m.2, \delta = -24°22.0')$
- M20: $(\alpha = 18^h02^m.4, \delta = -22°58.7')$
- M21: $(\alpha = 18^h04^m.2, \delta = -22°29.5')$
- M23: $(\alpha = 17^h57^m.0, \delta = -18°59.4')$

You may not change your choice.

(b) Point the telescope to the chosen cluster using the telescope controller. If necessary you may move the telescope slightly to obtain the best position in the frame of the CCD by checking the display of CCDops software.

(c) Display the region in The Sky software provided in the computer, to confirm that the telescope is pointed at the selected object in the sky. You may change the field of view of the sky chart.

(d) You may invert the background images into white, as in the chart mode. Copy and paste the sky chart from The Sky onto the answer page. Use the Ctrl-c and Ctrl-v buttons on the keyboard, respectively.

(e) Type the equatorial coordinates of the centre of that object in the answer page as indicated in The Sky.

(f) Take three photographs of the chosen object by using the attached CCD camera and CCDops software, with various exposure times. Choose exposure time in the range between 1 and 120 seconds. The image is automatically subtracted with a dark frame of the same exposure time.

(g) You must invert the background images into white. Copy and paste images from CCDops onto the answer page. Use the Ctrl-c and Ctrl-v buttons, respectively, on the keyboard.

(h) Save your answer page in a hard disk in Microsoft Word file format.

(i) Print your answer page which consists of the photographs and the corresponding sky chart.

(j) Go to the identification room and bring with you the prints-out of the sky chart and the photographs. Ask for help from the technical assistant, if necessary.

(k) Choose the best of the three printed images and identify as many objects as possible on it.

(l) Use the assigned computer and The Sky software to identify objects. Type your identification in your answer page.

(m) Type on the answer page the names (or catalogue number), RA, declination, and magnitude of each identified star and put the sequential number on the photograph. Make sure that you list the stars on the answer page following the same order and number as on the photograph.

(n) Estimate the limiting magnitude of the photograph you chose, empirically.

10.4 Planetarium Based Questions

1. The planetarium is projecting the sky of Beijing (longitude: 116°48'E, latitude: 40°32'N), on some day, just about 1 hour after sunset. Estimate which month (use 1–12) it should be according to the displayed night sky. What is the age[1] of the Moon (in 1–30 days)?

(I10 - O03 - B)

2. The sky projected on the dome corresponds to Suceava (longitude: 26°15'), at 18:00 UT, on a certain day of a certain month.   (I14 - O02 - B)

   (a) Two arcs of a circle will now be projected. The arcs are segmented. Each segment represents an interval of some degrees. This interval is not the same for each arc. Identify each arc by circling the correct name and give the angular size of each segment (in degrees).

   (b) Estimate the local sidereal time of the sky you see in the dome.

   (c) Determine the month to which the projected sky would correspond at the given time.

---

[1] Age of the moon is number of days since the last new moon

The arcs are now turned off and a red laser arrow is used to point at various objects for the rest of the questions. Each object is pointed at for 2 minutes with 30 seconds on a 10-second off cycle.

(d) The locations of the three Messier objects will be pointed to one by one. For each Messier object pointed to, write its Messier catalogue number and the number which indicates its type (1 for galaxy, 2 for nebula, 3 for open cluster, 4 for globular cluster). Also, for each object, write the IAU abbreviation of the constellation where the object is located.

(e) Three stars will be pointed to successively. Write either the proper name of the star or the Bayer designation and the number which indicates its type (1 for single, 2 double). Also, for each star, write the IAU abbreviation of the constellation where the star is located.

3. Simulation of the Earth sky   (I11 - O01 - C)

(a) In the sky projected, one can notice a cresent moon, a nova and a comet. On the map of the sky (use Fig. 10.4), mark the nova with a cross and label it. Mark the Moon with a Moon symbol and draw the shape and position of the comet.

(b) In the table below, circle only those objects which are above the astronomical horizon.

M20 – Triffid Nebula	o Cet – Mira	δ CMa – Wezen
α Cyg – Deneb	M57 – Ring Nebula	β Per – Algol
δ Cep – Alrediph	α Boo – Arcturus	M44 – Praesepe

                                                                   (Beehive cluster)

(c) The coordinate grid will now be switched on. When it is visible, mark on the map the northern part of the local meridian (from the zenith to the horizon) and the ecliptic north pole (with a cross and marked P).

(d) For the displayed sky, note down:

Geographical latitude of the observer (ϕ):

Local Sidereal Time (θ):

Approximate time of year (by circling the calendar month):

Jan, Feb, Mar, Apr, May, Jun, Jul, Aug, Sep, Oct, Nov, Dec.

(e) Give the names of the objects, whose approximate horizontal coordinates are:

Azimuth $A_1 = 45°$ and altitude $h_1 = 58°$:

Azimuth $A_2 = 278°$ and altitude $h_2 = 20°$:

(If you can, use Bayer designations, IAU abbreviations and Messier numbers or English or Latin names.)

(f) Give the horizontal coordinates (azimuth, altitude) of:

Sirius (α CMa): $A_3 =$ $;h_3 =$

The Andromeda Galaxy (M31): $A_4 =$ $; h_4 =$

(g) Give the equatorial coordinates of the star marked on the sky with a red arrow:

$$\alpha =   ; \delta =$$

4. Simulation of Martian sky: The sky projected now is as it appears for an observer standing at some distance from a Martian base. The Martian base is visible on the horizon.

                                                                   (I11 - O02 - C)

(a) Give the aerographic (Martian) latitude of the observer : $\varphi =$

(b) Give the altitudes of the upper (h_u) and lower (h_l) culmination of:

Pollux (β Gem): $h_u =$; $h_l =$
Deneb (α Cyg) : $h_u =$; $h_l =$

(c) Give the areocentric (Martian) declination of:

Regulus (α Leo) $\delta =$

Toliman (α Cen) $\delta =$

(d) Sketch diagrams to illustrate your working in the two Questions 4b and 4c above:

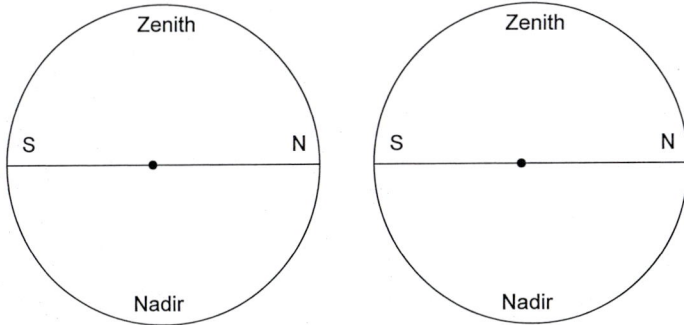

(e) On the map of the sky in Fig. 10.4, mark the Martian celestial north pole with a cross and label it.

(f) Estimate the azimuth (measured from the South) of the observer as seen from the Martian base visible on the horizon.

(g) Estimate the location of the base on Mars and circle the appropriate description:

a. near the northern Tropic circle   b. near the Equator

c. near the northern Arctic circle   d. near the North Pole

(h) The time axis below shows the Martian year and the seasons in the northern hemisphere. Mark the date corresponding to the sky on the axis.

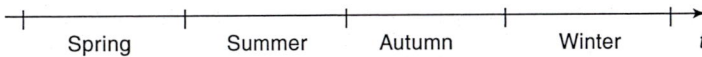

11

Solutions: Celestial Mechanics

11.1 Theory

1. (Perihelion distance) + (Aphelion distance) = (Major axis of the orbit).

   Thus, the semi-major axis, $a = \dfrac{31.5 + 0.5}{2} = 16$ AU

   According to Kepler's third law, we have

   $$T^2 \propto a^3 \tag{11.1}$$

   $$T^2 = (\text{constant}) \, a^3$$

   This constant is $1\dfrac{(year)^2}{(AU)^3}$ for our Solar System, which follows from the fact that the earth revolves around the Sun from 1 AU distance in 1 year. Thus, T is measured in years and a in AU. This is a useful trick to remember for comparison of periods of the Solar System object.

   Forth is comet we have,

   $$T^2 = 16^3 = \left(4^2\right)^6 = \left(4^3\right)^2$$

   $$T = 64.0 \text{ years} \tag{11.2}$$

2. This comet has a period of 64 years and semi-major axis measuring 16 AU.

   By Kepler's second law, the comet will sweep an equal area in equal time.

   $$\therefore \qquad \text{Area per year} = \frac{\text{Area of ellptical orbit}}{T} = \frac{\pi ab}{T} \tag{11.3}$$

   The perihelion distance is given by $a(1 - e) = 0.5$ AU, where e is the eccentricity.

   $$b^2 = a^2(1 - e^2) = a^2 - a^2 e^2 \tag{11.4}$$

   $$= (a + ae)(a - ae) \tag{11.5}$$

   $$= (\text{Aphelion distance}) \times (\text{Perihelion distance}) \tag{11.6}$$

   $$b^2 = 31.5 \times 0.5 \tag{11.7}$$

   $$\therefore \qquad b = 3.97 \text{ AU} \tag{11.8}$$

   $$\therefore \qquad \text{Area per year} = \frac{\pi \times 16 \times 3.97}{64}$$

   $$= 3.1 \ (\text{AU})^2/\text{yr} \tag{11.9}$$

EA: It is tricky to decide on the number of digits in the final answer. One should remember following rules:

- If different input values have a different number of significant digits, the number of digits in the final answer will be equal to the least number of digits of all the input values.
- However, if the input values are measurements, i.e., they are accompanied by units, then you should take into account the least count of measurements as denoted by the input values. In this case, the least uncertain measurement, i.e., the one with the largest least count, will govern the number of significant digits in the final answer.
- In the intermediate steps, you may retain at least one digit more than what is required so that you can minimise rounding errors.

In this question, both measurements (0.5 AU and 31.5 AU) have the same least count. Thus, the final answer can also be expressed with the same least count. Just because 0.5 AU has one significant digit, one should not round off the answer as 3 AU²/yr.

3. As the comet is entering the inner Solar System, its perihelion distance will be of the order of 10 AU or less, which is very small when compared to the aphelion distance.

$$a = \frac{d_{\text{peri}} + d_{ap}}{2} \tag{11.10}$$

$$\approx \frac{d_{ap}}{2} = \frac{3500}{2}$$

$$a = 17500 \text{ AU} \tag{11.11}$$

$$T = a^{1.5} \tag{11.12}$$

$$= 2.3 \times 10^6 \text{ years} \tag{11.13}$$

As the orbit is symmetric with respect to the major axis,

$$t_{journey} = \frac{T}{2} \tag{11.14}$$

$$= 1.2 \times 10^6 \text{ years} \tag{11.15}$$

4. Let us assume that a man can jump vertically up to 50 cm on the Earth. This number is purely a rough estimate and one can choose any number between 10 cm and 50 cm. One may think that a typical person's feet can move more than 50 cm away from the ground, but it should be remembered that vertical shift in his/her centre of gravity will be much smaller.

$$v_{jump} = \sqrt{2gh} \tag{11.16}$$

$$v_{escape} = \sqrt{\frac{2GM}{R}} \tag{11.17}$$

$$\because \quad v_{jump} = v_{escape}$$

$$\therefore \quad 2gh = \frac{2GM}{R} = \frac{2G}{R} \frac{4\pi \rho R^3}{3}$$

$$R = \sqrt{\frac{3gh}{4\pi \rho G}} \tag{11.18}$$

$$= \sqrt{\frac{3 \times 9.81 \times 0.5}{4\pi \times 5515 \times 6.6741 \times 10^{-11}}}$$

$$= 1.78 \times 10^3 \text{ m} \tag{11.19}$$

$$R \approx 2 \text{ km or smaller} \tag{11.20}$$

5. The mass of the asteroid is

$$m = \frac{4}{3}\pi r^3 \rho \tag{11.21}$$

$$= \frac{4}{3}\pi (1.1 \times 10^3)^3 \times 2.2 \times 10^3$$

$$= 1.23 \times 10^{13} \text{ kg} \tag{11.22}$$

Since, $m_{astronaut} \ll m$, it can be safely ignored. Then, the critical velocity is,

$$v_{crit} = \sqrt{\frac{Gm}{r}} \tag{11.23}$$

$$= \sqrt{\frac{6.6741 \times 10^{-11} \times 1.23 \times 10^{13}}{1100}}$$

$$= 0.86 \text{ km/s} \tag{11.24}$$

If the velocity of the astronaut is greater than or equal to v_{crit}, he/she will start orbiting the asteroid. That mean he/she will not be able to walk on the asteroid.

If the astronaut wants to complete a circle along the equator of the asteroid on foot within 2.2 hours,

$$v_{walk} = \frac{2\pi \times 1100}{2.2 \times 3600} \tag{11.25}$$

$$= 0.87 \text{ km/s} \tag{11.26}$$

As $v_{walk} > v_{crit}$, the astronaut will NOT be able to complete the circle on foot within the stipulated time.

Another way of reaching the same conclusion would be to find the oribital period of a body orbiting close to the surface of the asteroid, i.e., exactly with $v = v_{crit}$. This period is about one and a half minutes longer than 2.2 hours.

6. The escape velocity of an object on the edge of the cluster is given by,

$$v_{esc} = \sqrt{\frac{2GM_{cl}}{R_{cl}}} \tag{11.27}$$

$$\therefore \qquad M_{cl} = NM_\odot = \frac{R_{cl} v_{esc}^2}{2G}$$

$$\therefore \qquad N = \frac{R_{cl} v_{esc}^2}{2GM_\odot} \tag{11.28}$$

$$= \frac{20 \times 3.0856 \times 10^{16} \times (6 \times 10^3)^2}{2 \times 6.6726 \times 10^{-11} \times 1.9891 \times 10^{30}}$$

$$N \approx 8 \times 10^4 \tag{11.29}$$

Thus, the cluster contains about 80,000 stars.

7. As all the stars are part of the cluster, the rms velocity must be smaller than the escape velocity. As a rough estimate, one can take

$$v_{esc} = \sqrt{2}v_{rms} \tag{11.30}$$

However, this is just a convenient assumption and one is free to make other similar assumptions.

$$v^2_{esc} = \frac{2GM}{R} \tag{11.31}$$

$$\therefore \quad v^2_{rms} = \frac{GM}{R}$$

$$\therefore \quad M = \frac{Rv^2_{rms}}{G} \tag{11.32}$$

$$= \frac{20 \times 3.0856 \times 10^{16} \times (3 \times 10^3)^2}{6.6726 \times 10^{-11}}$$

$$\approx 8 \times 10^{34} \text{kg} \tag{11.33}$$

$$M \approx 4 \times 10^4 \, M_\odot \tag{11.34}$$

8. To determine the type of orbit, we must find the total energy of the spacecraft.

$$E_{Tot} = KE + PE$$

$$= \frac{1}{2}mv^2 - \frac{GM_\odot m}{R} \tag{11.35}$$

$$= m\left(\frac{(17062)^2}{2} - \frac{6.6726 \times 10^{-11} \times 1.9891 \times 10^{30}}{116.406 \times 1.4960 \times 10^{11}}\right)$$

$$E_{Tot} = 1.3793 \times 10^8 \, m \tag{11.36}$$

$$\therefore \quad E_{Tot} > 0 \tag{11.37}$$

Hence, the orbit is **hyperbolic**.

The magnitude of the Sun will be given by,

$$m_1 - m_2 = -2.5\log\left(\frac{f_1}{f_2}\right) \tag{11.38}$$

$$m_1 - m_2 = -2.5\log\left(\frac{d_2}{d_1}\right)^2$$

$$m_1 = m_2 + 5\log\left(\frac{d_1}{d_2}\right) \tag{11.39}$$

$$= -26.72 + 5\log\left(\frac{116.406}{1}\right)$$

$$m_1 = -16.39$$

9. Ratio of average densities of the Sun and the Earth will be given by,

$$\frac{\rho_\oplus}{\rho_\odot} = \frac{M_\oplus}{(R_\oplus)^3} \frac{(R_\odot)^3}{M_\odot} \qquad (11.41)$$

Now we should manipulate physical expressions for the given data so as to obtain quantities in the RHS of this equation.

Firstly, by Kepler's third law,

$$T_\oplus = 2\pi \sqrt{\frac{a^3}{GM_\odot}} \qquad (11.42)$$

Let $\theta_\odot$ be the angular diameter of the Sun in radians.

$$\theta_\odot = \frac{2R_\odot}{a_\oplus} \qquad (11.43)$$

$$\Rightarrow a_\oplus = \frac{2R_\odot}{\theta_\odot}$$

Combining the two, we get

$$T_\oplus^2 = 4\pi^2 \times \frac{8R_\odot^3}{GM_\odot \theta_\odot^3}$$

$$\Rightarrow \frac{R_\odot^3}{M_\odot} = \frac{GT_\oplus^2 \theta_\odot^3}{32\pi^2} \qquad (11.44)$$

The distance between latitudes will be measured along the longitudes. Two opposite longitudes form a circle. Thus, the distance between two latitudes, separated by φ radians, can be obtained by finding the arc length (S) on a circle with radius $R_\oplus$.

$$R_\oplus \varphi = S$$

$$\frac{1}{R_\oplus} = \frac{\varphi}{S} \qquad (11.45)$$

By definition of g

$$g = \frac{GM_\oplus}{(R_\oplus)^2}$$

$$\Rightarrow \frac{M_\oplus}{(R_\oplus)^2} = \frac{g}{G} \qquad (11.46)$$

Combining equations 11.44, 11.45 and 11.46, we get

$$\frac{\rho_\oplus}{\rho_\odot} = \frac{M_\oplus}{(R_\oplus)^2} \frac{1}{R_\oplus} \frac{(R_\odot)^3}{M_\odot}$$

$$= \left(\frac{g}{G}\right)\left(\frac{\varphi}{S}\right) \frac{GT_\oplus^2 \theta_\odot^3}{32\pi^2}$$

$$= \frac{g\varphi\theta_\odot^3 T_\oplus^2}{32\pi^2 S} \qquad (11.47)$$

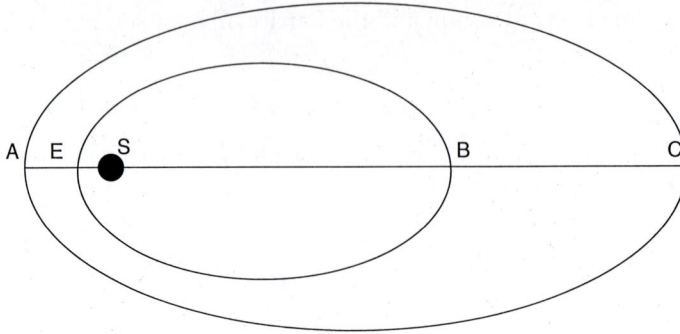

Fig. 11.1 *Orbits of Seneca and the Earth*

$$= g \times \frac{\pi}{180} \times \left(\frac{\pi}{360}\right)^3 \times \frac{T_\oplus^2}{32\pi^2 S}$$

$$= \frac{g T_\oplus^2 \pi^2}{32 \times 180 \times (360)^3 S} \tag{11.48}$$

$$= \frac{9.81 \times (3.1557 \times 10^7)^2 \pi^2}{32 \times 180 \times (360)^3 \times 111 \times 10^3}$$

$$\frac{\rho_\oplus}{\rho_\odot} = 3.23 \tag{11.49}$$

10. In Figure 11.1, the outer orbit represents the orbit of Seneca (justification provided later) and the inner orbit is the orbit of the Earth.

(a) From Figure 11.1, it is clear that the signal travelling from Seneca to the Earth will take the least time when the Earth is at 'E' and Seneca is at 'A'. The signal will take the longest time if the Earth is at 'E' and Seneca is at 'C'.

$$AE = AS - ES = ct_1$$

$$a_s(1 - e_s) - a_\oplus = (2 \times 60)c \tag{11.50}$$

$$EC = SC + ES = ct_2$$

$$\therefore \qquad a_s(1 + e_s) + a_\oplus = (39 \times 60)\,c \tag{11.51}$$

Adding the two equations, we get

$$2a_s = (41 \times 60)c$$

$$a_s \approx 3.687 \times 10^{11} \text{ m}$$

$$\approx 2.46 \text{ AU} \tag{11.52}$$

$$e_s = 1 - \frac{(2 \times 60)c - a_\oplus}{a_s}$$

$$= 1 - \frac{4}{41} - \frac{1.496 \times 10^{11}}{3.687 \times 10^{11}}$$

$$e_s \approx 0.50 \tag{11.53}$$

Notice that $a_s > 1$AU. That is why the orbit of Seneca is drawn outside the Earth's orbit.

(b) Using Kepler's third law, we compare Seneca with the corresponding ratio for the Earth's orbit. We assume that Seneca and the Earth are both revolving around the Sun in the same direction.

$$\frac{T_S^2}{a_S^3} = \frac{T_\oplus^2}{a_\oplus^3} = \frac{1^2}{1^3} = 1$$

$$T_S^2 = a_S^3 \approx 2.46^3$$

$$\approx 14.98$$

$$T_S \approx 3.87 \text{ years} \tag{11.54}$$

$$\frac{1}{T_{syn}} = \frac{1}{T_\oplus} - \frac{1}{T_S}$$

$$= \frac{1}{1} - \frac{1}{3.87}$$

$$= 0.74$$

$$T_{syn} = 1.35 \text{ years} \tag{11.55}$$

(c) In this section, we should note that the mass of Jupiter cannot be ignored when calculating the orbital period of Jupiter. We first calculate the mass of the Sun using Seneca's orbit. Then we apply the same process to Jupiter's orbit.

$$GM_\odot = \frac{4\pi^2 a_S^3}{T_S^2}$$

$$M_\odot = \frac{4\pi^2 \times (3.687 \times 10^{11})^3}{6.6726 \times 10^{-11} \times (3.87 \times 3.1557 \times 10^7)^2}$$

$$M_\odot = 1.99 \times 10^{30} \text{kg} \tag{11.56}$$

In Jupiter's case,

$$G(M_\odot + M_J) = \frac{4\pi^2 a_J^3}{T_J^2}$$

$$\therefore \qquad \frac{(M_\odot + M_J)}{M_\odot} = \frac{a_J^3 T_S^2}{a_S^3 T_J^2} \tag{11.57}$$

$$= \frac{5.204^3 \times 3.87^2}{2.46^3 \times 11.8618^2}$$

$$= 1.0016$$

$$\therefore \qquad M_J = 0.0016 \, M_\odot$$

$$\approx 3.26 \times 10^{27} \text{ kg} \tag{11.58}$$

11. Here we have to balance the gravitational attraction of the Sun with the radiation pressure. The force of radiation pressure is simply the solar radiation flux received by an object divided by the speed of light. Assuming that the dust grains completely absorb all the radiation incident on them,

Force due to radiation process $=\dfrac{L}{4\pi a^2}\dfrac{\pi r^2}{c}=\dfrac{Lr^2}{4a^2c}$

Where r is the radius of the dust grain at distance a from the Sun.

Force due to gravitational attraction $=\dfrac{GMm}{r^2}$

In the solar system, at 1 AU,

$$F_{RP}=\frac{L_\odot}{4\pi a_\oplus^2}\frac{\pi r_{dust}^2}{c} \tag{11.59}$$

$$F_{grav}=F_{RP}\ \text{[equilibrium condition]} \tag{11.60}$$

$\therefore$
$$\frac{GM_\odot m}{a_\oplus^2}=\frac{L_\odot r_{dust}^2}{4a_\oplus^2 c}$$

$$m=\frac{L_\odot r_{dust}^2}{4GM_\odot c}$$

$$\frac{4\pi}{3}r_{dust}^3\rho=\frac{L_\odot r_{dust}^2}{4GM_\odot c}$$

$\therefore$
$$r_{dust}=\frac{3L_\odot}{16\pi\rho GM_\odot c} \tag{11.61}$$

$$=\frac{3\times3.826\times10^{26}}{16\pi\times10^3\times6.6741\times10^{-11}\times1.9891\times10^{30}\times3\times10^8}$$

$$r_{dust}\approx0.6\ \mu m \tag{11.62}$$

12. The torque is decelerating the Earth's rotation.

$$\tau=I\alpha=\frac{2}{5}M_\oplus R_\oplus^2\alpha$$

$\therefore$
$$\alpha=\frac{5\tau}{2M_\oplus R_\oplus^2} \tag{11.63}$$

$$\omega_i=\omega_f+\alpha t \tag{11.64}$$

$$=\frac{2\pi}{(day)_{sidereal}}+\frac{\tau}{\frac{2}{5}M_\oplus R_\oplus^2}\times6\times10^8\times(1year)$$

$$=\frac{2\pi}{23^h56^m4.1^s}+\frac{5\times6\times10^{16}\times6\times10^8\times3.1557\times10^7}{2\times5.9736\times10^{24}\times(6.3708\times10^6)^2}$$

$$\omega_i=8.463\times10^{-5}\ rad/s \tag{11.65}$$

As the revolution period (side real year) remains unchanged,

$$(days)_i=\frac{1\,\text{sidereal year}}{T_i}=\frac{1\,\text{sidereal year}\times\omega_i}{2\pi} \tag{11.66}$$

$$= \frac{3.15 \times 10^7 \times 8.463 \times 10^{-5}}{2\pi}$$

$$= 424.3 \text{ days}$$

$$(days)_i \approx 420 \text{ days} \qquad (11.67)$$

Now based on the Mesopotamian calendar, we can carry out similar calculations and obtain the answer as,

$$\omega_i = 7.292 \times 10^{-5} + 1 \times 10^{-10}$$

$$\approx \omega_f \qquad (11.68)$$

Thus, at the scale of a few thousand years, there will not be any significant change in the length of the year.

13. We can solve the question in two ways:

(I) **Algebraic Solution**

As the space craft is stationary at (0, 0), let $y = mx$ be the line of sight of the telescope.

Then, the intersection of the line of sight and the circle is

$$x^2 + (mx)^2 - 10x - 8(mx) + 40 = 0 \qquad (11.69)$$

$$(1 + m^2)x^2 - (10 + 8m)x - 40 = 0$$

The equation will have a solution if its discriminant ($D = b^2 - 4ac$) is greater than or equal to zero.

$$D = b^2 - 4ac \geq 0 \qquad (11.70)$$

$$(-10 - 8m)^2 - 4(1 + m^2)\,40 \geq 0$$

$$64m^2 + 160m + 100 - 160m^2 - 160 \geq 0$$

$$-96m^2 + 160m + 60 \geq 0$$

$$-24m^2 + 40m - 15 \geq 0 \qquad (11.71)$$

The solution of the inequality is

$$\frac{(10 - \sqrt{10})}{12} \leq m \leq \frac{(10 + \sqrt{10})}{12} \qquad (11.72)$$

Therefore, these extreme values will be values of $\tan \phi$.

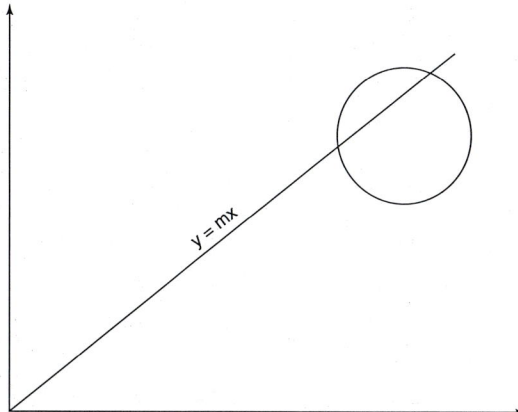

(II) Geometric Solution

$$x^2 + y^2 - 10x - 8y + 40 = 0$$

$$x^2 - 10x + 25 + y^2 - 8y + 16 - 1 = 0$$

$$(x-5)^2 + (y-4)^2 = 1 \tag{11.73}$$

The centre of the circle is (5, 4) and the radius is 1 unit. Now, we should find tangents from the origin to this circle to give the minimum and maximum angles of elevation. For this purpose, we define angle α as the angle made by the centre of the disk with the x-axis and angle β as the angle subtended by the radius of the disk at the origin.

$$\tan \alpha = \frac{4}{5} \tag{11.74}$$

$$\tan \beta = \frac{1}{\sqrt{5^2 + 4^2 - 1}} = \frac{1}{\sqrt{40}} = \frac{1}{2\sqrt{10}} \tag{11.75}$$

$$\tan \phi_{min} = \tan(\alpha - \beta)$$

$$= \frac{\tan \alpha - \tan \beta}{1 + \tan \alpha \tan \beta} \tag{11.76}$$

$$= \frac{\dfrac{4}{5} - \dfrac{1}{2\sqrt{10}}}{1 + \dfrac{4}{10\sqrt{10}}}$$

$$= \frac{(8\sqrt{10} - 5)}{(10\sqrt{10} + 4)}$$

$$= \frac{(8\sqrt{10} - 5)(10\sqrt{10} - 4)}{(10\sqrt{10} + 4)(10\sqrt{10} - 4)}$$

$$= \frac{(800 - 50\sqrt{10} - 32\sqrt{10} + 20)}{(1000 - 16)}$$

$$= \frac{82(10 - \sqrt{10})}{82 \times 12}$$

$$= \frac{(10 - \sqrt{10})}{12} \tag{11.77}$$

$$\tan \phi_{max} = \tan(\alpha + \beta)$$

$$= \frac{\tan \alpha + \tan \beta}{1 - \tan \alpha \tan \beta} \tag{11.78}$$

$$= \frac{(10 + \sqrt{10})}{12} \tag{11.79}$$

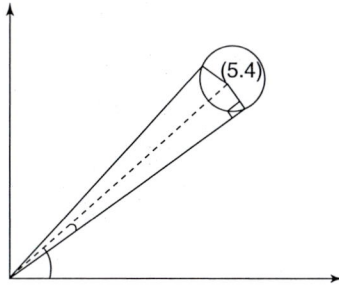

14. Mechanical energy is conserved and has the form

$$E = \frac{p^2}{2m} \quad \frac{GMm}{r} = \frac{p^2}{2m} \quad GMmu \tag{11.80}$$

$$\frac{p_A^2}{2m} - GMmu_A = \frac{p_B^2}{2m} - GMmu_B$$

$$GMmu_B - GMmu_A = \frac{p_B^2}{2m} - \frac{p_A^2}{2m}$$

$$GMm(u_B - u_A) = \frac{(p_B^2 - p_A^2)}{2m}$$

$$\therefore \qquad m = \sqrt{\frac{(p_B^2 - p_A^2)}{2GM(u_B - u_A)}} \tag{11.81}$$

$$m = \sqrt{\frac{(1.94 \times 10^9)^2 - (0.052 \times 10^9)^2}{2 \times 6.6726 \times 10^{-11} \times 5.9736 \times 10^{24} \times (194.17 - 5.15) \times 10^{-8}}}$$

$$= 5.00 \times 10^4 \text{kg} \tag{11.82}$$

To find the energy,

$$E_A = \frac{p_A^2}{2m} - GMmu_A$$

$$E = \frac{(5.2 \times 10^7)^2}{2 \times 50000} - 6.6726 \times 10^{-11} \times 5.9736 \times 10^{24} \times 5.00 \times 10^4 \times 5.15 \times 10^{-8}$$

$$= -1.0 \ 10^{12} \text{ J} \tag{11.83}$$

The total energy is negative. Thus, this PHO is in a closed elliptical orbit. However, it is important to remember that the question does not ask us to sketch the shape of the orbit from A to B. It asks for the shape of the function u vs. p. To sketch this curve, we use the equation

$$E = \frac{p^2}{2m} - GNMmu$$

$$\Rightarrow \frac{p^2}{2GMm^2} = u + \frac{E}{GMm} \tag{11.84}$$

This is similar to the form $ax^2 = y + b$. Thus, it is a parabolic curve.

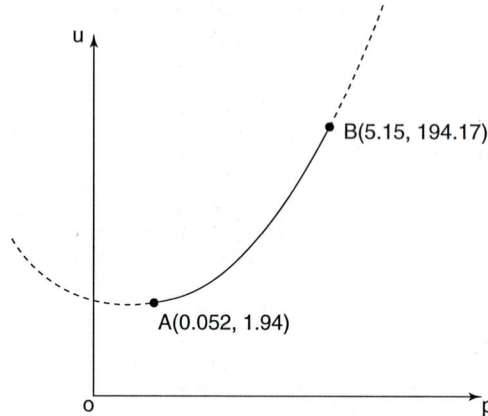

15. For the cloud, let O be the centre and A be some point on the surface. Thus, the object is travelling from O to A. Let V_i be the gravitational potential at point i.

    If the particle was free-falling, then its velocity at the surface would be be zero.

$$KE_A + PE_A = KE_O + PE_O \tag{11.85}$$

$$0 + V_A = \frac{GMm}{2R} + V_O \tag{11.86}$$

$$\therefore \quad V_O = V_A - \frac{GMm}{2R}$$

$$= -\frac{GMm}{R} - \frac{GMm}{2R}$$

$$V_O = \frac{3GMm}{2R} \tag{11.87}$$

To escape, the total energy of the particle should be zero. If $v_O = v_{esc}$,

$$KE_O + PE_O = 0 \tag{11.88}$$

$$\frac{1}{2}mv_{esc}^2 + V_O = 0 \tag{11.89}$$

$$\frac{1}{2}v_{esc}^2 = \frac{3GM}{2R}$$

$$\therefore \quad v_{esc} = \sqrt{\frac{3GM}{2R}} \tag{11.90}$$

16. Let us take at op-view of the system, as shown in the figure below. In this figure, D is the centre of the Moon. The Moon's gravitational acceleration at A and the centre of the Earth C are given by,

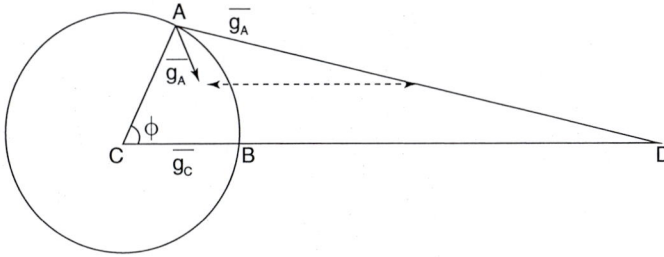

$$\vec{g_A} = -\frac{GM_m}{r_A^3}\vec{r_A} \tag{11.91}$$

$$\vec{g_C} = -\frac{GM_m}{r_C^3}\vec{r_C} = -\frac{GM_m}{a_\oplus^3}\vec{r_C} \tag{11.92}$$

Both these vectors point towards the Moon.

From the figure, $r_A = AD$ and $r_C = CD$.

The Moon's net gravitational acceleration felt by a test mass at A is,

$$\vec{g_A'} = \vec{g_A} - \vec{g_C} = -\left(\frac{GM_m}{r_A^3}\vec{r_A} - \frac{GM_m}{a_\oplus^3}\vec{r_C}\right) \tag{11.93}$$

From the figure, $\vec{r_A} = \vec{r_C} - \vec{R_\oplus}$. Thus,

$$\vec{g_A'} = \frac{GM_m}{r_A^3}\vec{R_\oplus} - \left(\frac{GM_m}{r^3} - \frac{GM_m}{a_\oplus^3}\right)\vec{r_C} \tag{11.94}$$

Distance r_A can be found by the cosine rule.

$$r_A^2 = a_\oplus^2 + R_\oplus^2 - 2R_\oplus a_\oplus \cos\phi \tag{11.95}$$

Now, the first term of the RHS in Equation 11.94 is purely radial. Thus, for horizontal acceleration of sea water at A, we need to take only the horizontal component of the second term.

$$\overrightarrow{g_{A\,(hori)}} = \frac{GM_m}{a^3}\frac{GM_m}{r_A^3}a\ \sin \tag{11.96}$$

$$= \left|\frac{1}{a_\oplus^3} - \frac{1}{(a_\oplus^2 + R_\oplus^2 - 2R_\oplus a_\oplus \cos\phi)^{3/2}}\right|GM_m a_\oplus \sin\phi \tag{11.97}$$

17. This problem can be solved in two slightly different ways. We can either assume the centre of the Sun to coincide with the centre of mass of the system (a valid approximation) or take it as a separate explicit point. The angular velocity of a particle (around the Sun) at any Lag range point is the same as that of the angular velocity of the Earth. At L_3, the gravitational forces of the Sun and Earth are balanced by the centrifugal force. Let us assume that the distance to point L_3 from the centre of the Sun exceed 1 AU by x kilometres. If L_3 lies inside the orbit, we will obtain the value of x as negative.

If the centre of the Sun coincides with the centre of the system then,

$$F_{cf} = F_\odot + F_\oplus \tag{11.98}$$

$$\not{m}(a_{\oplus} + x)\omega^2 = \frac{GM_{\odot}\not{m}}{(a_{\oplus} + x)^2} + \frac{GM_{\oplus}\not{m}}{(2a_{\oplus} + x)^2} \tag{11.99}$$

$$(a_{\oplus} + x)\frac{GM_{\odot}}{(a_{\odot}^3)} = \frac{GM_{\odot}}{(a_{\oplus} + x)^2} + \frac{GM_{\oplus}}{(2a_{\oplus} + x)^2} \qquad \left(\because \omega^2 = \frac{GM_{\odot}}{a_{\odot}^3} \right)$$

$$\frac{a_{\oplus} + x}{a_{\oplus}} = \frac{a_{\oplus}^2}{(a_{\oplus} + x)^2} + \frac{M_{\oplus}a_{\oplus}^2}{M_{\odot}(2a_{\oplus} + x)^2}$$

$$1 + \frac{x}{a_{\oplus}} = (1 + \frac{x}{a_{\oplus}})^{-2} + \frac{M_{\oplus}}{4M_{\odot}}\left(1 + \frac{x}{2a_{\oplus}}\right)^{-2}$$

$$\approx 1 - \frac{2x}{a_{\oplus}} + \frac{M_{\oplus}}{4M_{\odot}}\left(1 - \frac{x}{a_{\oplus}}\right)$$

$$\frac{3x}{a_{\oplus}} = \frac{M_{\oplus}}{4M_{\odot}}\left(1 - \frac{x}{a_{\oplus}}\right)$$

$$\frac{x}{a_{\oplus}} = \frac{\dfrac{M_{\oplus}}{4M_{\odot}}}{3 + \dfrac{M_{\oplus}}{4M_{\odot}}}$$

$$\therefore \qquad x = \frac{M_{\oplus}}{12M_{\odot} + M_{\oplus}}a_{\oplus} \tag{11.100}$$

$$= \frac{5.9736 \times 10^{24} \times 1.4960 \times 10^8}{12 \times 1.9891 \times 10^{30} + 5.9736 \times 10^{24}}$$

$$x = 37.44 \text{km} \tag{11.101}$$

As x has a positive sign, our initial assumption that L_3 lies outside the Earth's orbit is correct.

Alternatively, let us say that the centre of the Sun is y km away from the centre of mass of the system.

$$\therefore \qquad y = \frac{M_{\oplus}a_{\oplus}}{M_{\odot}} = 449.3 \text{km}$$

Comparing with Equation 11.99,

$$(a_{\oplus} + x + y)\frac{M_{\odot} + M_{\oplus}}{a_{\oplus}^3} = \frac{M_{\odot}}{(a_{\oplus} + x)^2} + \frac{M_{\oplus}}{(2a_{\oplus} + x)^2} \tag{11.102}$$

$$\frac{(a_{\oplus} + x + y)\left(1 + \dfrac{y}{a_{\oplus}}\right)}{a_{\oplus}} = \frac{a_{\oplus}^2}{(a_{\oplus} + x)^2} + \frac{ya_{\oplus}}{(2a_{\oplus} + x)^2}$$

Ignoring the second order terms

$$1 + \frac{2y}{a_{\oplus}} + \frac{x}{a_{\oplus}} = 1 - \frac{2x}{a_{\oplus}} + \frac{y}{4a_{\oplus}}$$

$\therefore$

$$\frac{3x}{a_\oplus} = \frac{-7y}{4a_\oplus}$$

$\therefore$

$$x = \frac{-7M_\oplus a_\oplus}{12M_\odot} \tag{11.103}$$

$$= \frac{-7 \times 5.9736 \times 10^{24}}{12 \times 1.9891 \times 10^{30}} \times 1.4960 \times 10^8 \text{ km}$$

$$x = -262.1 \text{ km} \tag{11.104}$$

$\therefore$

$$a_\oplus + x + y = a_\oplus - 262.1 + 449.3$$

$$> a_\oplus \tag{11.105}$$

This proves that the Lagrange point L_3 is outside the Earth's orbit.

However, its separation from the centre of the Sun is less than 1 AU.

18. The reference to the dates of perihelion (early January) and aphelion (early July) in the question makes it clear that the Earth's orbit is to be taken as elliptical. The shape of the new orbit after the solar catastrophe will depend on the moment of catastrophe. Let the new semi-major axis, after the catastrophe, be a_f. As the catastrophe is instantaneous, the kinetic energy of the Earth will not change in the process.

(a) On 3rd July, the Earth is at aphelion. By Virial Theorem,

$$\frac{-GM_\odot m_\oplus}{2a} = \frac{1}{2}m_\oplus v_a^2 - \frac{GM_\odot m_\oplus}{a\,(1+e)} \tag{11.106}$$

$\therefore$

$$v_a^2 = \frac{GM_\odot}{a_\oplus}\left[\frac{2}{1+e_\oplus} - 1\right]$$

$$= \frac{GM_\odot}{a_\oplus}\left[\frac{1-e_\oplus}{1+e_\oplus}\right] \tag{11.107}$$

After the catastrophe,

$$\frac{-GM_\odot/2}{2a_f} = \frac{1}{2}v_a^2 - \frac{GM_\odot/2}{a_\oplus(1+e_\oplus)} \tag{11.108}$$

$$\frac{-GM_\odot}{4a_f} = \frac{GM_\odot}{2a_\oplus}\left[\frac{1-e_\oplus}{1+e_\oplus}\right] - \frac{GM_\odot}{2a_\oplus(1+e_\oplus)}$$

$$\frac{1}{4a_f} = \frac{1}{2a_\oplus}\left[\frac{1}{1+e_\oplus} - \frac{1-e_\oplus}{1+e_\oplus}\right]$$

$$\frac{1}{a_f} = \frac{2}{a_\oplus}\left[\frac{e_\oplus}{(1+e_\oplus)}\right]$$

$\therefore$

$$a_f = \frac{a_\oplus(1+e_\oplus)}{2e_\oplus} \tag{11.109}$$

One can see from the equations above that the total energy is still negative. Hence, the orbit is still elliptical. As a_f is much larger than $a_\oplus$, the orbit will be larger and hence there is no threat of the Earth colliding with the Sun.

$$T_f^2 = \frac{4\pi^2 a_f^3}{GM_\odot/2}$$

$$= 2\left(\frac{4\pi^2 a_\oplus^3}{GM_\odot}\right)\left(\frac{1+e_\oplus}{2e_\oplus}\right)^3$$

$$= \frac{T_\oplus^2}{4}\left(\frac{1+e_\oplus}{e_\oplus}\right)^3$$

$$T_f = \frac{T_\oplus}{2}\left(\frac{1+e_\oplus}{e_\oplus}\right)^{\frac{3}{2}}$$

$$= \frac{1}{2}\left(\frac{1+0.0167}{0.0167}\right)^{\frac{3}{2}}$$

$$T_f = 237.5 \text{ years} \tag{11.110}$$

(b) On 3rd January, the Earth is at perihelion.

$$\frac{-GM_\odot}{2a_\oplus} = \frac{1}{2}v_p^2 - \frac{GM_\odot}{a_\oplus\left(1-e_\oplus\right)}$$

$$\therefore \qquad v_p^2 = \frac{GM_\odot}{a_\oplus}\left[\frac{1+e_\oplus}{1-e_\oplus}\right] \tag{11.111}$$

$$\text{Total energy} = \frac{1}{2}v_p^2 - \frac{GM_\odot}{2a_\oplus\left(1-e_\oplus\right)} \tag{11.112}$$

$$= \frac{GM_\odot}{2a_\oplus}\left[\frac{1+e_\oplus}{1-e_\oplus} - \frac{1}{1-e_\oplus}\right]$$

$$= \frac{GM_\odot}{2a_\oplus}\left[\frac{e_\oplus}{1-e_\oplus}\right]$$

$$\therefore \qquad \text{Total energy} > 0 \tag{11.113}$$

Thus, the Earth will move in a hyperbolic orbit and there is no period for this orbit.

19. First and foremost we must remember that when the projectile moves from the surface to high altitude, the gravitation acceleration will be variable along the path. Hence, approximated relations, which assume a constant g, cannot be used.

In Figure 11.2, the projectile is launched from point A on the surface of the earth, it reaches its highest point at H and then hits the Earth's surface at B. The principal focus of the orbit is on the centre of the Earth (O). Point M is on the surface of the Earth along the major axis (LOH). Line AB cuts the major axis at C, and O' is the other focus of the ellipse. The tangent at point A meets the major axis between M and O'.

(a)Total energy of the projectile is

$$E = \frac{1}{2}mv_0^2 - \frac{GM_\oplus m}{R_\oplus} \tag{11.114}$$

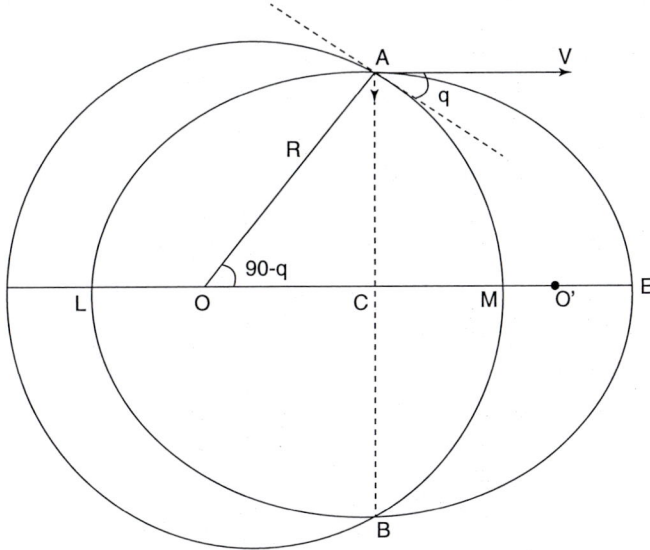

Fig. 11.2   *High-altitude projectile*

$$= \frac{GM_\oplus m}{2R_\oplus} - \frac{GM_\oplus m}{R_\oplus}$$

$$= -\frac{GM_\oplus m}{2R_\oplus} < 0 \qquad (11.115)$$

As the total energy is less than 0, The orbit might be an ellipse or a circle. As $\theta > 0$, the orbit is an ellipse. Total energy for an ellipse is

$$E = -\frac{GMm}{2a} \qquad (11.116)$$

Comparing equations 11.115 and 11.116, we conclude

$$a = R \qquad (11.117)$$

(b) Now for any ellipse, as O and O′ are the two foci, and A is some random point on the ellipse,

$$l(AO) + l(AO') = 2a = 2R \qquad (11.118)$$

$$R + l(AO') = 2R$$

$$\therefore \qquad\qquad l(AO') = R = l(AO) \qquad (11.119)$$

The same will be true for B. This means that A and B lie on the minor axis of the ellipse. Hence, C is the centre of the ellipse.

Let b be the semi-minor axis of the orbit.

$$b = a\sqrt{1 - e^2}$$

$$= R_\oplus \sqrt{1 - e^2} \qquad (11.120)$$

As A is on the minor axis, $\vec{v}_A$ is parallel to the major axis.

$$\therefore \qquad \angle AOC = \frac{\pi}{2} - \frac{\pi}{6} = \frac{\pi}{3} \qquad (11.121)$$

$$b = R_\oplus \sin\frac{\pi}{3} = \frac{\sqrt{3}}{2} R_\oplus \qquad (11.122)$$

$$\therefore \qquad \sqrt{1-e^2} = \frac{\sqrt{3}}{2}$$

$$1 - e^2 = \frac{3}{4}$$

$$e^2 = \frac{1}{4}$$

$$\therefore \qquad e = 0.5 \qquad (11.123)$$

$$r_{max} = R_\oplus (1 + e) \qquad (11.124)$$

$$= 1.5 R_\oplus \qquad (11.125)$$

$$\therefore \qquad h_{max} = HM = HO - OM \qquad (11.126)$$

$$= r_{max} - R_\oplus$$

$$h = 0.5 R_\oplus \qquad (11.127)$$

(c) As there is no air drag or other dissipative force, path AHB will be symmetric about the major axis. As $\angle AOC = \frac{\pi}{3}$, we can conclude, $\angle AOB = \frac{2\pi}{3}$. Thus range from A to B along the surface will be,

$$R = \text{Arclength } (AB) = \frac{2\pi}{3} \times \frac{1}{2\pi} \times 2\pi R_\oplus \qquad (11.128)$$

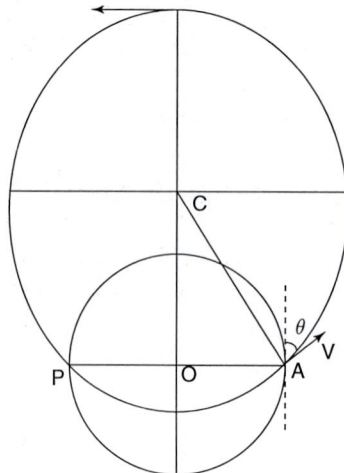

Fig. 11.3   *Projectile to antipode*

$$R = \frac{2\pi}{3} R_{\oplus} \tag{11.129}$$

(d) As already shown in Equation 11.123, $e = 0.5$

(e) Now by Kepler's second law, the time spent to cover a particular part of the orbit will be proportional to the area swept by the radius vector.

Thus, we needs to find $Area(OAHBO)$.

$$Area(OAHBO) = Area(CAHBC) + Area(\triangle AOB) \tag{11.130}$$

$$= \frac{\pi ab}{2} + \frac{1}{2} \times l\left(\overline{OC}\right) \times l\left(\overline{AB}\right) \tag{11.131}$$

$$= \frac{\pi ab}{2} + \frac{1}{2} \times a \times e \times 2b$$

$$= \frac{\pi ab}{2} + \frac{ab}{2}$$

$$Area(OAHBO) = \frac{(\pi+1)ab}{2} \tag{11.132}$$

$$T = \sqrt{\frac{4\pi^2 a^3}{GM_{\oplus}}} \tag{11.133}$$

$$\therefore \quad \frac{t}{T} = \frac{Area(OAHBO)}{Area(LAHBL)} \tag{11.134}$$

$$\therefore \quad t = \frac{(\pi+1)ab}{2\pi ab} \times 2\pi \sqrt{\frac{a^3}{GM_{\oplus}}} \tag{11.135}$$

$$= (\pi+1)\sqrt{\frac{a^3}{GM_{\oplus}}} \tag{11.136}$$

$$= (\pi+1)\sqrt{\frac{\left(6.3708 \times 10^6\right)^3}{6.6726 \times 10^{-11} \times 5.9736 \times 10^{24}}}$$

$$= 3335.7 \ sec \tag{11.137}$$

$$t = 55^m 35.7^s \tag{11.138}$$

20. In the following equations, subscript '0' corresponds to the launching position and subscript '1' corresponds to the antipode position.

(a) As the two positions are diametrically opposite,

$$\lambda_1 = (180° - \lambda_0) \ West$$

$$\lambda_1 = 150° \ West \tag{11.139}$$

$$\phi_1 = (\phi_0) \ South$$

$$\phi_1 = 44° \ West \tag{11.140}$$

(b) As the launching position and its antipode are both points on the trajectory and as the centre of the Earth is at the primary focus, it is obvious that the diameter of the Earth connecting the launching position and its antipode forms the latus rectum of the trajectory.

$$r_{apo} = H + R_\oplus = a(1 + e)$$

$$a(1 + e) = 6R_\oplus + R_\oplus$$

$$a(1 + e) = 7R_\oplus \tag{11.141}$$

$$r_0 = a(1 - e^2)$$

$$R_\oplus = a(1 + e)(1 - e)$$

$$= 7R_\oplus (1 - e)$$

$$\therefore \qquad e = 1 - \frac{1}{7} = \frac{6}{7} \tag{11.142}$$

$$\therefore \qquad a = \frac{7R_\oplus}{1 + e} = \frac{7R_\oplus}{1 + \dfrac{6}{7}}$$

$$a = \frac{49R_\oplus}{13} \tag{11.143}$$

$$v_0 = \sqrt{GM_\oplus \left(\frac{2}{r_0} - \frac{1}{a} \right)} \tag{11.144}$$

$$= \sqrt{GM_\oplus \left(\frac{2}{R_\oplus} - \frac{13}{49R_\oplus} \right)}$$

$$= \sqrt{\frac{GM_\oplus}{R_\oplus} \times \frac{(98 - 13)}{49}}$$

$$= \sqrt{\frac{6.6726 \times 10^{-11} \times 5.9736 \times 10^{24} \times 85}{6.3708 \times 10^6 \times 49}}$$

$$v_0 = 10.418 \text{ kms}^{-1} \tag{11.145}$$

Let us say that the projectile was launched at launch angle θ with respect to the local horizon. In Figure11.3, $\angle OAC = \theta$. Thus,

$$\tan \theta = \frac{l(OC)}{l(OA)} = \frac{ae}{a(1 - e^2)} \tag{11.146}$$

$$= \frac{\frac{6}{7}}{\left(1 - \left[\frac{6}{7}\right]^2\right)} = \frac{6 \times 49}{7 \times (49 - 36)}$$

$$\theta = \tan^{-1} \left(\frac{42}{13} \right)$$

$$\theta = 72.80° \tag{11.147}$$

(c) Due to symmetry of the orbit, the speed at the antipode would be the same as the launching speed.

(d)

$$v_{apo} = \sqrt{GM_\oplus \left(\frac{2}{r_{apo}} - \frac{1}{a} \right)} \tag{11.148}$$

$$= \sqrt{GM_\oplus \left(\frac{2}{7R_\oplus} - \frac{13}{49R_\oplus} \right)}$$

$$= \sqrt{\frac{GM_\oplus}{R_\oplus} \times \frac{(14-13)}{49}}$$

$$= \sqrt{\frac{6.6726 \times 10^{-11} \times 5.9736 \times 10^{24}}{6.3708 \times 10^6 \times 49}}$$

$$v_{apo} = 1.130 \text{ kms}^{-1} \tag{11.149}$$

(e) In an elliptical orbit with high eccentricity, we can perform a first order approximation that the length of the radius vector does not change much from the perigee to the end of the latus rectum (i.e., point A). Thus, the area on the other side of the latus rectum would be approximately twice the difference between the area swept by the radius vector while going from the perigee to A and the area of triangle OCA. To obtain the time of flight, we must take the ratio of the remaining area with the total area of the ellipse.

$$t = \frac{\pi ab - \left[a^2 \sin\left(90° - \theta\right) - \frac{1}{2} ae \frac{b^2}{a} \right]}{\pi ab} T \tag{11.150}$$

$$= \left[1 - \frac{2a^2 \sin\left(90° - 72.80°\right) - b^2 e}{2\pi ab} \right] \sqrt{\frac{4\pi^2 a^3}{GM_\oplus}}$$

$$= \left[1 - \frac{2a^2 \times 0.2957 - a^2 e\left(1-e^2\right)}{2\pi a^2 \sqrt{1-e^2}} \right] \times \frac{2\pi}{\sqrt{GM_\oplus}} \times \left(\frac{49R_\oplus}{13} \right)^{1.5}$$

$$= \left[1 - \frac{0.5914 - \frac{6}{7}\left(1 - \left(\frac{6}{7}\right)^2\right)}{2\pi \sqrt{1 - \left(\frac{6}{7}\right)^2}} \right] \times \frac{2\pi \times \left(\frac{6.3708 \times 10^6 \times 49}{13} \right)^{1.5}}{\sqrt{6.6726 \times 10^{-11} \times 5.9736 \times 10^{24}}}$$

$$= 0.8875 \times 3.7032 \times 10^4$$

$$= 32866s$$

$$\therefore \qquad t = 9.13h \tag{11.151}$$

(f) We use lunar data to obtain an estimate of the solar flux incident on the projectile. The Moon reflects 14% of the sunlight incident on it. We should note that at maximum height we will see the first quarter phase of the projectile. Thus, only half the area is visible.

$$f_{reflect'M} = \alpha_M f_{in'M}$$

$$= \alpha_M S\pi R_M^2 \text{ (where } S \text{ is the solar constant)}$$

$$m_{apo} - m_M = -2.5\log\left(\frac{f_{apo}}{f_M}\right) \tag{11.152}$$

$$m_{apo} = m_M - 2.5\log\left(\frac{\frac{1}{2}S\pi r^2}{4\pi(6R_\oplus)^2} \times \frac{4\pi d^2}{\alpha S\pi R_M^2}\right)$$

$$= m_M - 2.5\log\left(\frac{r^2 d^2}{72 R_\oplus^2 R_M^2}\right)$$

$$= m_M + 5\log\left(\frac{6\sqrt{2}R_\oplus R_M}{rd}\right) \tag{11.153}$$

$$= -12.74 + 5\log\left(\frac{6\sqrt{2} \times 6.3708 \times 10^6 \times 1.7374 \times 10^6}{0.4 \times 3.78 \times 10^8}\right) \tag{11.154}$$

$$m_{apo} = +16.23 \tag{11.155}$$

Thus, the projectile will be too faint to be visible to the unaided eye.

21. As the orbit is parabolic,

$$E_{sat} = \left(\frac{-GM_\odot}{r_{sat}} + \frac{1}{2}v_{sat}^2\right)m_{sat} = 0 \tag{11.156}$$

$$\therefore \qquad v_{sat} = \sqrt{\frac{2GM_\odot}{r_{sat}}} \tag{11.157}$$

This will be an expression for total velocity of the satellite at all points in its orbit, when neglecting the influence of the planets.

(a) Angular momentum of the satellite at launch is,

$$L = m_{sat}v_{sat'\oplus}a_\oplus$$

$$= m_{sat}\sqrt{2GM_\odot a_\oplus} \tag{11.158}$$

Let v_T be the tangential velocity of the satellite at Mars' orbit. For conserving angular momentum, one has to take into account only the tangential component of the velocity $\left(\overrightarrow{v_T}\right)$, as $\left|\overrightarrow{r}\times\overrightarrow{v_{rad}}\right| = 0$

$$m_{sat}\sqrt{2GM_\odot a_\oplus} = m_{sat}v_T a_m$$

$$\therefore \qquad v_T = \frac{\sqrt{2GM_\odot a_\oplus}}{a_m} \tag{11.159}$$

$$\cos\psi = \frac{v_T}{v} = \frac{\sqrt{2GM_\odot a_\oplus}}{a_m}\sqrt{\frac{a_{am}}{2GM_\odot}} \tag{11.160}$$

$$= \sqrt{\frac{a_\oplus}{a_m}} = \sqrt{\frac{1}{1.524}}$$

$$= 0.8100 \tag{11.161}$$

$$\therefore \qquad \psi = 35.90° \qquad (11.162)$$

(b) If Mars is very close to the satellite, then the orbital velocity of Mars $\left(\overrightarrow{v_m}\right)$ will be parallel to the tangential velocity of the satellite.

$$\overrightarrow{v_{rel}} = \overrightarrow{v_{rad}} + \overrightarrow{v_T} - \overrightarrow{v_m} \qquad (11.163)$$

$$= v_{rad}\hat{r} + \left(v_T - v_m\right)\hat{\theta} \qquad (11.164)$$

$$= \sqrt{\frac{6.6726\times10^{-11}\times1.9891\times10^{30}}{1.524\times1.4960\times10^{11}}}$$

$$v_m = 24.13 \text{ km/s} \qquad (11.165)$$

$$v_{sat} = \sqrt{\frac{2GM_\odot}{r_m}} = \sqrt{2}v_m$$

$$= 34.13 \text{ km/s} \qquad (11.166)$$

$$v_{sat} = v_{sat} \cos\psi = 34.13 \times 0.8100$$

$$= 27.64 \text{ km/s} \qquad (11.167)$$

$$v_{rad} = v_{sat} \sin\psi$$

$$= 20.01 \text{ km/s} \qquad (11.168)$$

$$\overrightarrow{v_{rel}} = 20.01r + 3.15\theta \qquad (11.169)$$

$$\left|\overrightarrow{v_{rel}}\right| = 20.32 \text{ km/s} \qquad (11.170)$$

$$\theta = \tan^{-1}\left(\frac{3.15}{20.01}\right) \qquad (11.171)$$

$$= 10.07° \qquad (11.172)$$

Thus, the angle is about 10° east wards. As the satellite has been launched in the direction of the Earth's motion, and given the fact that Mars and the Earth have same sense of revolution around the Sun, $\overrightarrow{v_T}$ and $\overrightarrow{v_m}$ are in the same direction and hence the magnitudes must be subtracted.

22. In this question, the trick is to realise that the two angles α and β are not in the same plane. In other words, the impulse given $\left(\Delta\overrightarrow{p}\right)$ is not in the plane of the orbit of the satellite. If the orbit is in the x—y plane, we can say,

$$\overrightarrow{p'} = \overrightarrow{p} + \Delta\overrightarrow{p} \qquad (11.173)$$

$$p'_{tangential} = p + p \cos\alpha \sin\beta \qquad (11.174)$$

$$p'_{radial} = p \cos\beta \qquad (11.175)$$

$$p'_z = p \sin\alpha \sin\beta \qquad (11.176)$$

We note that if $\cos\beta \neq 0$, then the point of explosion will no longer remain either perigee or apogee. As this is not what we want,

$$\beta = 90° \text{ or } 270° \tag{11.177}$$

Thus, we get

$$p' = \sqrt{p^2\left(1+\cos\alpha\right)^2 + p^2\sin^2\alpha} \tag{11.178}$$

$$= p\sqrt{1+\cos^2\alpha + 2\cos\alpha + \sin^2\alpha}$$

$$p' = p\sqrt{2\left(1+\cos\alpha\right)}$$

$$= p\sqrt{4\cos^2\left(\alpha/2\right)}$$

$$p' = 2\,p\,\cos(\alpha/2) \tag{11.179}$$

Now, for the orbit to remain circular, we need $p' = p$.

For a parabola, we need, $p' = \sqrt{2}p$.

For an ellipse, we need p' to be smaller than the value for the parabola and for a hyperbola, we need values greater than that of parabola. Thus,

Type		α		
Hyperbola	Perigee = initial point	$[0° : 90°)$	or	$(270° : 360°]$
Parabola	Perigee = initial point	$90°$	or	$270°$
Ellipse	Perigee = initial point	$(90° : 120°)$	or	$(240° : 270°)$
Circle		$120°$	or	$240°$
Ellipse	Apogee = initial point	$(120° : 180°)$	or	$(180° : 240°)$

At exactly $\alpha = 180°$, we get $p' = 0$ and the satellite will fall on the Earth. This also assumes the Earth to be a point object. However, in reality, for angles close to $\alpha = 180°$, the orbit will pass so close to the centre of the Earth that, the satellite will hit the Earth's surface.

11.2 Data Analysis

1. By Kepler's third law, the shorter the orbital radius, the shorter the period. We make the following observations:

   - Moon 4 is moving the slowest and in these three snapshots, it is the one which has travelled farthest from Jupiter.
   - Moon 3 is moving the fastest and it stays close to Jupiter.
   - Moon 2 is the second fastest and it has not gone as far away from Jupiter as Moon 1.

   Although this data is not full conclusive, with given the data, our best answer would be as follows:

   Moon 1 – Ganymede

   Moon 2 – Europa

   Moon 3 – Io

   Moon 4 – Callisto

12

Solutions: Celestial Coordinate Systems

12.1 Theory

1.
$$\alpha = \frac{\text{Diameter of Earth}}{\text{Distance to Moon}} \tag{12.1}$$

$$= \frac{D_\oplus}{d_M} \text{radians} = \frac{D_\oplus}{d_M} \times \frac{180 \times 60}{\pi} \text{arcminutes}$$

$$= \frac{12741.6}{378000} \times \frac{180 \times 60}{\pi} \text{arcminutes}$$

$$\alpha = 116' = \frac{116}{15} \text{ minutes of RA} \tag{12.2}$$

Thus, the difference in apparent right ascension is 7.73 minutes.

In reality, as the Moon is reasonably close to the Earth, when the Moon is exactly at the middle longitude of the two observers, the line of sight of both the diametrically opposite observers will be blocked by the solid Earth. So if two observers are stationed as far as possible on the surface of the Earth, such that they both see the Moon on the horizon (ignoring atmospheric refraction and taking the Moon to be a point object), the line of sight will be tangential to the surface of the Earth.

Thus

$$\frac{\Delta\lambda}{2} = \cos^{-1}\frac{D_\oplus}{d_M} \tag{12.3}$$

∴
$$\Delta\lambda = 2\cos^{-1}\left(\frac{12741.6}{378000}\right)$$

$$= 2 \times 88°4'$$

∴
$$\Delta\lambda = 176°8' \tag{12.4}$$

Thus, you can be only about 176° apart to see the Moon simultaneously.

2. To find the minimum declination, we have to consider various effects. Firstly, we have to note the latitude of the observer (ϕ). Then we note that the observer is at a high altitude. Hence, he/she will be able to see some part of the sky below the standard horizon. This is known as horizon depression (θ). Thirdly, atmospheric refraction at the horizon (α) is about 34'.

$$\cos\theta = \frac{R}{R+h} = \frac{6370.8}{6370.8+5.6} \tag{12.5}$$

$$\theta = 2.40° = 2°24' \tag{12.6}$$

$\therefore$
$$\delta = 90° - \phi - \theta - \alpha \tag{12.7}$$

$$= 90° - (35°57' + 2°24' + 34')$$

$$= 90° - 38°55'$$

$\therefore$
$$\delta = 51°5' \, \text{N} \tag{12.8}$$

3. For condition (a), we have to ensure that the ray of light, grazing the outer edge of the tabeshband, should hit the lower edge of the window. For condition (b), we have to ensure that the ray of light, grazing the outer edge of the tabeshband, should reach point A as in Fig. 2.1. The zenith angle of the Sun at the summer and winter solstice will be given by

$$z_s = \phi - 23.5° = 12.5° \tag{12.9}$$

$$z_w = \phi + 23.5° = 59.5° \tag{12.10}$$

From Fig. 2.1, at summer solstice we have

$$\tan(z_s) = \frac{x}{h} \tag{12.11}$$

$$= \tan 12.5° = 0.222 \tag{12.12}$$

And in winter solstice, we have

$$\tan(z_w) = \frac{D+x}{H} \tag{12.13}$$

$$= \tan 59.5° = 1.70 \tag{12.14}$$

$\therefore$
$$x = 1.70H - D$$

$$x = 0.593 \, \text{m} \tag{12.15}$$

$$h = \frac{x}{0.222}$$

$$h = 2.67 \, \text{m} \tag{12.16}$$

4. Recall the coordinate transformation relations between the equatorial and horizontal coordinates.

$$\sin a = \sin \delta \sin \phi + \cos \delta \cos \phi \cos H \tag{12.17}$$

For the special case of rising or setting of an astronomical object, the altitude (a) of the Sun is zero and the relation is reduced to a simplified form

$$\cos H = - \tan \delta \tan \phi \tag{12.18}$$

For 21 December, $\delta_\odot = -23.5°$ and the question states $\phi_{obs} = 42.5°$. Thus

$$H = \cos^{-1}(- \tan(-23.5°) \tan(42.5°))$$

$$= \cos^{-1}(0.4348 \times 0.9163)$$

$$= \cos^{-1}(0.3984)$$

$$H \approx 4^h26^m5^s \tag{12.19}$$

Thus, the Sun rises 4 hours 26 minutes before local noon or at 07:34 hr local time.

Next, we notice that the longitude of the observer is $\lambda_{obs} = 71°$ E.

As local time changes by 4 minutes for every degree of longitude, his local time must be 4 hours and 44 minutes ahead of GMT. But the problem states that his civil time is 5 hours after GMT.

This means his civil time is 16 minutes behind his local time.

Applying this correction, the time of sunrise as per the observer's watch will be

$$t = 7:34 - 0:16 = 7:18 \text{ am} \tag{12.20}$$

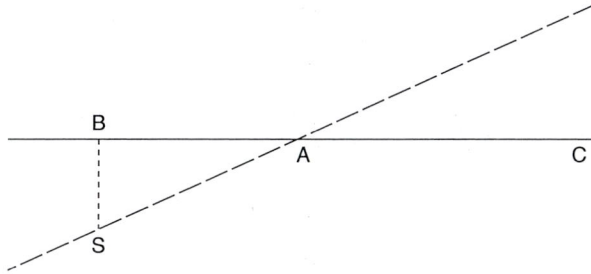

EA: Correction for atmospheric refraction is roughly 34' and angular radius of the solar disk can be up to 15'. As a combined effect of these two factors, the top edge of the Sun becomes visible when the centre of the Sun is about 49' below the horizon.

In the figure, $\overline{BAC}$ is the horizon line. $\overline{SA}$ marks the path of the Sun. A is the position where the centre of the Sun will rise. B is the position where the top edge of the Sun becomes visible when the centre of the Sun is at S. Thus, $l(\overline{BS}) = 49'$. As the plane of the daily path of the Sun is perpendicular to the Earth's axis, it is inclined with respect to the horizon by $(90 - \phi_{obs})$ degrees. Thus

$$\angle BSA = \phi_{obs} \tag{12.21}$$

$$\therefore \qquad l(\overline{AS}) = \frac{l(\overline{BS})}{\cos\phi} = \frac{49'}{\cos 42.5°} \approx 66.5' \tag{12.22}$$

As this is a small length, we approximate the Sun's speed as 4 minutes per degree. Thus, the Sun will rise about 4.5 minutes earlier due to these two factors. The equation of time shows that the Sun will be about 2 minutes (1.7 minutes to be precise) ahead on 21 December. Thus, the total error introduced by all these effects is about 6 minutes.

5. The wall of the observatory is in the plane of the prime vertical, i.e., the great circle through East, West, Zenith and the sundial is facing North. This means that whenever the Sun is to the south of the prime vertical, the sundial will not work.

(a) When the Sun is to the south of the equator, i.e., $-23°26' < \delta < 0°$, it will rise south of East and set south of West, i.e., on the southern side of the prime vertical. Thus, for this period from 23 September to 21 March, there will be at least some part of the day for which the Sun will not cast any shadow on the sundial. This corresponds to the spring and summer seasons of the southern hemisphere.

(b) It will not work the whole day, if the Sun is to the south of the prime vertical for the whole day; i.e., it should cross the local meridian on the south of zenith. This will happen when the declination of the Sun is less than the latitude of the place.

$$-\epsilon < \delta < \phi \qquad (12.23)$$

$$-23°26' < \delta < -22°54' \qquad (12.24)$$

If the Sun's ecliptic coordinates are $(\beta = 0, \lambda)$, then

$$\sin \delta = \sin \epsilon \sin \lambda \cos \beta + \cos \epsilon \sin \beta \qquad (12.25)$$

$$\therefore \qquad \sin \delta = \sin \epsilon \sin \lambda$$

$$\lambda = \sin^{-1}\left(\frac{\sin \delta}{\sin \epsilon}\right)$$

$$= \sin^{-1}(-0.9785)$$

$$258°6' < \lambda < 281°54' \qquad (12.26)$$

As the motion of the mean Sun (i.e., ignoring the equation of time) along the ecliptic is uniform, the λ will change linearly in time. Thus, this 12° window in λ corresponds to about 12 days on the either side of winter solstice (21 December).

6. Note that the date of observation (June 19) is very close to summer solstice. Thus, the equatorial coordinates for the Sun are

$$\delta \approx +23°26' \text{ and } \alpha \approx 6^h$$

At full moon, the Moon is nearly diametrically opposite the Sun along the ecliptic. The diametrically opposite position will be

$$\delta \approx -23°26' \text{ and } \alpha \approx 18^h$$

We further note that the Moon can be up to 5.14° above or below the ecliptic. Thus, δ can be between −18.29° and −28.57° depending on the position of the node. Thus, by Equation 12.18

$$\cos H = - \tan \delta \tan \phi \qquad (12.27)$$

$$\therefore \qquad H_1 = \cos^{-1}(- \tan \delta \tan \phi)$$

$$= \cos^{-1}(- \tan(-18.29°) \tan(-6°49'))$$

$$H_1 = 92.26° = 6^h9^m \qquad (12.28)$$

$$\therefore \qquad H_2 = \cos^{-1}(- \tan \delta \tan \phi)$$

$$= \cos^{-1}(- \tan(-28.57) \tan(-6°49'))$$

$$H_2 = 93.73° = 6^h15^m \qquad (12.29)$$

As a first approximation, the duration will be given by $2H$, i.e., the duration for which the Moon will be above the horizon can be from at least 12 hours 18 minutes to a maximum of 12 hours 30 minutes.

EA: However, we have to include two important corrections to this value. Firstly, due to the lunar orbital motion, the Moon is moving backwards by slightly less than 53 minutes per day. Thus, in 12.5 hours, it will move backwards by nearly 27 minutes and will be visible for 27 additional minutes.

Secondly, as the refraction near the horizon is nearly half a degree, the moon will be seen longer by 2 minutes each at rising and setting. Thus, total correction will be for 31 minutes. Hence, extreme possible values are 12 hours 49 minutes and 13 hours 1 minute.

One may note that some of the data given in this problem like longitude, civil time and elevation is not used in the solution. It is expected that the student solving such problems chooses data judiciously and does not get confused by excess data.

7. If the Moon was always on the ecliptic, its maximum declination would be ϵ. However, the orbit of the Moon is inclined w.r.t. the ecliptic by 5.3°. Further, we have to take into account the geocentric parallax and atmospheric refraction.

$$a_{ecl} = 90° - \phi + \epsilon \tag{12.30}$$
$$= 90° - 40°37' + 23°26'$$
$$= 72°49'$$

$$a_{moonorbit} = aecl + 5.3° \tag{12.31}$$
$$= 78°3'$$

We find geocentric parallax (θ_{gp}) using Fig. 12.1. 'C' is the centre of the Earth, 'M' is the Moon and 'O' is the observer's position. In this triangle

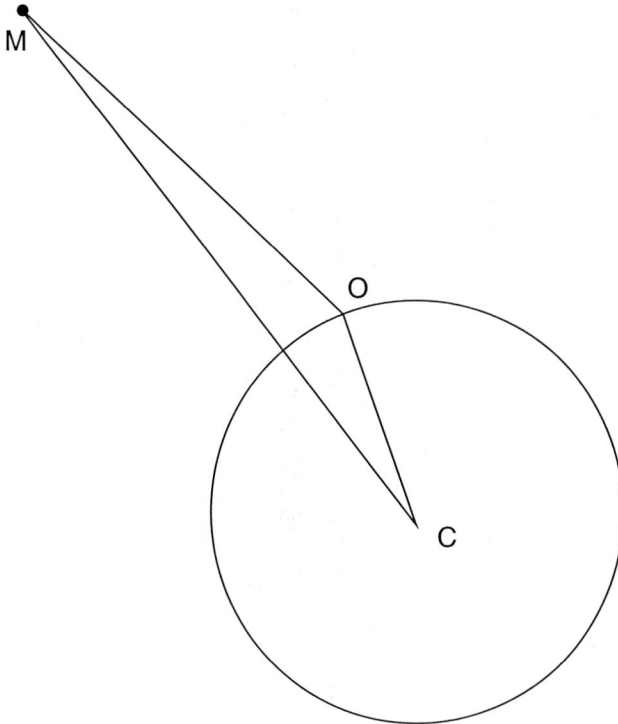

Fig. 12.1 *Geocentric parallax for the Moon*

$$\angle CMO = \theta_{gp} \tag{12.32}$$

$$\angle MCO = 90° - a_{moon\ orbit} \tag{12.33}$$

$$MC = d_M = 3.78 \times 10^8 \text{ m} \tag{12.34}$$

$$CO = R_\oplus = 6.3708 \times 10^6 \text{ m} \tag{12.35}$$

Using the cosine rule

$$MO^2 = MC^2 + CO^2 - 2(MC)(CO)\cos(\angle MCO)$$

$$= (3.78 \times 10^8)^2 - (6.3708 \times 10^8)^2 + 2 \times 3.78 \times 10^8 \times 6.3708 \times 10^6 \times \cos 11°57'$$

$$\therefore \qquad MO = 3.72 \times 10^6 \text{ m}$$

Using the sine rule

$$\frac{\sin \angle CMO}{CO} = \frac{\sin \angle MCO}{MO} \tag{12.36}$$

$$\therefore \qquad \sin \theta_{gp} = \frac{6.3708 \times 10^6}{3.72 \times 10^8} \sin 11°57'$$

$$= 0.00355$$

$$\theta_{gp} = 12'12'' \tag{12.37}$$

$$\theta_{refrac} = 60.3'' \tan z \tag{12.38}$$

$$= 60.3'' \tan(\angle MCO)$$

$$= 60.3'' \tan(11°57')$$

$$\theta_{refrac} = 13'' \tag{12.39}$$

$$\therefore \qquad a_{max} = a_{moon\ orbit} - \theta_{gp} - \theta_{refrac} \tag{12.40}$$

$$= 78°3' - 12'12'' - 13''$$

$$a_{max} = 77°51' \tag{12.41}$$

8. As FOV is expected to be very small, the motion of Vega across the FOV can be approximated by a straight line. We will calculate the angle of rotation of the sky near Vega's location. We must remember to include the declination effect. If the trace-out time (t) corresponds to the angle of rotation θ

$$\therefore \qquad \theta = 360° \times \frac{t}{T_{sidereal}} \times \cos \delta \tag{12.42}$$

$$= 360° \times \frac{5.3}{(23 \times 60 + 56)} \times \cos 39°$$

$$\theta \approx 62' \tag{12.43}$$

Thus, in 5.3 minutes, the sky near Vega will move through 62'. This is the same as the field of view (FOV) of the telescope. Hence, FOV is 1°2'.

9. Refer to Fig. 12.2. The horizontal circle is the galactic equator and point P is the south galactic pole. The triangle PV_1V_2 is a spherical triangle. Applying the cosine rule

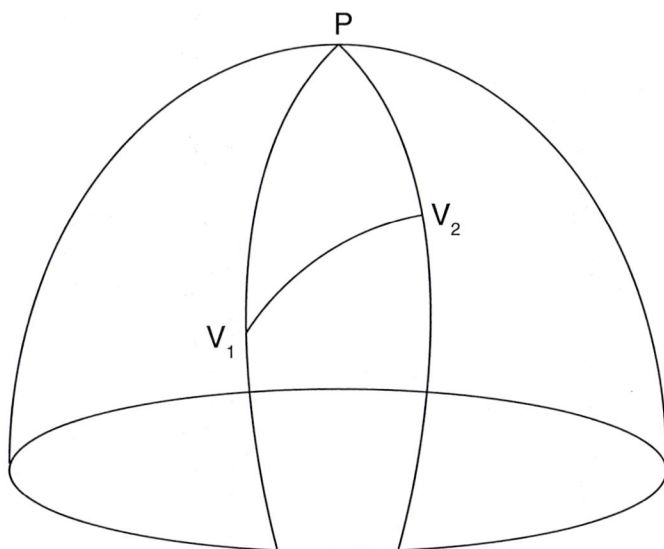

Fig. 12.2 *Spherical triangle Galati V1 and Galati V2*

$$\cos(V_1V_2) = \cos(PV_1)\cos(PV_2) + \sin(PV_1)\sin(PV_2)\cos(RV_1PV_2) \qquad (12.44)$$
$$= \cos(90° - b_1)\cos(90° - b_2) + \sin(90° - b_1)\sin(90° - b_2)\cos(l_2 - l_1)$$
$$= \sin b_1 \sin b_2 + \cos b_1 \cos b_2 \cos(l_2 - l_1)$$
$$= \sin(-11.35°)\sin(-16.177°) + \cos(-11.35°)\cos(-16.177°)\cos(1.105°)$$
$$= 0.9963$$

$$V_1V_2 = 4.945° \qquad (12.45)$$

10. In Fig. 12.3, 'N' stands for North, 'E' for East and 'W' for South. The north celestial pole is marked by 'P', zenith by 'Z' and the star at 'S'. N-W-A-E is the observer horizon and W-B-E is the celestial equator. The great circle arc PS meets the equator at 'B' and the great circle arc ZS meets the horizon at 'A'.

In such an arrangement, triangle PZS is a spherical triangle. Let us call the declination as δ and hour angle as H. In this triangle

$$PZ = 90° - NP = 90° - \phi \qquad (12.46)$$
$$ZS = z \qquad (12.47)$$
$$PS = 90° - SB = 90° - \delta \qquad (12.48)$$
$$RPZS = RNZA = 180° - A \qquad (12.49)$$
$$RZPS = H \qquad (12.50)$$

Using the cosine rule

$$\cos(PS) = \cos(ZS)\cos(PZ) + \sin(ZS)\sin(PZ)\cos(RPZS)$$
$$\cos(90 - \delta) = \cos z \cos(90 - \phi) + \sin z \sin(90 - \phi)\cos(180 - A)$$

$$\sin \delta = \cos z \sin \phi - \sin z \cos \phi \cos A \qquad (12.51)$$

$$\sin \delta = \cos 30° \sin 40° - \sin 30° \cos 40° \cos 50°$$

$$= 0.866 \times 0.643 - 0.500 \times 0.766 \times 0.643$$

$$= 0.310$$

$$\therefore \qquad \delta = 18°5' \qquad (12.52)$$

Using the sine rule

$$\frac{\sin(\angle ZPS)}{\sin(ZS)} = \frac{\sin(\angle PZS)}{\sin(PS)}$$

$$\frac{\sin H}{\sin z} = \frac{\sin(180° - A)}{\sin(90° - \delta)}$$

$$\sin H = \frac{\sin A \sin z}{\cos \delta} \qquad (12.53)$$

$$\sin H = \frac{\sin 30° \sin 50°}{\cos(18°5')}$$

$$= \frac{0.5 \times 0.766}{0.951}$$

$$= 0.402$$

$$H = 23°45'42''$$

$$\therefore \qquad H = 1^h \, 35^m \, 03^s \qquad (12.54)$$

11. By definition, when the star culminates in Lisbon, its hour angle as observed from Lisbon is exactly $0°$. Therefore, its hour angle in Thessaloniki is

$$H_1 = H_2 + (\lambda_1 - \lambda_2) \qquad (12.55)$$

$$= 0° + (1^h \, 32^m + 0^h \, 36^m)$$

$$H_1 = 2^h \, 8^m = 32° \qquad (12.56)$$

Using the cosine rule in Fig. 12.3

$$\cos(ZS) = \cos(PS) \cos(PZ) + \sin(PS) \sin(PZ) \cos(RZPS)$$

$$\cos z = \cos(90 - \delta) \cos(90 - \phi_1) + \sin(90 - \delta) \sin(90 - \phi_1) \cos H$$

$$\cos z = \sin \delta \sin \phi_1 + \cos \delta \cos \phi_1 \cos H$$

$$= \sin 38°47' \sin 40°37' + \cos 38°47' \cos 40°37' \cos 32°$$

$$= 0.9096$$

$$z = 24°33' \qquad (12.57)$$

12. Recall that the hour angle of a star (H), its RA (α) and local sidereal time (t) are related by

$$\alpha = t - H \qquad (12.58)$$

At lower culmination, the hour angle is 12 hours. Hence, the sidereal time at that moment will be

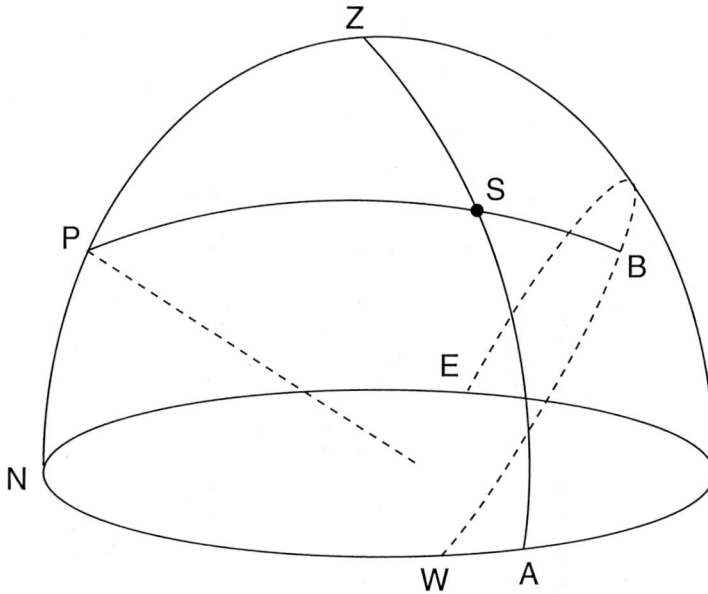

Fig. 12.3 *Spherical triangle for Alt–Az to equatorial conversion*

$$t = \alpha + H$$

$$= 14^h51^m + 12^h00^m$$

$$t = 2^h51^m \tag{12.59}$$

This will be your lowermost marker on the dial. Next we should ensure that the scale is marked anti-clockwise as that will be the direction of motion of the stars. On the UT side of the card, we again note that the lowermost point will correspond to 03:15 for the given date and the scale will again be anti-clockwise. Now, as the sidereal day is shorter than the solar day by 4 minutes, the clock will need a second dial to calibrate for this effect. This can be done easily by calibrating the inner dial with dates.

13. If the current local sidereal time (LST) is θ and the RA of the northern galactic pole (NGP) is α_G, then the hour angle of NGP will be given by

$$H_G = \alpha_G - \theta$$

$$= 12^h51^m - 0^h51^m$$

$$H_G = 12^h00^m \tag{12.60}$$

i.e., the NGP is at its lower culmination.

In Fig. 12.4, P is NCP, G is NGP and line EW marks the galactic equator. Plane NWS shows the horizon where letters represent directions. In Equation 2.1, ε corresponds to the angle between the poles of the two coordinates. Thus, it will be replaced by arcangle ZG. Also, from the figure, it is clear that the altitude of galactic equator will be maximum at $A = 0°$ (North) and minimum at $A = 180°$ (South). Note that $A = 90°$ is at the point where the galactic equator meets the horizon.

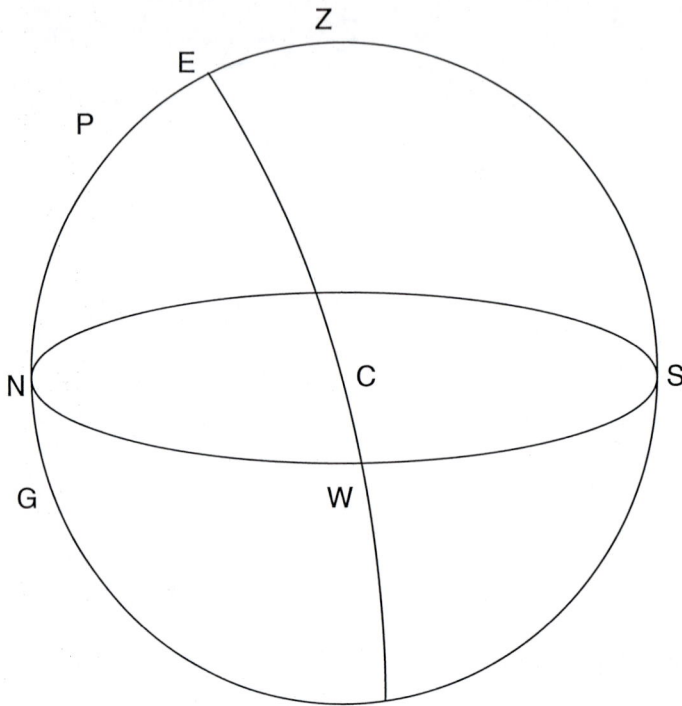

Fig.12.4 *Galactic plane in horizontal coordinates*

Similarly, RA is zero at the meeting point of the celestial equator and the ecliptic. Also, as NGP is below the horizon, the direction of increasing coordinates is opposite. Thus, $\sin \alpha$ should be replaced by $- \cos A$.

$$ZG = PG + PZ \qquad (12.61)$$

$$= 90° - \delta_G + 90° - \phi$$

$$= 180° - (\delta_G + \phi)$$

$$= 180° - 27°8' - 49°34'$$

$$= 180° - 76°42' \qquad (12.62)$$

$$h = \tan^{-1}[- \cos A \tan(ZG)]$$

$$h = \tan^{-1}[\cos A \tan 76°42'] \qquad (12.63)$$

14. One should always remember that precession does not change the ecliptic latitudes of the stars.

   In the Northern hemisphere, declination of the never-rising stars is $\delta < \varphi - 90°$, where φ stands for latitude, and declination of the never-setting stars is $\delta > 90° - \varphi$. So in Krakow,

$$\delta_{no-rise} < -39.9° \qquad (12.64)$$

$$\delta_{no-set} > 39.9° \qquad (12.65)$$

stars with intermediate declinations will rise and set. As an appproximate solution, we notice that both the stars are reasonably close to 6^h RA Let us assume their RA to be exactly 6 hours. Currently, at this RA, declination of the ecliptic (δ_{ec}) is +23.5°, which is the highest possible. If it changes to its lowest possible value, i.e., $\delta_{ec} = -23.5°$, then the declination of both the stars will decrease by 47°.

$$\therefore \qquad \delta_{Sirius} \approx -63° \qquad (12.66)$$

$$\delta_{Canopus} \approx -80° \qquad (12.67)$$

It is not possible for the declination of canopus to be much higher than its current declination. So it will never be possible for it to rise at Krakow. However, the new declination of Sirius is well inside the never-rising region of the sky for Krakow. So it can become a never-rising star.

One can solve this more rigorously using the spherical trigonometric formula given below.

$$\sin \beta = \sin \delta \cos \epsilon - \cos \delta \sin \epsilon \sin \alpha \qquad (12.68)$$

$$\sin \lambda \cos \beta = \sin \epsilon \sin \delta + \sin \alpha \cos \delta \cos \epsilon \qquad (12.69)$$

and $\qquad \sin \delta = \sin \epsilon \sin \lambda \cos \beta + \cos \epsilon \sin \beta \qquad (12.70)$

However, as the new declinations by approximate method are far away from the boundary of the never-rising region, such detailed treatment is not necessary.

15. (a) In this section, we are ignoring atmospheric refraction. For the duration of sunset, we should recall that the path of the Sun is inclined to the horizon. Since it is vernal equinox day, $\delta_\odot = 0°$.

   i. For the astronomer

$$\theta = \frac{\theta_\odot}{\sin \phi} = \frac{2R_\odot}{a_\oplus \sin 45°} \qquad (12.71)$$

$$= \frac{2\sqrt{2} 6.955 \times 10^8}{1.4960 \times 10^{11}}$$

$$\theta = 0.01315 \text{ rad}$$

$$t_{as} = \frac{\theta}{2\pi} \times 24 \text{ h}$$

$$= \frac{0.01315}{2\pi} \times 1440 \text{ min}$$

$$t_{as} \approx 3.0136 \text{ min} \qquad (12.72)$$

   ii. For the two eagles, the horizon dip will affect the exact time of sunset as well as the duration of sunset. We first calculate the horizon dip for both the eagles.

$$\cos \gamma_1 = \frac{R_\oplus}{R_\oplus + H} \qquad (12.73)$$

$$= \frac{6.3708 \times 10^6}{6.3708 \times 10^6 + 2300}$$

$$\therefore \qquad \gamma_1 = 1.5394° \qquad (12.74)$$

$$\cos \gamma_2 = \frac{R_\oplus}{R_\oplus + H + h}$$

$$= \frac{6.3708 \times 10^6}{6.3708 \times 10^6 + 2300 + 39.3}$$

$$\therefore \qquad \gamma_2 = 1.5524° \qquad (12.75)$$

For the duration of sunset, we can add γ to latitude and the effective latitude may be used for calculation.

$$t_1 = \frac{\theta_1}{2\pi} \times 24\,\text{h}$$

$$= \frac{2R_\odot}{2\pi a_\oplus \sin(\phi + \gamma_1)} \times 1440\,\text{min}$$

$$= \frac{6.955 \times 10^8}{\pi \times 1.4960 \times 10^{11} \times \sin(46.5394°)} \times 1440\,\text{min}$$

$$t_1 \approx 2.9358\,\text{min} \qquad (12.76)$$

Similarly

$$t_2 = \frac{R_\odot}{\pi a_\oplus \sin(\phi + \gamma_2)} \times 1440\,\text{min}$$

$$= \frac{6.955 \times 10^8}{\pi \times 1.4960 \times 10^{11} \times \sin(46.5524°)} \times 1440\,\text{min}$$

$$t_2 \approx 2.9352\,\text{min} \qquad (12.77)$$

iii. The eagle at the base of the monument would see the Sun set first as its horizon is smaller.

On any given day, all other factors like equation of time and hour angle at sunset would be the same for both the eagles and the difference between the final moments of sunset will only be due to two factors: time difference between start of sunset and difference in duration of sunset.

$$\delta t = \frac{\gamma_2 - \gamma_1}{2\pi \sin\left(\phi + \frac{\gamma_1 + \gamma_2}{2}\right)} \times 1440 + t_2 - t_1 \qquad (12.78)$$

$$= \frac{1.5524° - 1.5394°}{360° \times \sin(45° + 1.5459°)} \times 1440 + 2.9352 - 2.9358$$

$$= \frac{0.0130°}{360° \times \sin(46.5459)} \times 1440 - 0.0006$$

$$= 0.0710\,\text{min}$$

$$\delta t = 4.26\,\text{s} \qquad (12.79)$$

(b) The shadow length will be minimum when the Sun is at meridian. Assuming $\delta_\odot$ does not change much the next day, its altitude at meridian will be the same as the latitude of the place.

i. The distance between the eagles will be

$$d_1 = \frac{h}{\sin \phi} = \frac{39.3}{\sin 45°}$$

$$= 39.3 \times \sqrt{2}$$

$$d_1 = 55.58 \text{ m} \tag{12.80}$$

The distance of the second eagle from the cross is the same as the height of the pillar (as altitude is 45°). Thus, $d_2 = 39.3$ m.

ii. Similarly, if the shadow of one of the arms at this moment is 7 m, then the length of the arm on one side is also 7 m. This would mean the total length of the horizontal bar is 14 m. Note that the horizontal bar is along the North–South direction. Hence, the shadow of the arm will fall on the vertical pillar.

(c) If the altitude of the place was 0 metres and there was no atmospheric refraction. The circumpolar circle would have radius $= 90° - \phi$. We should subtract the horizon dip and atmospheric refraction from this.

$$\delta_{min} = 90° - \phi - \gamma_2 - \xi \tag{12.81}$$

$$= 90° - 45° - 1.5524° - 34'$$

$$\delta_{min} = 42°53' \tag{12.82}$$

$$a_{max} = \phi + \delta min \tag{12.83}$$

$$= 45° + 42°53'$$

$$a_{max} = 87°53' \tag{12.84}$$

16. Summer solstice in the Southern hemisphere is December 23. On that day, declination of the Sun is $\delta = -\epsilon - 23.45°$. Thus, the altitude of the Sun at this island on that noon will be

$$a_0 = 90° + \varphi - \delta \tag{12.85}$$

$$= 90° - 66.55° - (-23.45°)$$

$$a_0 = 46.9° \tag{12.86}$$

At sunset, the centre of the Sun will just touch the horizon and then start rising again, i.e., the lowest point of the declination circle along which the Sun travels on that day is just touching the horizon. This means that at that instant, the shadow extends to infinity and hence the locus is not a closed curve. The locus of the tip of the shadow will be symmetric on either side of the prime meridian (North–Zenith–South). Thus, as shown in the figure, the equation of the locus will be that of a parabola, with origin at the focus. Let us take a generalised parabola equation and find its coefficients.

$$y = px^2 + q_x + r \tag{12.87}$$

Firstly, as the focus of the parabola is at the origin, q will be zero. We will take coordinates at noon as (x_0, y_0), and the coordinates when the Sun is at prime vertical (East–Zenith–West), say pre-noon, as (x_1, y_1). To find this second set of coordinates, we have to find the altitude of the Sun when it crosses the prime vertical. We use the fact that the plane of declination circle is inclined to the horizon at ϵ degrees. Let us say that R is the radius of the imaginary celestial sphere and z_1 is the projected height of the Sun on the z-axis. Therefore

$$x_0 = 0 \tag{12.88}$$

$$y_1 = 0 \tag{12.89}$$

$$y_0 = px_2^0 + r \tag{12.90}$$

$$r = \frac{-h_{chirst}}{\tan a_0} \tag{12.91}$$

$$= \frac{-39.60}{\tan 49.6}$$

$$\therefore \qquad r = -37.06 \text{ m} \tag{12.92}$$

$$z_1 = R \sin a_1 \tag{12.93}$$

$$\tan \epsilon = \frac{z_1}{R} = \sin a_1 \tag{12.94}$$

$$\therefore \qquad a_1 = \sin^{-1}(\tan \epsilon) = 25°42' \tag{12.95}$$

$$x_1 = \frac{h_{chirst}}{\tan a_1} \tag{12.96}$$

$$= 82.26$$

Now

$$p = \frac{-r}{x_1^2} \tag{12.97}$$

$$p = 0.0055 \tag{12.98}$$

$$\therefore \qquad y = 0.0055x^2 - 37.06 \tag{12.99}$$

17. It is important to understand what is asked in the question. Imagine that you are standing inside a huge rotating sphere and various stars are attached to the sphere. Now one of these stars at the given location comes loose at the given time and flies off tangentially to infinity. We would like to know the final apparent coordinates of this star and also the time required for it to travel a certain distance.

Let R be the radius of the celestial sphere and (x, y, z) a coordinate system with origin at the observer, z is the down–up axis, y is the east–west axis and x is the south–north axis. At the superior culmination, we have

$$a = 90° - \varphi + \delta = 49.35° + 7.41° \tag{12.100}$$

$$a = 56.76° \tag{12.101}$$

$$\vec{v} = v_0 \hat{y} = 2\pi R \hat{y} / day \tag{12.102}$$

$$\vec{r_0} = R(-\cos ax + \sin az) \tag{12.103}$$

Now the object flies off at this stage. At any point in the future, its location will be given by

$$\vec{r(t)} = \vec{r_0} + \vec{v}t \tag{12.104}$$

$$a(t) = \tan^{-1}\left(\frac{z}{\sqrt{x^2 + y^2}}\right) \tag{12.105}$$

When $t \to \infty$, the x and z coordinates of the star remain constant, while $y \to \infty$ and we have

$$a = \tan^{-1}\left(\frac{z}{\infty}\right) = \tan^{-1} 0 = 0° \tag{12.106}$$

Similarly, the final azimuth is the West direction ($A = 90°\ or\ A = 270°$, depending on the system used). For the magnitude

$$m_0 - m_6 = -2.5 \log \left(\frac{F_0}{F_6}\right) = -5 \log \left(\frac{R_6}{R_0}\right) \tag{12.107}$$

$$R_6 = 10^{\frac{(6.00-0.45)}{5}} R$$

$$R_6 = 12.9 R_0 \tag{12.108}$$

$$|\overrightarrow{r(t)}| = \sqrt{x^2 + y^2 + z^2} \tag{12.109}$$

$$= \sqrt{x_0^2 + (2\pi R t)^2 + z_0^2}$$

$$= \sqrt{R^2 + 4\pi^2 R^2 t^2}$$

$$= R\sqrt{1 + 4\pi^2 t^2} = 12.9 R \tag{12.110}$$

$$\therefore \qquad 12.9^2 = 1 + 4\pi^2 t^2$$

$$t = \sqrt{\frac{12.9^2 - 1}{4\pi^2}}$$

$$t = 2.04 \text{ days} \tag{12.111}$$

18. As seen from an inertial reference frame outside the Earth, the observer must describe a circle parallel to the ecliptic, with constant speed, in a period of one sidereal day. Note that the observer starts observing when the ecliptic pole is just rising, i.e., on the horizon. Since the ecliptic poles should stay at zero latitude, this circle must be a great circle.

But in the reference frame of the Earth, the total motion will be the motion in inertial frame (as described above) plus motion to compensate for the rotation of the Earth. In other words, the displacement of the observer is the vectorial addition of rotation through some angle φ along the ecliptic and rotation through the same angle φ around the Earth's rotation axis. But this is exactly the same construction which would describe the analemma of the Sun, if the Earth would have been in exact circular orbit around the Sun. So the resultant path of the observer will appear like an analemma for the circular orbit (symmetrical figure of 8).

- It must be a closed curve, bound by latitudes $= \pm\epsilon$.
- It should be symmetric around the equator as well as a chosen longitude.
- It should have the shape of 8.

As the observer starts in the Southern hemisphere, he will cross the equator for the first time in the direction south–north. Its velocity relative to an inertial reference frame will have magnitude $v = \dfrac{2\pi R}{T}$ and azimuth (the angle with the north–south direction) $A_1 = 90° - \epsilon$. The velocity of the Earth's surface will have the same magnitude and azimuth $A_2 = 90°$. Subtracting the vectors

$$v_{combined} = v\sqrt{2(1 - \cos \epsilon)} \tag{12.112}$$

$$A_{combined} = -\frac{\epsilon}{2} = -11.72° \tag{12.113}$$

12.2 Data Analysis

1. This is an interesting problem as there is a lot of data but only a small part of it will actually be used to solve the question. Thus, the key to the solution is to first understand which data should be picked up from the table.

   (a) We start by examining the dates of solstices and equinoxes, and the position of object A:

		Right Ascension					
		h	m	s	°	'	"
Mar	21	23	59	51.47	− 0	1	1.44
Mar	22	0	3	30.11	+0	22	40.3
Jun	21	5	56	41.18	+23	26	13.51
Jun	22	6	0	50.78	+23	26	20.99
Sep	23	11	58	23.75	+0	10	27.2
Sep	24	12	1	59.32	−0	12	54.79
Dec	22	17	58	42.17	−23	26	27
Dec	23	18	3	8.7	−23	26	21.28

This matches exactly with expected positions of the Sun on these dates. Thus, **object A is the Sun**.

Now, we see how other objects move with respect to the Sun. If we scan through the entire table, we notice that the difference between the RA of the Sun and that of object C is never more than 3 hours. Thus, it is an inner planet. The elongation of this planet can be found by calculating the difference between the RA of the two. We note that on 1 January, the difference in RA is

$$e = 18^h44^m7^s.11 - 15^h28^m49^s.55$$

$$= 3^h15^m17^s.56$$

$$\approx 48°49' \tag{12.114}$$

Here, the implicit assumption is that the planet is exactly on the ecliptic and hence the difference in RA will correctly give the elongation. Now, in the case of Mercury, the orbital radius is about 0.4 AU. Thus, its maximum elongation will be about 28°. Orbital radius of Venus is about 0.72 AU and the maximum elongation (assuming circular orbits) is about 47°. Thus, we note that elongation of object C is much more than the maximum elongation of Mercury but reasonably close to the maximum elongation of Venus. The small difference could be entirely due to our approximations (measuring only the difference along the RA and assuming circular orbits). We can safely conclude that **object C** is **Venus**. A clear sign of an outer planet is that during the course of the year, it can be seen sometimes at opposition. In terms of coordinates, it means that the difference between the RA of the object and the RA of the Sun should be 12 hours. Both object B (3 February) and object D (31 August) can be seen at opposition. Thus, they are outer planets. We next note that object D is changing coordinates much faster than object B. Let us concentrate on object B first.

These objects are changing coordinates from day to day. However, we must remember that this change is due to the combined effect of the changing position of the Earth and the changing position of the object. Usually, it will be difficult to separate the two contributions. However, as the table provides coordinates over an entire year, we can say that the orbital position of the Earth as on 1 January will be nearly the same as that on 31 December. Thus, the difference in coordinates of the objects between these two dates will be entirely because of the changing position of the object.

For object B, the difference in the RA over one year is nearly 2^h, i.e., it will taken early 12 years to go through the full circle (24^h). We can recall that the synodic period of Jupiter is 12 years and conclude that **object B** is **Jupiter**. As the synodic period of object D is smaller than Jupiter, we conclude that the **object D** is **Mars**.

(b) To be visible for the longest duration at night, the object should rise at sunset and set nearly at sunrise. This again means that it should be at opposition. We already know the dates of opposition of Jupiter and Mars from the table above. Next we note that winter nights are longer than summer nights. As the observer is based in the Northern hemisphere, we can say that February nights will be longer than August nights. Thus, we will conclude that **Jupiter** will be seen for the longest duration at night.

(c) The corresponding date will be the date of opposition, i.e., **3 February**.

(d) To place all the objects in the orbit diagram as on 3 February, we must take the RA of each of these objects. As we are viewing the Solar System perfectly face-on, declination is not relevant here. To place the Earth, we take the RA of the Sun. The orbit diagram shows the direction of vernal equinox. If the Earth was exactly opposite that direction (lower part of the paper), the observer will see the RA of the Sun as 0^h. The radial vector of the Earth currently makes an angle with the vertical line. When viewed from the top, the planets move anti-clockwise. As we are at few days before vernal equinox, the Earth's position will be to the left of the vertical line. The four circles denote the orbits of Venus, Earth, Mars and Jupiter. So we place the Earth making an angle of $44°$ with the vertical line on the second (from inside) orbit on the lower left part.

$$e = 24^h0^m0^s - 21^h4^m47^s.25$$

$$= 2^h55^m12^s.75$$

$$\approx 44° \tag{12.115}$$

Jupiter is at opposition on that date. So it will be placed in the last orbit, exactly along the Sun–Earth line. Next, we note that the vernal equinox direction points to reference at infinity. Hence, the direction of 0^h as drawn from the Earth will also be exactly vertically up. From that direction, as we move anti-clockwise, the RA will keep on increasing. We will place Venus and Mars in their resepctive orbits as per their RA.

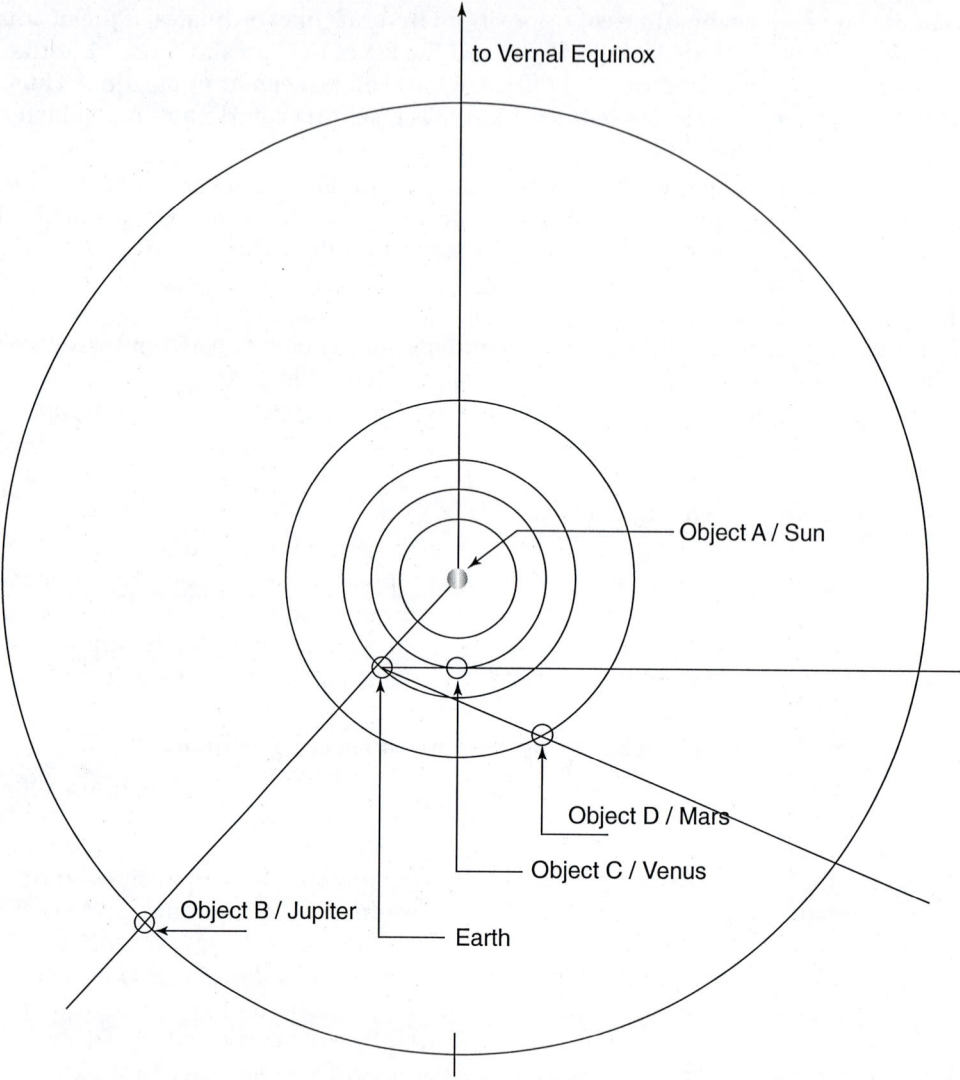

to Vernal Equinox

Object A / Sun

Object D / Mars

Object C / Venus

Object B / Jupiter

Earth

13

Solutions: Geometric Astronomy and Time

13.1 Theory

1. The apparent angular separation between the Sun and Venus as seen from the Earth is maximum when $\angle SVE = 90°$.

$$\therefore \qquad d_{SV} = d_{\odot - \oplus} \sin 46° \tag{13.1}$$

$$= (1 \text{ AU}) \times 0.719$$

$$\approx 0.72 \text{ AU} \tag{13.2}$$

2. During a full moon, we see the whole face of the Moon. Hence

$$\text{Angle in radians} \approx \frac{\text{Diameter of the Moon}}{\text{Distance to the Moon}} \tag{13.3}$$

$$\therefore \qquad \text{Distance to the Moon} = \frac{\text{Diameter of the Moon}}{\text{Angle in radians}}$$

$$= \frac{2 \times 1.7374 \times 10^6}{(0.46\pi)/180}$$

$$= \frac{2 \times 1.7374 \times 10^6 \times 180}{0.46\pi}$$

$$= 4.3 \times 10^8 \text{ m} \tag{13.4}$$

3. From the definition of the unit parsec

$$\text{Angle measured in arcsec} = \frac{\text{Diameter of orbit in AU}}{\text{Distance in parsec}} \tag{13.5}$$

$$= \frac{2}{100} = 0.02" \tag{13.6}$$

4. As the solar day is measured from noon to noon, it is slightly longer than the rotation period of the Earth (sidereal day). Over the course of one solar year, this small time difference is accumulated to one additional sidereal day. Thus, in exactly half a year, it would have accumulated to 0.5 extra days.

Thus, there will be 183.5 sidereal days from the noon of 1 July to the noon of 31 December. Mathematically, the sidereal day is $3^m\ 56^s$ shorter than the solar day.

$\therefore$ 183 solar days $= 183^d + 183 \times (3^m56^s)$

$$= 183^d11^h50^m48^s$$

$$\approx 183.5 \text{ days} \tag{13.7}$$

5. Let us find the orbital period of Mars first. By Kepler's third law

$$\frac{T_M^2}{T_E^2} = \frac{a_M^3}{a_E^3} \tag{13.8}$$

$$T^2{}_M = 1.524^3 \times (365.2564)^2$$
$$T_M = 1.52^{1.5} \times 365.2564$$
$$T_M = 687.19 \text{ days} \tag{13.9}$$

To find the time between successive oppositions, we must find the synodic period of Mars.

$$\frac{1}{T_{Sy}} = \frac{1}{T_E} - \frac{1}{T_M} \tag{13.10}$$

$$\frac{1}{T_{Sy}} = \frac{1}{365.2564} - \frac{1}{687.19}$$

$$T_{Sy} = 779.67 \text{ days} \tag{13.11}$$

Thus, the time between successive oppositions (synodic period) of Mars is 780 days.

6. As in the previous question, we first find the orbital period and then the synodic period of Mars.

$$T_M = 687.19 \text{ days} \tag{13.12}$$
$$T_{sy} = 779.67 \text{ days} \tag{13.13}$$

This means there is an opposition of Mars about every 780 days. To find the date of Great Opposition in the year 2018, we must find the number of days between 28/08/2003 and 28/08/2018 and the number of synodic periods in that interval.

$$15 \times 365 + 4 = 5479 \text{ days} \tag{13.14}$$

$$\frac{5479}{779.67} = 7.0273 \tag{13.15}$$

It means that there will be seven oppositions between 28 August 2003 and 28 August 2018. So the date for the Great Opposition in 2018 should be

$$5479 - 7 \times 779.67 = 21.31 \text{ days} \tag{13.16}$$

i.e., 21 days and 7.5 hours before the matching date and time in 2018. Now the 2003 opposition took place on the evening of 28 August. Thus, 7.5 hours will not change the date of opposition. Thus, the opposition will take place on 7 August 2018.

7. The current length of the solar day is exactly 24 hours. But a sidereal day is a little less than a solar day because of the yearly motion of the Sun. Now, in one solar year, the Earth completes 365.25 solar days but it completes one additional rotation around itself. Thus, the number of sidereal days will be 366.25.

$$T_{sid} = T_{sol} \times \frac{n}{n+1} \tag{13.17}$$

$$= 24^h \times \frac{365.25}{365.25+1}$$

$$= 23^h56^m4^s \tag{13.18}$$

Now, if the Earth rotates in the opposite direction, then the exact opposite will happen; i.e., the Earth will complete one rotation less than the number of solar days in a solar year.

On the other hand, the sidereal day will remain the same as its magnitude does not depend on the direction of rotation (neglecting the precession).

$$T'_{sol} = T_{sid} \times \frac{n-1}{n} \tag{13.19}$$

$$= T_{sol} \times \frac{n}{n+1} \times \frac{n-1}{n}$$

$$= 24^h \times \frac{365.25-1}{365.25+1}$$

$$= 23^h52^m8^s \tag{13.20}$$

8. In Fig. 13.1, the observer in Tehran is located at O and the satellite is at S.

Thus
$$\angle OES = \varphi \tag{13.21}$$

$$\angle EOS = 180° - z = 180° - 46.0°$$

$$= 134° \tag{13.22}$$

$$\delta = 180 - \varphi - \angle EOS$$

$$= 10.4° \tag{13.23}$$

By the sine rule

$$\frac{R_s}{\sin(\angle EOS)} = \frac{R_\oplus}{\sin \delta} \tag{13.24}$$

$$\frac{R_s}{R_\oplus} = \frac{\sin(\angle EOS)}{\sin \delta}$$

$$= \frac{\sin 134°}{\sin 10.4°}$$

$$\therefore \qquad R_s = 3.98 R_\oplus \tag{13.25}$$

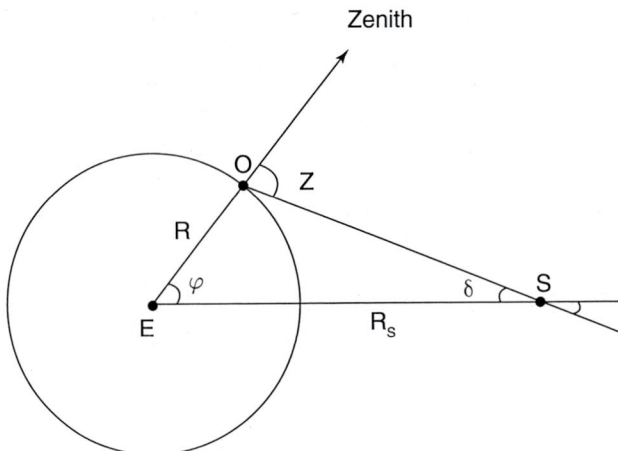

Fig. 13.1 *Geocentric parallax of the satellite*

The angle δ is called the geocentric parallax of that satellite with respect to the observer in Tehran.

9. If the observer was at the centre of Mars (C), Phobos would have been visible above the horizon for exactly half the period. However, the observer is on the Martian surface (O). Thus, as shown in Fig. 13.2, Phobos will set at point P. The orbital period of Phobos will be given by

$$T_{ph} = 2\pi \sqrt{\frac{a_{ph}^3}{GM_{Mars}}} \tag{13.26}$$

$$= 2\pi \sqrt{\frac{(9.38 \times 10^6)^3}{6.6726 \times 10^{-11} \times 6.421 \times 10^{23}}}$$

$$= 2.76 \times 10^4 \text{ s}$$

$$T_{ph} \approx 7.660 \text{ hrs} \tag{13.27}$$

To find out the relative motion of Phobos as seen from O, we should find its synodic period with respect to the Martian rotation.

$$\frac{1}{T_{syn}} = \frac{1}{T_{ph}} - \frac{1}{P_{Mars}} \tag{13.28}$$

$$T_{syn} = \frac{P_{Mars} T_{ph}}{P_{Mars} - T_{ph}}$$

$$= \frac{24.623 \times 7.660}{24.623 - 7.660}$$

$$= 11.12 \text{ hrs} \tag{13.29}$$

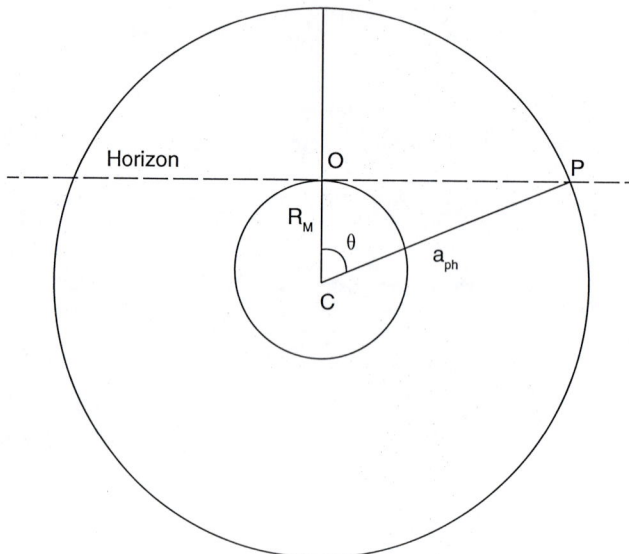

Fig. 13.2   *Horizon for the Martian observer*

This is the synodic period of Phobos for a Martian observer. Now

$$\theta = \cos^{-1}\left(\frac{R_{Mars}}{a_{Ph}}\right) \tag{13.30}$$

$$t = \frac{2\theta}{360°} \times T_{syn}$$

$$= \frac{T_{syn}}{180°} \cos^{-1}\left(\frac{R_{Mars}}{a_{Ph}}\right) \tag{13.31}$$

$$= \frac{11.12}{180°} \cos^{-1}\left(\frac{3393}{9380}\right) = \frac{11.12}{180°} \times 68.79°$$

$$= 4.25 \text{ hrs} \tag{13.32}$$

Hence, Phobos will be visible in the Martian sky for about 4 hours and 15 minutes.

10. If we go into the reference frame of the Earth, Mars will complete one revolution in its synodic period. In Fig. 13.3, Mars is at opposition at M_1 and at quadrature at M_2. Length SM_2 is the orbital radius of Mars (a_m) and SE is the orbital radius of the Earth ($a_\oplus$). The angle between the two positions is θ.

$$\frac{1}{T_{sy}} = \frac{1}{T_\oplus} - \frac{1}{T_m} \tag{13.33}$$

$$\therefore \quad T_{sy} = \frac{T_m T_\oplus}{(T_m - T_\oplus)} \tag{13.34}$$

$$= \frac{687 \times 365}{(687 - 365)}$$

$$\therefore \quad T_{sy} = 778.7 \text{ days} \approx 779 \text{ days} \tag{13.35}$$

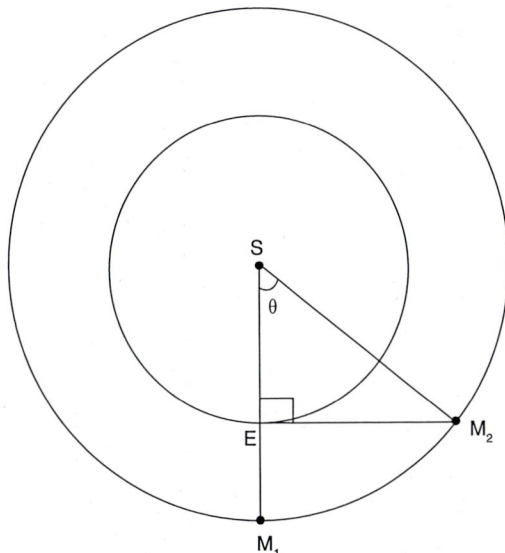

Fig. 13.3 *Mars at opposition and at quadrature*

$$\theta = \frac{t}{T} \times 360° = \frac{106}{779} \times 360° \tag{13.36}$$

$$= 49.00° \tag{13.37}$$

$$a_\oplus = a_m \cos\theta \tag{13.38}$$

$$a_m = \frac{1}{\cos 49.00°}$$

$$a_m = 1.52 \text{ AU} \tag{13.39}$$

11 If there is no phase factor, the apparent magnitude of the Moon as seen from the Earth will be given by

$$m_m = M_m + 5\log\left(\frac{d_m}{a_\oplus}\right) \tag{13.40}$$

$$= 0.25 + 5\log\left(\frac{3.78 \times 10^8}{1.496 \times 10^{11}}\right)$$

$$m_\mu = -12.737 \tag{13.41}$$

With the phase factor, we will modify the formula as

$$m_m = -12.737 - 2.5\log P\,(\Psi) \tag{13.42}$$

a) On a full moon day, $\Psi = 0°$. Hence

$$P\,(\Psi) = \frac{2}{3}\left[\left(1 - \frac{0}{\pi}\right)\cos 0 + \frac{1}{\pi}\sin 0\right]$$

$$= \frac{2}{3} \tag{13.43}$$

$$m_m = -12.737 - 2.5\log\left(\frac{2}{3}\right)$$

$$m_m = -12.30 \tag{13.44}$$

a) On the first quarter day, $\Psi = 90°$. Hence

$$P(\Psi) = \frac{2}{3}\left[\left(1 - \frac{\pi}{2\pi}\right)\cos 90° + \frac{1}{\pi}\sin 90°\right]$$

$$= \frac{2}{3\pi} \tag{13.45}$$

$$m_m = -12.37 - 2.5\log\left(\frac{2}{3\pi}\right)$$

$$m_m = -11.05 \tag{13.46}$$

12. (a) Drawing a scaled diagram is impossible. A rough sketch is accepted.

(b) There are 10 days and nights per Tarisyear. The obliquity is $+3°$, which means that the planet's rotation is in the same direction as its orbit. Thus, the total number of rotations per year is $10 + 1 = 11$.

This is similar to the fact that the Earth will complete one additional rotation in one year.

Note:

- The obliquity is positive (similar to the Earth / Mars / Jupiter). This means we have to ADD one rotation. Subtracting one rotation by assuming opposite rotation (like Venus) is not correct.

(c) By Kepler's third law

$$\frac{T_{en}^2}{R_{en}^3} = \frac{T_{ex}^2}{R_{ex}^3} \tag{13.47}$$

$$R_{ex}^3 = \frac{1.6^2 R_{en}^3}{0.2^2}$$

$$R_{ex} = \sqrt[3]{64} R_{en} = 4 R_{en}$$

$$= 4 \text{ Endorlengths} \tag{13.48}$$

(d) Using same logic as above

$$\frac{T_C^2}{R_C^3} = \frac{T_T^2}{R_T^3} \tag{13.49}$$

$$T_C^2 = \frac{9^3 R_T^3 T_T^2}{R_T^3}$$

$$T_C = \sqrt{729} R_T = 27 R_T$$

$$= 27 \text{ Tarisyears} \tag{13.50}$$

(e) As Corulus is in opposition, Sola–Taris–Corulus form a straight line (in that order). Distance $= 9 - 1 = 8$ Tarislengths.

(f) In Fig. 12d, S is Sola, A and B are the start of the year positions of Taris and Corulus and T and C are their positions after 'n' days. Angles are named from a to f. The dashed line is parallel to line SB. Triangle SCT is used for the sine rule as well as the answer in the next part. The figure is not to scale.

$$a + b + c = \pi \tag{13.51}$$

$$b + d + e = \pi \tag{13.52}$$

$$d = f + c \tag{13.53}$$

As Taris goes around Sola in 10 days,

$$f + c = \frac{2\pi n}{10} \tag{13.54}$$

Similarly, using the orbital period of Corulus

$$f = \frac{2\pi n}{270} \tag{13.55}$$

$$\therefore \qquad c = \frac{2\pi n}{10} - \frac{2\pi n}{270}$$

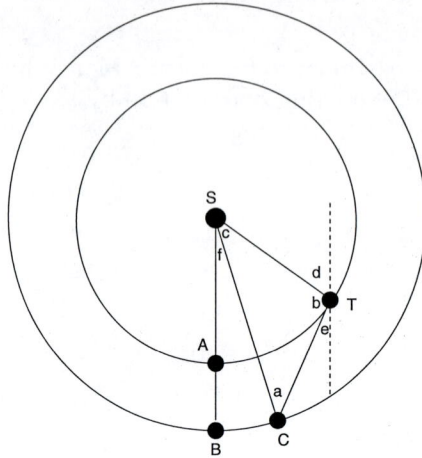

$$c = \frac{52\pi n}{270} \tag{13.56}$$

$$\frac{\sin a}{ST} = \frac{\sin b}{SC} = \frac{\sin b}{9ST} \tag{13.57}$$

$$\therefore \qquad \sin b = 9 \sin a \tag{13.58}$$

$$e = \pi - b - d \tag{13.59}$$

$$= \pi - b - c - f$$

$$e = a - f \tag{13.60}$$

$$b = \pi - (a + c) \tag{13.61}$$

$$b = \pi - \left(a + \frac{52\pi n}{270}\right) \tag{13.62}$$

$$9 \sin a = \sin\left[\pi - \left(a + \frac{52\pi n}{270}\right)\right] \tag{13.63}$$

$$= \sin\left(a + \frac{52\pi n}{270}\right)$$

$$= \left[\sin a \cos\left(\frac{52\pi n}{270}\right) + \cos a \sin\left(\frac{52\pi n}{270}\right)\right] \tag{13.64}$$

$$9 = \cos\left(\frac{52\pi n}{270}\right) + \cot a \sin\left(\frac{52\pi n}{270}\right)$$

$$\cot a = \frac{9 - \cos\left(\dfrac{52\pi n}{270}\right)}{\sin\left(\dfrac{52\pi n}{270}\right)} \tag{13.65}$$

$$a = \tan^{-1}\left[\frac{\sin\left(\dfrac{52\pi n}{270}\right)}{9 - \cos\left(\dfrac{52\pi n}{270}\right)}\right] \tag{13.66}$$

At the beginning of the year, The Solaptic longitude of Sola is zero. Hence, the Solaptic longitude of Corulus is 180°. At the new position, the Solaptic longitude of Corulus is

$$\lambda = \pi - e \tag{13.67}$$

$$= \pi + f - a$$

$$\lambda = \pi + \frac{2\pi n}{270} - \tan^{-1}\left[\frac{\sin\left(\dfrac{52\pi n}{270}\right)}{9 - \cos\left(\dfrac{52\pi n}{270}\right)}\right] \tag{13.68}$$

(g) When $n = 1$

$$\text{Area} = \frac{1}{2} \times l(ST) \times l(SC) \times \sin c \tag{13.69}$$

$$= \frac{1}{2} \times 1 \times 9 \times \sin\left(\frac{52\pi n}{270}\right)$$

$$= 4.5 \times 0.5688$$

$$= 2.56 \tag{13.70}$$

The area is about 2.5 Tarislength².

13. Since the observer is close to the pole, the effect of the Earth's rotation on the transit can be ignored. The Sun's angular size for the observer will be

$$\theta_\odot = \frac{2R_\odot}{a_\oplus} \tag{13.71}$$

$$= \left(\frac{2 \times 6.955 \times 10^8}{1.496 \times 10^{11}}\right) \times \frac{206\,265''}{60}$$

$$\theta_\odot \approx 32.0\text{ʃ} \tag{13.72}$$

$$\theta_{Venus} = \frac{2R_{Venus}}{d_{V-E}} \tag{13.73}$$

$$= \frac{2 \times 0.949 \times 6.371 \times 10^6 \times 206\,265''}{(1 - 0.723) \times 1.496 \times 10^{11} \times 60}$$

$$\theta_{Venus} \approx 1.00' \tag{13.74}$$

The angular velocity of Venus around the Sun with respect to the Earth will be

$$\omega_{sy} = \omega_{Venus} - \omega_{Earth} = \frac{2\pi}{T_{Venus}} - \frac{2\pi}{T_{Earth}} \tag{13.75}$$

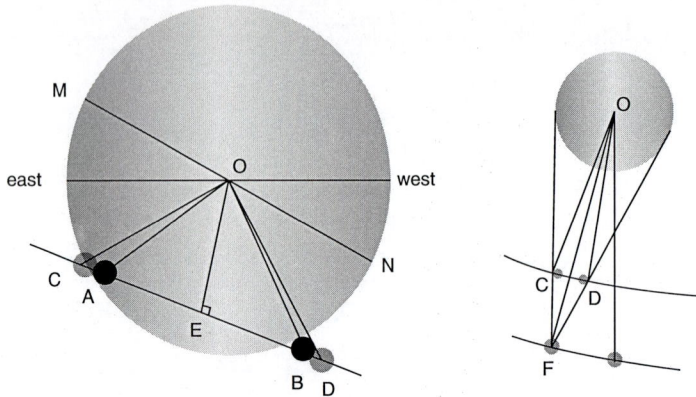

Fig. 13.4 *Venus transit geometry*

$$= \frac{2\pi \times 206\,265''}{86400 \times 60} \left(\frac{1}{224.70} - \frac{1}{365.25}\right)$$

$$\approx 4.28 \times 10^{-4} \text{ arcmin/s} \tag{13.76}$$

For the observer on the Earth, let us say that Venus moved through angle θ during the whole transit. Let OE be perpendicular to AB (Fig. 13.4).

$$OA = \frac{1}{2}\theta_\odot$$

$$\angle AOB = 90°$$

$$MN \parallel AB$$

$\therefore$

$$OE = \frac{1}{2}\theta_\odot \sin 45°$$

$$= 11.3' \tag{13.77}$$

$$OC = \frac{(\theta_{Venus} + \theta_\odot)}{2}$$

$$= 16.5' \tag{13.78}$$

$$CE = \sqrt{OC^2 - OE^2} \tag{13.79}$$

$$= \sqrt{16.0^2 - 11.3^2}$$

$$\approx 12.0' \tag{13.80}$$

$$CD = 2CE$$

$\therefore$

$$CD = \angle CFD = \theta = 24.0' \tag{13.81}$$

However, CFD is the angle measured from the Earth, which is different from the angle measured from the Sun. The angle measured from the Sun ($\theta' = \angle COD$) is the actual angle that Venus covered during the transit.

$$\frac{\sin\left(\frac{\theta'}{2}\right)}{\sin\left(\frac{\theta}{2}\right)} = \frac{a_{Venus}}{d_{V_E}} \tag{13.82}$$

$$= \frac{0.723}{(1-0.723)}$$

$$\theta' = 2\sin^{-1}\left(\frac{\sin 12.0'}{2.610}\right) = 9.195' \tag{13.83}$$

$$t_{transit} = \frac{\theta'}{\omega_{sy}} \tag{13.84}$$

$$= \frac{9.195'}{4.28 \times 10^{-4}}$$

$$t_{transit} = 5^h 58^m \tag{13.85}$$

So the transit will finish at about $14^h 58^m$.

14. Let us call the semi-major axis of the Moon's orbit as a, its eccentricity as e, the revolution period T, apparent radius r, the distance between the Earth and the Moon as d and apparent radius of the Sun as $r_\odot$. When the Moon is at perigee, the total eclipse will be longest and when the Moon is at apogee, the annular eclipse will be longest.

By conserving angular momentum

$$d_{ap}^2 \omega_{ap} = d_{peri}^2 \omega_{peri} \tag{13.86}$$

$$\therefore \quad \frac{\omega_{peri}}{\omega_{ap}} = \left(\frac{a(1+e)}{a(1-e)}\right)^2$$

$$= \frac{(1+e)^2}{(1-e)^2} \tag{13.87}$$

As the Earth's orbit around the Sun is circular, we can assume $\omega_\oplus$ is constant. Thus, time of eclipse at these two points

$$t_{ap} = \frac{2(r_\odot - r_{ap})}{\omega_{ap}} \tag{13.88}$$

$$t_{peri} = \frac{2(r_{peri} - r_\odot)}{\omega_{peri}} \tag{13.89}$$

$$\frac{t_{ap}}{t_{peri}} = \frac{\omega_{peri}}{\omega_{ap}} \frac{2(r_\odot - r_{ap})}{2(r_{peri} - r_\odot)}$$

$$= \frac{(1+e)^2}{(1-e)^2} \frac{(r_\odot - r_{ap})}{(r_{peri} - r_\odot)} \tag{13.90}$$

Now we try to obtain $r_\odot$ in terms of r_{ap}.

$$\frac{r_{ap}}{r_{peri}} = \frac{a(1-e)}{a(1+e)} \tag{13.91}$$

$$\frac{(r_\odot - r_{ap})}{(r_{peri} - r_\odot)} = \frac{t_{ap}}{t_{peri}} \frac{(1-e)^2}{(1+e)^2} = k$$

$$(r_\odot - r_{ap}) = k\left(\frac{(1+e)}{(1-e)} r_{ap} - r_\odot\right)$$

$$(1+k)r_\odot = \left(\frac{(1+e)}{(1-e)} k + 1\right) r_{ap} \tag{13.92}$$

Evaluating

$$k = \frac{12.5}{7.5} \times \frac{(1-0.0549)^2}{(1+0.0549)^2}$$

$$= 1.667 \times (0.8959)^2$$

$$k = 1.3378 \tag{13.93}$$

$$r_\odot = \left(\frac{\left(0.8959^{-1} \times 1.3378 + 1\right)}{(1.3378 + 1)}\right) r_{ap} \tag{13.94}$$

$$r_\odot = 1.0665 r_{ap} \tag{13.95}$$

Now, for an elliptical orbit, we find θ for which $r_\odot = r$.

$$d_\theta = \frac{a(1-e^2)}{1 - e\cos\theta} \tag{13.96}$$

$$d_{ap} r_{ap} = d_\theta r_\odot \tag{13.97}$$

$$a(1+e)r_{ap} = \frac{a(1-e)(1+e)}{1 - e\cos\theta} 1.0665 r_{ap}$$

$$1 - e\cos\theta = 1.0665(1 - e)$$

$$\cos\theta = -(0.0549) - 1(0.0665 - 1.0665e)$$

$$= -0.145 \tag{13.98}$$

Thus, annular eclipses will take place for about 98° orbit on either side of apogee. Our assumption here is that the Moon's orbit is in the same plane as the Earth's. As the eccentricity of the Moon's orbit is small, we make a further approximation by assuming average ω throughout the motion. Thus, the ratio of the number of eclipses

$$\frac{f_A}{f_T} \approx \frac{\Delta\theta_A}{\Delta\theta_T} \tag{13.99}$$

$$\approx \frac{98.32}{\left(180 - 98.32\right)} \tag{13.100}$$

$$\approx 1.2 \tag{13.101}$$

EA: The assumption in the last part (constant ω) is a poor one. However, calculating the area swept will require the use of calculus and hence will be deemed beyond the scope of this book. We note that the Moon will move slower near apogee and faster near perigee. Hence this estimate is a lower end estimate.

Inclination of the Moon's orbit, positions of its nodes and precession of its nodes will complicate the calculation further.

13.2 Data Analysis

1. From the figures of the Moon's phases, we see that the Moon is almost full on 10 June as well as on 11 June. Thus, we can conclude that the full moon occurs on 11 June (± 0.5 days) 2006. We are going to use this full moon as the reference for calculating the Moon's age on Albert Einstein's birthday (14 March 1879).

   Approximate time span between 11 June 2006 and 14 March 1879 is 127 years. There are 31 leap years between the two years.

   So, there are $365 \times 127 + 31 = 46{,}386$ days from 1 January 2006 to 1 January 1879. As a result, there are 46,475 days starting from 11 June 2006 to 14 March 1879.

   Thus, the number of lunar months will be

   $$N = \frac{46475}{29.5306} = 1573.79 \tag{13.102}$$

   This means 1573 lunar months and $0.79 \times 29.5306 = 23.37$ days. As we are going backwards in time, this means 23 and half days before full moon.

   $$p = \frac{29.5306 \times 3}{2} - 23.37 = 44.30 - 23.37 = 20.93 \tag{13.103}$$

   That is, 8.6 days before the new moon or 20.9 days since last the new moon.

   We note that our first assumption of the exact date of the full moon is accurate only to ± 0.5 days. Errors in other quantities taken in this calculation are much smaller. Hence, the error in our answer will also be about ± 0.5 days.

   Thus, the Moon's age on Albert Einstein's birthday (14 March 1879) is 20.9 ± 0.5 days.

2. (a) Examine Fig. 13.5. In this figure, the Sun–Earth distance is taken as r_e, the Sun–Venus distance is taken as r_v and the Earth–Venus distance is taken as Δ. In the figure on the right, the circle represents Venus as seen from the top. Earth is in the direction of $L\left(\overrightarrow{KL}\right)$. The Sun is in the direction of $\left(\overrightarrow{OP}\right)$. Thus, Region IOJKN will be dark and the other half will be illuminated. Region MONILPM will be visible from the Earth.

   $$\angle SVE = \angle LOP$$

   $$= \angle ION \tag{13.104}$$

   $$= \angle OIQ \tag{13.105}$$

To obtain $\angle ION$, we have to convert phase information (which gives the illuminated area as a percentage) to angle. We can imagine the illuminated area as an addition of half-circle and half-ellipse (see the middle picture of Fig. 13.5). For the circular part, the radius is r and for elliptical part, the semi-major and semi-minor axes are given by r and r', respectively. From the figure on the right

$$l(\overline{OI}) = r$$

$$l(\overline{IQ}) = r'$$

$$\therefore \qquad r' = r\cos \angle SVE \qquad (13.106)$$

$$A_{illu} = \frac{\pi r^2}{2} + \frac{\pi r r'}{2} \qquad (13.107)$$

$$A_{tot} = \pi r^2 \qquad (13.108)$$

$$\text{phase} = \frac{A_{illu}}{A_{tot}} = \left(\frac{\frac{\pi r^2}{2} + \frac{\pi r r'}{2}}{\pi r^2} \right) \times 100 \qquad (13.109)$$

$$= \left(\frac{\frac{\pi r^2}{2} + \frac{\pi r^2 \cos(\angle SVE)}{2}}{\pi r^2} \right) \times 100$$

$$= \frac{100(1 + \cos(\angle SVE))}{2}$$

$$= 100\cos^2\left(\frac{\angle SVE}{2}\right)$$

$$\angle SVE = 2\cos^{-1}\left(\frac{\sqrt{\text{phase}}}{10}\right) \qquad (13.110)$$

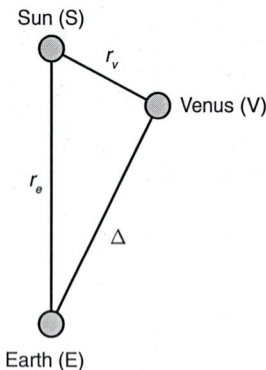

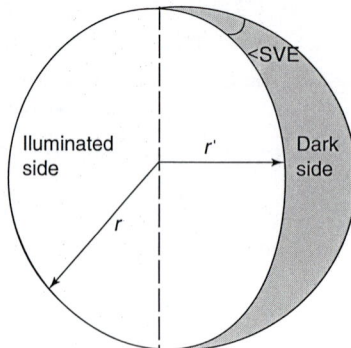

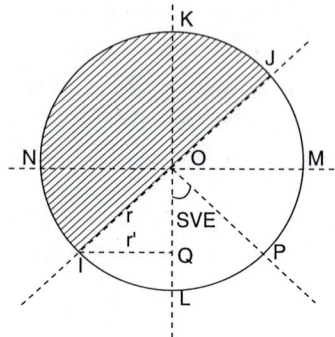

Fig. 13.5   *Venus phase geometry*

We use this equation to obtain values of $\angle SVE$ for each value of the phase given in Table 3.2. The values are listed in column 2 of Table 13.1.

(b) Using the sine rule in $\triangle SEV$, we realize that

$$\frac{r_e}{\sin(\angle SVE)} = \frac{r_v}{\sin(\angle SVE)}$$

$$r_v = \frac{r_e \sin(\angle SEV)}{\sin(\angle SEV)} \tag{13.111}$$

With the help of this equation, we compute the Sun–Venus distance as listed in column 3 of Table 13.1.

(c) Column 1 and column 3 of Table 13.1 are plotted in Fig. 13.6.

(d) From the graph in Fig. 13.6, we get

$$r_{v\,max} = 0.728 \text{AU} \tag{13.112}$$

$$r_{v\,min} = 0.718 \text{AU} \tag{13.113}$$

(e) Semi-major axis is

$$a = \frac{(r_{v\,max} + r_{v\,min})}{2} = 0.723 \text{AU} \tag{13.114}$$

(f) Eccentricity could be calculated from both aphelion and perihelion distances as

$$e = \frac{(r_{v\,max} - r_{v\,min})}{2a} = 0.00612 \tag{13.115}$$

Table 13.1   *Venus computations*

Date	$\angle SVE$	r_v
20/09/08	39.825	0.7255
10/10/08	47.156	0.7276
20/10/08	50.802	0.7283
30/10/08	54.549	0.7284
09/11/08	58.264	0.7283
19/11/08	62.095	0.7281
29/11/08	66.172	0.7268
19/12/08	74.811	0.7245
29/12/08	79.630	0.7230
18/01/09	90.573	0.7206
07/02/09	104.833	0.7188
17/02/09	114.079	0.7184
27/02/09	125.591	0.7186
19/03/09	157.518	0.7211

Venus orbit

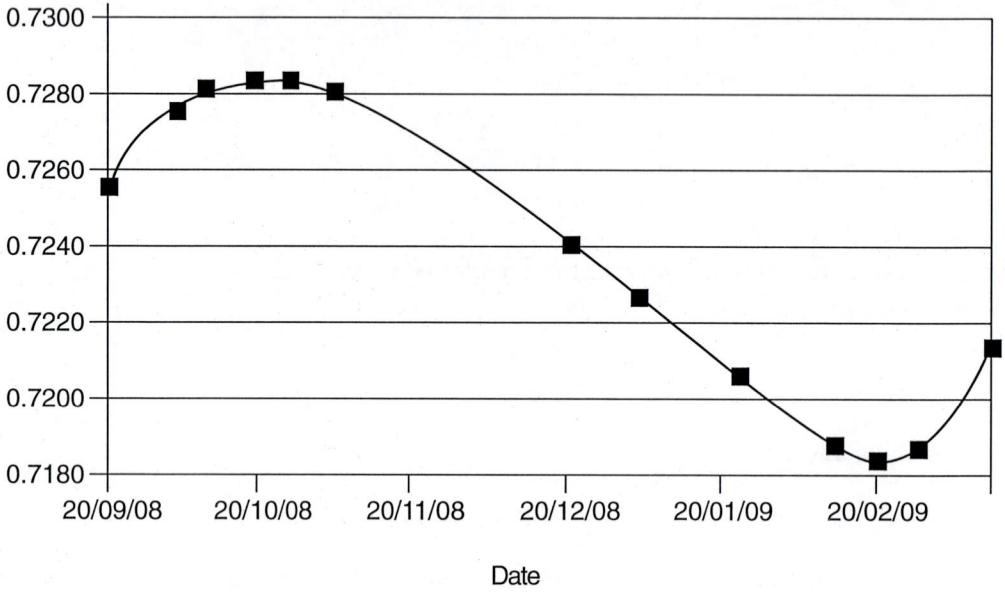

Fig. 13.6   *Venus FWMH*

14

Solutions: Optics and Detectors

14.1 Theory

1. Let us say that diametrically opposite points on the said crater subtend an angle ϕ at our eye. If the minimum separation between these two points to make them resolvable is x, then

$$\phi \geq 1.22 \frac{\lambda}{D_{eye}} \tag{14.1}$$

$$\phi = \frac{x}{\text{Distance from the Earth to the Moon}} = \frac{x}{d_M} \tag{14.2}$$

$$\therefore \qquad x \geq \frac{1.22 \lambda d_M}{D_{eye}} = \frac{1.22 \times 6 \times 10^{-7} \times 3.78 \times 10^8}{6 \times 10^{-3}}$$

$$\approx 46 \text{ km} \tag{14.3}$$

As this is less than 80 km, the said crater can be resolved. Alternatively

$$\phi \geq 1.22 \frac{\lambda}{D_{eye}}$$

$$\text{L. H. S} = \phi = \frac{80 \text{ km}}{d_M}$$

$$= \frac{80 \times 10^3 \text{ km}}{3.78 \times 10^8 \text{ m}} = 2.11 \times 10^{-4} \text{ rad} \tag{14.4}$$

$$\text{R. H. S} = 1.22 \frac{\lambda}{D_{eye}}$$

$$= \frac{1.22 \times 6 \times 10^{-7}}{6 \times 10^{-3}} = 1.22 \times 10^{-4} \text{ rad} \tag{14.5}$$

Thus, the inequality is true and it is possible to resolve the 80-km-diameter crater with the naked eye. Note the particular choice of wavelength which makes the calculations easier.

2. Since the resolution of both the telescopes is the same

$$1.22 \frac{\lambda_1}{D_1} = 1.22 \frac{\lambda_2}{D_2}$$

$$D_2 = \frac{D_1 \lambda_2}{\lambda_1} \tag{14.6}$$

$$= \frac{0.1 \times 0.01}{5 \times 10^{-7}}$$

$$= 2 \text{ km} \tag{14.7}$$

Answers may vary slightly depending on your choice of optical wavelength. For this reason, the final answer is rounded to a single significant digit.

3. A 5 AU orbital radius around some star 1 pc away would subtend an angle of 5″ at the Earth. Thus, for a planetary system 250 pc away

$$\theta = \frac{\angle 5''}{250} = \frac{1}{50 \cdot 206265} \text{rad}$$

$$\theta = 9.70 \approx 10^{-8} \text{ rad} \tag{14.8}$$

$$\therefore \qquad D = 1.22 \frac{\lambda}{\theta} = \frac{1.22 \times 5 \times 10^{-7}}{9.70 \times 10^{-8}}$$

$$D \approx 6 \text{ m} \tag{14.9}$$

4. One should use the angular size of the galactic black hole to find the resolution.

$$\theta_{BH} = \frac{\text{Diameter of event horizon}}{\text{Distance to galactic centre}} = \frac{2R_{BH}}{d_{GC}} \tag{14.10}$$

$$\theta_{tel} = \frac{1.22\lambda}{\text{Diameter of the Earth}} = \frac{1.22\lambda}{2R_\oplus} \tag{14.11}$$

$$\theta_{BH} \geq \theta_{tel} \tag{14.12}$$

$$\frac{2R_{BH}}{d_{GC}} \geq \frac{1.22\lambda}{2R_\oplus}$$

$$\lambda \leq \frac{4R_{BH}R_\oplus}{1.22 d_{GC}} \tag{14.13}$$

$$\leq \frac{12 M_{BH} R_\oplus}{1.22 d_{GC} M_\odot}$$

$$\leq \frac{12 \times 4 \times 10^9 \times 6.371 \times 10^6}{1.22 \times 8.3 \times 10^3 \times 3.086 \times 10^{16}}$$

$$\lambda \leq 0.98 \text{ mm} \tag{14.14}$$

$$\lambda \leq 0.9 \text{ mm} \tag{14.15}$$

This means that we need to observe in sub-mm wavelengths, which is in the radio or far-infrared band. We have rounded the limit on λ to 0.9 mm instead of 1.0 mm as the answer is in terms of an inequality. Thus, we must respect the direction of inequality.

5. Let us assume the Moon is at the maximum possible separation from the ecliptic plane. We know that the displacement of the Earth and Moon are inversely proportional to their mass. Let us call the distance between the Earth and the Moon as d_m, semi-amplitude of

the Earth's oscillation as x and distance between the centre of the Earth and barycentre of the Earth–Moon system as y.

$$\frac{x}{y} = \tan 5.14° \tag{14.16}$$

$$M_\oplus y = M_m \left(d_m - y\right) \tag{14.17}$$

$$\therefore \quad y = \frac{M_m d_m}{M_\oplus + M_m} \tag{14.18}$$

$$x = \frac{M_m d_m}{M_\oplus + M_m} \tan 5.14° \tag{14.19}$$

$$= \frac{7.4377 \times 10^{22} \times 3.78 \times 10^8}{\left(597.36 + 7.4377\right) \cdot 10^{22}} \times 0.0900$$

$$= 4.248 \times 10^5 \, \text{m} \tag{14.20}$$

$$\therefore \quad 2x = 849.6 \, \text{km} \tag{14.21}$$

Note that points L_4 or L_5 are at exactly 1 AU distance from the Earth. Also note that the resolution of the telescope improves with decreasing wavelength. As the telescope is capable of observing in near-UV, we will use a reasonable wavelength in the near-UV range (say 350 nm) to determine the smallest possible diameter.

$$\alpha \geq \frac{2x}{d_{L4}} = 1.22 \frac{\lambda}{D} \tag{14.22}$$

$$\therefore \quad D \geq \frac{1.22 d_{L4} \lambda}{2x}$$

$$\geq \frac{1.22 \times 1.496 \times 10^{11} \times 350 \times 10^{-9}}{2 \times 4.248 \times 10^5}$$

$$D \geq 7.5 \, \text{cm} \tag{14.23}$$

6 (a) We note that the longest separation one can fit on a CCD in a single frame would be along the diagonal of the CCD.

$$S = \sqrt{756^2 + 510^2} \times 9 \mu\text{m} \tag{14.24}$$

$$= 919.4 \times 9 \, \mu\text{m} \approx 8.27 \, \text{mm} \tag{14.25}$$

$$f = 10780 \, \text{mm} \tag{14.26}$$

$$\theta = \frac{S}{f} = \frac{206\,265'' \times 8.27}{10780} \tag{14.27}$$

$$= 158.3'' = 2.64' \tag{14.28}$$

As the two stars are very close to each other, one can approximate the situation to plane geometry. Hence, the angular separation between them is

$$\gamma = \sqrt{\Delta\alpha^2 + \Delta\delta^2} \tag{14.29}$$

$$\therefore \quad \Delta\alpha = 20^\text{h}18^\text{m}03^\text{s}.3 - 20^\text{h}17^\text{m}38^\text{s}.9 = 0^\text{m}24^\text{s}.4 \tag{14.30}$$

$$\therefore \qquad \Delta\delta = -12°32'41" + 12°30'30" = -2'11" \tag{14.31}$$

$$\therefore \qquad \gamma = \sqrt{\left(\left(0^m24^s.4\right)\times15^2\right)+\left(-2'11"\right)^2} \tag{14.32}$$

$$= \sqrt{(366")^2+(-131")^2}$$

$$\approx 389" \tag{14.33}$$

This is much larger than 158.3". Thus, the stars will not fit in a single frame.

One can also make an even simpler argument of simply noting that the separation in RA (24^s.40) itself is bigger than the CCD diagonal. It should be noted that plane trigonometry works only for stars that are reasonably close to each other. For other cases, spherical trigonometry must be used.

(b) To find the position angle, we note that the secondary star is towards the southwest of the primary star. As position angle (ϕ) is measured from the north in anti-clockwise fashion, we expect the value to be between 90° and 180°.

$$\phi = \tan^{-1}\left(\frac{\Delta\alpha}{\Delta\delta}\right) \tag{14.34}$$

$$= \tan^{-1}\left(\frac{366"}{131"}\right) = \tan^{-1}2.794 \tag{14.35}$$

$$\approx 109°42' \tag{14.36}$$

7. The light beam arriving from Vega can be considered paraxial, due to the distance from it to the observer on the Earth. As the star is not along the optical axis of the lens, in the absence of any mirror, all rays would concentrate at point Σ_1. Now, the mirror reflects some of these rays and we get a second image Σ_2. This is shown in Fig. 14.1 (left). Effectively, all rays within the unshaded region contribute to Σ_2, whereas rays within the shaded region contribute to Σ_1.

If we visualise the circular beam incident on the lens, the same picture would correspond to Fig.14.1 (right). The ratio between the light fluxes concentrated into the two image points will directly depend on the ratio of the two sectors areas. As triangle MOC and triangle $MN\Sigma_1$ are similar

$$OC = \frac{r}{2}$$

$$\therefore \qquad \angle CBO = 30° \tag{14.37}$$

$$\angle BOC = 60°$$

$$\angle AOB = 120°$$

$$\therefore \qquad \frac{S_2}{S_1} = \frac{\frac{\pi}{3}r^2 - \frac{1}{2}\times\frac{r}{2}\times\sqrt{3}r}{\frac{2\pi}{3}r^2 + \frac{1}{2}\times\frac{r}{2}\times\sqrt{3}r} \tag{14.38}$$

$$= \frac{\frac{\pi}{3}-\frac{\sqrt{3}}{4}}{\frac{\pi}{3}+\frac{\sqrt{3}}{4}}$$

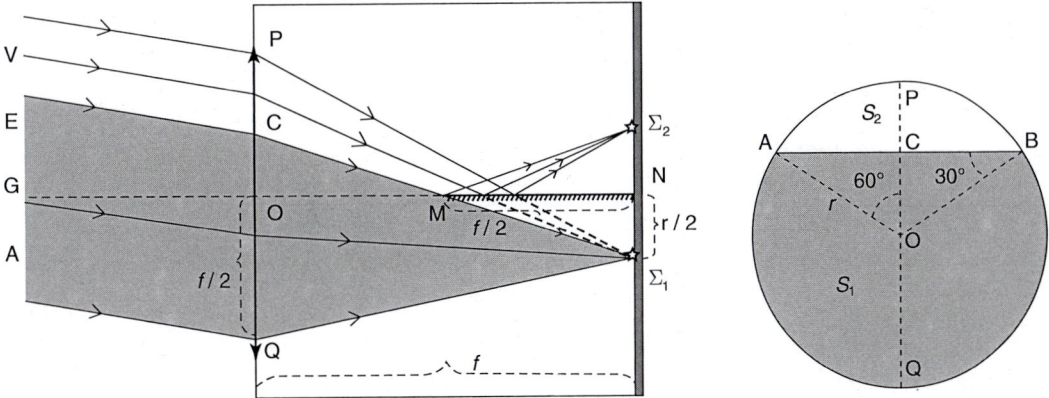

Fig. 14.1 *Light beam from Vega*

$$\approx 0.243$$

$\therefore$

$$m_{\Sigma_2} - m_{\Sigma_1} = -2.5 \log\left(\frac{S_2}{S_1}\right)$$

$$= -2.5 \log 0.243$$

$$m_{\Sigma_2} - m_{\Sigma_1} = 1.536 \tag{14.39}$$

8. We first find the image scale of the picture in arcseconds per mm. The focal ratio of the telescope is the ratio of its aperture and focal length. Thus

$$S = \frac{206\,265''}{f} = \frac{206\,265''}{D/F} \tag{14.40}$$

$$= \frac{206\,265'' F}{D} = \frac{206\,265''}{100} \times \frac{1}{15}$$

$$= 137.51''/\text{mm} \tag{14.41}$$

Thus, we can obtain the angular diameter and then, by dividing the physical diameter by the angular diameter, the distance can be obtained.

$$\theta_\odot = 137.51 \times 13.817 \tag{14.42}$$

$$= 1900.0'' = 31'40'' \tag{14.43}$$

$$d_\odot = \frac{2R_\odot}{\theta_\odot} = \frac{2 \times 6.955 \times 10^8 \times 180}{(31'40'') \times \pi} \tag{14.44}$$

$$= 1.510 \times 10^{11}\ \text{m} \tag{14.45}$$

$$\theta_{moon} = 137.51 \times 13.235 \tag{14.46}$$

$$= 1820.0'' = 30'20'' \tag{14.47}$$

$$d_{moon} = \frac{2R_{moon}}{\theta_{moon}} = \frac{2 \times 1.7374 \times 10^6 \times 180}{(30'20'') \times \pi} \tag{14.48}$$

$$= 3.772 \times 10^8\ \text{m} \tag{14.49}$$

The percentage of the solar disk covered by the Moon is

$$\left(\frac{13.235}{13.817}\right)^2 \times 100\% = 91.75\% \tag{14.50}$$

9. The focal length of the telescope is $f = 10 \times 0.1 = 1$ m. Next, we find the angular distance (on the solar disk) of the active region from the centre of the disk. Using the cosine rule for a spherical triangle

$$\alpha = \cos^{-1}(\cos 40°\cos 8°) \tag{14.51}$$

$$= 40°40' \tag{14.52}$$

The tangential plane of the active region is inclined at 40°40" to the normal plane. Let $\theta_{1,2}$ be the angular diameters of the active region seen from the Earth and let S be its size seen on CCD. Let $d_{1,2}$ be the actual size and A denote the area of the active region.

$$S = (5 \times 4) \times 9 \ \mu m \times 9 \ \mu m$$

$$S = 45 \ \mu m \times 36 \ \mu m \tag{14.53}$$

$$S = f\theta \tag{14.54}$$

$$\theta = \frac{45 \mu m \times 36 \mu m}{1m}$$

$$= (45 \times 36) \times 10^{-6} \ \text{rad} \tag{14.55}$$

$$\theta_{1,2} = \frac{d_{1,2}\cos\alpha}{d_\odot} \tag{14.56}$$

Also

$$\frac{32' \times 60}{206\,265"} = \frac{2R_\odot}{d_\odot} \tag{14.57}$$

$$d_{1,2} = \frac{\theta_1 \times \theta_2 \times 2R_\odot \times 206\,265"}{32' \times 60 \times \cos\alpha}$$

$$= \frac{(45 \times 36) \times 10^{-6}}{960 \times 0.7585} R_\odot$$

$$= (0.0127 \ R_\odot \times 0.0102 \ R_\odot)$$

$$A = (0.0127 \times 0.0102) R_\odot^2 \tag{14.59}$$

Area of hemisphere

$$2\pi R_\odot^2 \tag{14.60}$$

$$\frac{A}{A_{hemi}} = \frac{0.0127 \times 0.0102}{2\pi}$$

$$= 0.00002069 \approx 20.69 \ \text{msh} \tag{14.61}$$

Thus, the area of the active region is 20.69 msh.

14.2 Data Analysis

1. We calculate the angular distance, φ, between two bright stars of Ursa Major. To minimise the error while converting the angular distance to length scale in the photograph, it is preferable to choose pairs of stars with larger angular separation. To further improve the estimate, we take five such pairs and obtain their mean.

   Angular distance can be estimated using the cosine rule.

   $$\varphi = \cos^{-1}(\sin\delta_1 \sin\delta_2 + \cos\delta_1 \cos\delta_2 \cos(\alpha_1 - \alpha_2)) \tag{14.62}$$

Table 14.1 *Focal length estimation for different pairs of stars*

Pair of stars	$\Delta\theta$	Δl (mm)	$\Delta l S_{enlarge}$ (mm)	f (mm)
$\alpha-\eta$	25.7088°	100	15.70	68.80
$\beta-\eta$	25.5648°	100	15.70	69.20
$\alpha-\zeta$	19.3359°	75	11.78	69.12
$\beta-\zeta$	19.8694°	78	12.25	69.92
$\beta-\in$	15.5114°	61	9.58	70.32

Then we measure the corresponding distance on the image (Δl) using a ruler. This image size (as in the IOAA13 printed question paper) is 17.0 mm × 22.0 mm. The ratio of CCD size and image size will give the conversion factor from the angular distance to the image. However, the size of image is not the same as the size of the CCD. We measure the total size of the image and compare it with the size of the CCD to obtain the enlargement factor as

$$S_{enlarge} = \frac{\dfrac{\text{CCD length}}{\text{Image length}} + \dfrac{\text{CCD width}}{\text{Image width}}}{2} \tag{14.63}$$

$$= \frac{\dfrac{22.0}{140} + \dfrac{17.0}{108}}{2}$$

$$= \frac{0.1571 + 0.1574}{2}$$

$$= (0.157 \pm 0.002) \tag{14.64}$$

Using this enlargement factor, we find the final scaling factor between the angular distance and the CCD length scale. The focal length of the optical device will be given by

$$f = \frac{\Delta l * S_{enlarge}}{2 \tan \frac{\varphi}{2}} \tag{14.65}$$

See Table 14. 1 summarising the calculations. Thus, mean focal length would be

$$f = \frac{68.80 + 69.20 + 69.12 + 70.32}{5}$$

$$f = (70.0 \pm 0.4) \text{ mm} \tag{14.66}$$

Note: The error in the final answer is calculated as $\sqrt{5}\Delta f_i$, where Δf_i is the error in each estimation of the focal length, which is approximately the same.

2. (a) Refer to Fig. 14.2. Five bright stars are marked in the map. Note that as compared to the photograph, the map is rotated by 90° counter-clockwise.

(b) The boundaries of the photograph are drawn on Fig. 14.2. By measuring the field size using a measuring scale and converting it as per the coordinates of the grid, we find out that the size of field is about 26 arcminutes. Note that declination of the point at the centre of the field is roughly 7°. Strictly speaking, we have to correct the field size measured along the RA by the $\cos \delta$ factor. But, our placement of field boundaries is only approximate and based on visual estimation. Thus, for such a small declination, we can ignore the declination correction. One can check that the field size measured along the declination is also the same within the error bars.

(c) One can find the physical size of a CCD chip and hence the size of each pixel.

$$s = f\theta$$

$$= \frac{3.180 \times 26' \times 60}{206\,265''} \tag{14.67}$$

$$s = 24.1 \text{ mm} \tag{14.68}$$

$$\therefore \qquad s_{px} = \frac{24.1}{1024}$$

$$s_{px} \approx 23 \ \mu\text{m} \tag{14.69}$$

(d) From the images, we can see that the size of the star is roughly 10 pixels. This is 3.5 times the original FWHM (full width at half maximum). Thus, the original FWHM of the star is slightly smaller than 3 pixels. Now, as the field size of 26 arcminutes corresponds to 1024 pixels

$$\theta_{px} = \frac{26' \times 60}{1024} \approx 1.5'' \tag{14.70}$$

Thus, three pixels will correspond to about 4.5". This is the size of the seeing disk.

(e) Theoretical diameter of the diffraction disc will be

$$\theta_{diff} = \frac{2 \times 1.22\lambda}{D} \approx \frac{2.44 \times 5 \times 10^{-7} \times 206\,265''}{0.61} = 0.4'' \tag{14.71}$$

Thus, diffraction limit (0.4") is much smaller than the seeing disk.

(f) If seeing was 1", the FWHM would be roughly two-thirds of a pixel. Thus, if we increase contrast 3.5 times, the disk will appear to be about 3 pixels wide.

(g) We have to calculate the velocity of both the objects. For object 1, one can simply measure the length of the trail (in arcseconds) during the exposure time. For the second object, we have to measure the motion of its centre in number of pixels in the given time difference between two photos.

Object 1:

$$l \approx 107'' \tag{14.72}$$

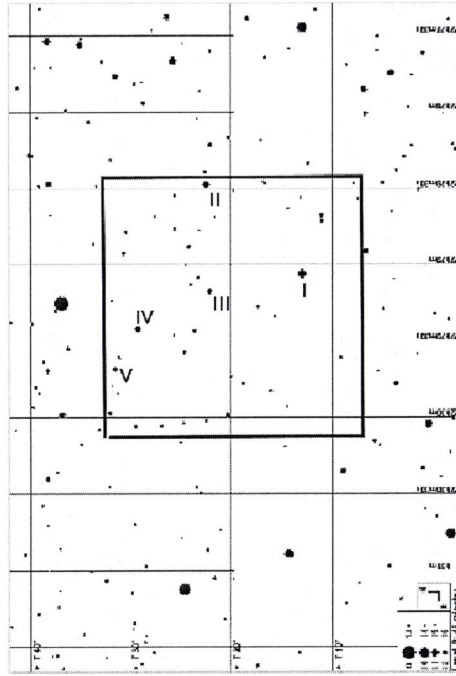

Fig. 14.2 Sky map with region of the sky and bright stars marked *Hydrae*

$\therefore$

$$\omega_1 = \frac{l}{t} = \frac{107''}{300} \approx 0.36''s^{-1}$$

$$\omega_1 = 1.73 \times 10^{-6} \text{rad s}^{-1} \tag{14.73}$$

Object 2:

$$\omega_2 = \frac{\text{pixel} \times \theta_{px}}{\Delta t} \tag{14.74}$$

$$= \frac{8 \times 1.5}{17^m 27^s} = 0.011''s^{-1}$$

$$\omega_2 = 5.6 \times 10^{-8} \text{ rad s}^{-1} \tag{14.75}$$

We convert these angular velocities to physical velocities at some sample distances. Let us consider two sample cases. In the first case the asteriod is going around the Earth with an orbit similar to the lunar orbit. The second sample case, is of an asteriod inside the asteriod belt going around the Sun with orbital radius of about 2 AU, i.e., about 1 AU away from the Earth.

Case	Typical Velocity	Object 1	Object 2
Around Earth	1 km/s	0.6 km/s	20 m/s
Around Sun	20 km/s	259 km/s	8.5 km/s

From the table it is clear that object 1 is most likely close to the Earth and is likely to be under the gravitational influence of the Earth. Object 2 is most likely to be an asteriod orbiting the Sun and is far from the Earth. Thus, the probable causes of different angular velocities are different orbital velocities and different distances from the Earth.

3. This problem closely simulates the process of converting a CCD reading to the magnitudes of stars. At the beginning, we notice that there are five regions with high pixel count. These are clearly the stars. The rest of the field is empty sky. The problem explicitly states that we should approximate the stars as squares. We can see that different stars have different sizes. The biggest of these (star 3) can be properly included in a 5×5 pixel square.

    We must realise that even dark sky gives us some non-zero pixel count. So the total pixel count of the square containing the stars also includes this contribution from overall sky brightness. To obtain the flux of the star, we have to subtract total pixel count from the equivalent area of the dark sky. As the pixel count in the dark sky appears random, we should measure pixel counts from squares over the dark sky at more than one place and then use the average. Now, if we take different square sizes for different stars, we will compound our difficulty as we have to measure the total count from the dark sky separately for each square size. Thus, for the sake of convenience, it makes sense to use square of the same size for all the stars. One should not be concerned about dark sky pixels getting included in the square as those contributions will automatically be subtracted when we subtract the average count of the dark sky.

    As mentioned above, we should take the minimum size of the square as 5×5 pixels. We can even opt for a bigger square, but it will unnecessarily increase our labour. Further, as we want the centre of the star to be at the centre of our square, the side of the square should be taken as an odd number. Thus, the choice is restricted to 5×5 pixels (correct size), 3×3 pixels (too small) or 7×7 pixels (too large).

    (a) We take five random 5×5 pixel squares of dark sky. Each region should be relatively far from any of the stars in the field. We obtain the counts as 121, 113, 115, 123 and 113. The average of these five counts is 117 (for 25 pixels).

    We note that instrumental magnitude (m_I) is the log of the flux received from the star. Now, when we talk about stellar magnitude, it is implicitly assumed that the integration time for the flux is of the order of 1 second. However, in this image, the CCD was exposed for 450 seconds. Thus

$$m_I = -2.5 \log \left(\frac{count_{st} - count_{sky}}{t_{exp}} \right) \tag{14.76}$$

Star	$count_{st}$	$count_{st} - count_{sky}$	m_I	m_t
1	7389	7272	−3.021	9.03
2	3313	3196	−2.128	−
3	98520	98403	−5.849	6.22
4	18668	18551	−4.083	8.02
5	949	832	−0.667	−

    (b) We correct for exinction next.

$$m_I = m_t + KX - Z_{mag}$$

$$Z_{mag_1} = m_{t_1} - m_{I_1} + KX$$

$$= 9.03 - (-3.02) + 0.3 \times \sec(25°)$$

$$= 9.03 + 3.02 + 0.3 \times 1.10$$

$$= 12.05 + 0.33$$

$$Z_{max_1} = 12.38 \tag{14.77}$$

$$\therefore \quad Z_{max_3} = 12.40 \tag{14.78}$$

$$\therefore \quad Z_{max_4} = 12.39 \tag{14.79}$$

Average Z_{mag} is therefore 12.39.

(c) For stars 2 and 5, we can calculate true magnitudes (m_t).

$$m_I = m_t + KX - Z_{mag}$$

$$\therefore \quad m_t = m_I - KX + Z_{mag}$$

$$m_{t_2} = -2.13 - 0.33 + 12.39$$

$$m_{t_2} = 9.93 \tag{14.80}$$

$$m_{t_5} = -0.67 - 0.33 + 12.39$$

$$m_{t_5} = 11.39 \tag{14.81}$$

(d) Pixel scale for this CCD is calculated

$$S = f\theta \tag{14.82} \text{ as}$$

$$\theta = \frac{25 \times 10^{-6} \times 206\,265''}{1.2}$$

$$= 4.3'' \tag{14.83}$$

(e) Average sky brightness of the dark sky is measured as magnitude per square arcseconds. As sky brightness is an isotropic intensity perceived by the observer, we need not worry about atmospheric extinction.

$$S_{sky} = m_{sky} + 2.5 \log A \tag{14.84}$$

$$= -2.5 \log \left(\frac{count_{sky}}{25 t_{exp}} \right) + Z_{mag} + 2.5 \log \theta^2$$

$$= -2.5 \log \left(\frac{count_{sky}}{25 t_{exp} \theta^2} \right) + Z_{mag} \tag{14.85}$$

$$= -2.5 \log \left(\frac{117}{25 \times 450 \times 4.3^2} \right) + 12.39$$

$$S_{sky} = 20.5 \,\text{mag/arcsec}^2 \tag{14.86}$$

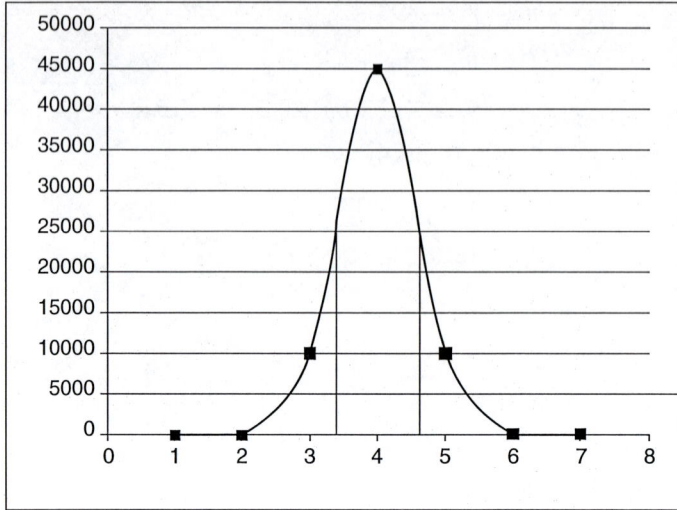

Fig. 14.3   Astronomical seeing

(f) To estimate astronomical seeing, we must know the FWHM size of the stellar disk. First, we plot pixel values along the vertical line as well as the horizontal line for one of the bright stars in the image. As Fig. 14.3 shows, the FWHM of pixel values which is plotted for star 3 is 1 pixel; hence, the astronomical seeing is equal to pixel scale $\cong 4''$.

We should not estimate seeing in terms of a fractional number of pixels as that is not physically possible.

15

Solutions: Physics of Stars and Planets

15.1 Theory

1. From Wien's displacement law

$$\lambda_{max} = \frac{2.898 \times 10^{-3}}{4000} \text{ m} \tag{15.1}$$

$$\lambda_{max} = 724.5 \text{ nm} \tag{15.2}$$

2. By Wien's law

$$T = \frac{0.002898}{\lambda_{max}} \tag{15.3}$$

$$= \frac{0.2898}{5 \times 10^{-7}} = 5800 \text{ K}$$

$$\approx 6000 \text{ K} \tag{15.4}$$

The temperature is rounded as the peak wavelength has only one significant digit.

3. From the Stefan–Boltzmann law

$$L = \sigma \, AT^4 = \sigma(4\pi R^2)T^4 \tag{15.5}$$

$$\therefore \quad \frac{L}{L_\odot} = \frac{R^2 T^4}{R_\odot^2 T_\odot^4} = \left(\frac{R}{R_\odot}\right)^2 \left(\frac{L}{L_\odot}\right)^4$$

$$= (2.5)^2 \left(\frac{7500}{5778}\right)^4 = 17.43$$

$$\therefore \quad L \approx 17 \, L_\odot \tag{15.6}$$

4. $$\quad L_1 = 4\pi\sigma R_1^2 T_1^4 \tag{15.7}$$

$$L_2 = 4\pi\sigma R_2^2 T_2^4$$

$$m_2 - m_1 = \Delta m = 2.5 \, \log\left(\frac{L_1}{L_2}\right) \tag{15.8}$$

$$2 = 2.5 \, \log\left(\frac{4\pi\sigma R_1^2 T_1^4}{4\pi\sigma R_2^2 T_2^4}\right)$$

$$2 = 5 \log\left(\frac{R_1 T_1^2}{R_2 T_2^2}\right) \tag{15.9}$$

$$\therefore \qquad \frac{R_1 T_1^2}{R_2 T_2^2} = 10^{0.4} \tag{15.10}$$

$$\frac{R_1}{R_2} = 2.512 \left(\frac{T_2}{T_1}\right)^2 \tag{15.11}$$

As both the stars are on the main sequence, we can assume that the star with the higher temperature is the brighter star. Thus, star 1 has the higher temperature.

$$\frac{R_1}{R_2} = 2.512 \left(\frac{5000}{6000}\right)^2 \tag{15.12}$$

$$\frac{R_1}{R_2} = 1.74 \tag{15.13}$$

5. The bolometric magnitude of the star remains constant, which means its luminosity remains constant. As stars can be approximated as black bodies

$$L_\star = 4\pi R_\star^2 \sigma T_\star^4 \tag{15.14}$$

$$4\pi R_1^2 \times \sigma T_1^4 = 4\pi R_2^2 \times \sigma T_2^4$$

$$R_1^2 T_1^4 = R_2^2 T_2^4$$

$$\frac{R_1}{R_2} = \frac{T_2^2}{T_1} \tag{15.15}$$

$$\frac{R_{5000K}}{R_{30000K}} = \left(\frac{30000}{5000}\right)^2$$

$$= 36 \tag{15.16}$$

6. As the escape velocity exceeds the speed of light

$$\sqrt{\frac{2GM_\odot}{R}} > c \tag{15.17}$$

$$R_{object} < \frac{2GM_\odot}{c^2} \tag{15.18}$$

$$R_{object} < \frac{2 \times 6.6726 \times 10^{-11} \times 1.9891 \times 10^{30}}{(2.9979 \times 10^8)^2}$$

$$R_{object} < 2953.6 \text{ m} \tag{15.19}$$

7. The radius of the event horizon is given by

$$R = \frac{2GM_\odot}{c^2} \tag{15.20}$$

$$R = \frac{2 \times 6.6726 \times 10^{-11} \times 1.9891 \times 10^{30}}{(2.9979 \times 10^8)^2} \, m$$

$$= 2953.6 \text{ m}$$

$$R = 2.9536 \text{ km} \tag{15.21}$$

8. The Schwarzschild radius of a black hole with mass M is $R = \dfrac{2GM}{c^2}$

$$\bar{\rho} = \frac{M}{V} = \frac{3M}{4\pi R_{sch}^3} \tag{15.22}$$

$$= \frac{3Mc^6}{4\pi(2GM)^3} = \frac{3c^6}{32\pi G^3 M^2}$$

$$= \frac{3\times(3\times10^8)^6}{32\pi(6.6726\times10^{-11})^3\times(10^8\times1.9891\times10^{30})^2}$$

$$= 1.85 \times 10^3 \text{ Kg/m}^3 \tag{15.23}$$

$$\approx 2 \times 10^3 \text{ Kg/m}^3 \tag{15.24}$$

It is interesting to note that this value is in fact lower than the mean density of the Earth. This occurs as all the mass of the black hole is concentrated at a single point in the centre and the rest of the region inside the event horizon is empty.

9. We can find mass defect by

$$\Delta m = 2M_{He_3} - M_{He} - 2M_H \tag{15.25}$$

$$= 2808.30 \times 2 - 3727.40 - 938.27 \times 2$$

$$\Delta m = 12.66 \text{ MeV/c}^2 \tag{15.26}$$

$$\therefore \qquad \frac{\Delta m}{2M_{He_3}} = \frac{12.66}{2\times2808.30}$$

$$\text{Mass Fraction} = 2.254 \times 10^{-3} = 0.2254\% \tag{15.27}$$

As masses are expressed in energy units, the energy released will be 12.66 MeV and mass fraction loss is 0.23%.

10. Since λ_1 and λ_2 both lie in the range

$$I(\lambda_1) = 1.1 I(\lambda_2)$$

$$\frac{2\pi hc^2}{\lambda_1^5\left(e^{\frac{hc}{\lambda_1 kT}} - 1\right)} = 1.1\frac{2\pi hc^2}{\lambda_2^5\left(e^{\frac{hc}{\lambda_2 kT}} - 1\right)} \tag{15.28}$$

$$\frac{2\pi hc^2}{\lambda_1^5\left(1 + \frac{hc}{\lambda_1 \kappa T} - 1\right)} = 1.1\frac{2\pi hc^2}{\lambda_2^5\left(1 + \frac{hc}{\lambda_2 \kappa T} - 1\right)} \qquad (\because e^x \approx 1 + x \text{ if } x \ll 1)$$

$$\left(\frac{\lambda_2}{\lambda_1}\right)^5 = 1.1\frac{\left(\frac{hc}{\lambda_1 \kappa T}\right)}{\left(\frac{hc}{\lambda_2 \kappa T}\right)}$$

$$= 1.1 \left(\frac{\lambda_2}{\lambda_1} \right)$$

$$\lambda_2^4 = 1.1 \lambda_1^4$$

$$\therefore \qquad \lambda_2 = \sqrt[4]{1.1} \lambda_1 \qquad (15.29)$$

EA: The original text of the problem specified the relation as $I(\lambda_1) = 2I(\lambda_2)$. However, in that case, the assumption $\Delta\lambda \ll \lambda$ is no longer valid.

11. The amount of energy emitted by the Sun per second will be

$$L_\odot = (\text{Area}) \times \sigma T_\odot^4$$

$$= 4\pi R_\odot^2 \sigma T_\odot^4 \qquad (15.30)$$

The amount of light received on the Earth will be given by

$$E_{\text{received}} = \frac{L_\odot R_\oplus^2}{4a_\oplus^2}$$

$$= 4\pi R_\odot^2 \sigma T_\odot^4 \times \frac{R_\oplus^2}{4a_\oplus^2} \qquad (15.31)$$

As the albedo is 0.39, it means that 39% of the energy will be be reflected back. The rest of the energy will be absorbed and, assuming the Stefan–Boltzmann law holds true for the Earth

$$(1 - \alpha)E_{\text{received}} = 4\pi R_\oplus^2 \sigma T_\oplus^4 \qquad (15.32)$$

$$(1 - \alpha)4\pi R_\odot^2 \sigma T_\odot^4 \times \frac{R_\oplus^2}{4a_\oplus^2} = 4\pi R_\oplus^2 \sigma T_\oplus^4$$

$$T_\oplus = T_\odot (1 - \alpha)^{\frac{1}{4}} \sqrt{\frac{R_\odot}{2a_\oplus}} \qquad (15.33)$$

$$= 5778 \times (1 - 0.39)^{\frac{1}{4}} \sqrt{\frac{6.955 \times 10^8}{2 \times 1.496 \times 10^{11}}}$$

$$= 246 \text{ K}$$

$$T_\oplus = -27°C \qquad (15.34)$$

12. The rate of energy radiated by the Sun $= \sigma 4\pi R_\odot^2 T_\odot^4$

Let d be the distance of the spaceship from the Sun.

Energy incident on the spaceship $= \dfrac{\sigma 4\pi R_\odot^2 T_\odot^4}{4\pi d^2} \pi R_N^2$

Energy emitted by the spaceship $= \sigma 4\pi R_N^2 T_N^4$

$$\therefore \qquad \frac{\sigma 4\pi R_\odot^2 T_\odot^4}{4\pi d^2} \pi R_N^2 = \sigma 4\pi R_N^2 T_N^4$$

$$4d^2 = \left(\frac{T_\odot}{T_N}\right)^4 \cdot R_\odot^2$$

$$d = \frac{R_\odot}{2}\left(\frac{T_\odot}{T_N}\right)^2 \tag{15.35}$$

$$m = m_\odot + 5\log\left(\frac{d}{a_\oplus}\right)$$

$$= m_\odot + 5\log\left(\frac{R_\odot}{2a_\oplus}\right) + 10\log\left(\frac{T_\odot}{T_N}\right) \tag{15.36}$$

$$\alpha = \frac{2R_\odot}{d}$$

$$= \frac{4R_\odot}{R_\odot}\left(\frac{T_N}{T_\odot}\right)^2$$

$$\therefore \qquad \alpha = \left(\frac{2T_N}{T_\odot}\right)^2 \tag{15.37}$$

13. As the Earth is in thermal equilibrium, the power of radiation received by the Earth from the Sun will be equal to the power transmitted by the Earth to outer space.

$$P_r = F_\odot A t_1 = \frac{L_\odot}{4\pi d_{\oplus-\odot}^2}\pi R_\oplus^2 t_1 \tag{15.38}$$

$$= \frac{4\pi R_\odot^2 \sigma T_\odot^4}{4\pi d_{\oplus-\odot}^2}\pi R_\oplus^2 t_1$$

$$P_r = \left(\frac{R_\odot R_\oplus}{d_{\oplus-\odot}}\right)^2 \pi\sigma T_\odot^4 t_1 \tag{15.39}$$

$$P_t = \sigma T_\oplus^4 4\pi R_\oplus^2 t_2 \tag{15.40}$$

$$P_t = P_r \tag{15.41}$$

$$\sigma T_\oplus^4 4\pi R_\oplus^2 t_2 = \left(\frac{R_\odot R_\oplus}{d_{\oplus-\odot}}\right)^2 \pi\sigma T_\odot^4 t_1$$

$$T_\oplus^4 = \left(\frac{R_\odot}{d_{\oplus-\odot}}\right)^2 \times \frac{t_1}{4t_2}T_\odot^4$$

$$T_\oplus = \sqrt{\frac{R_\odot}{2d_{\oplus-\odot}}}\sqrt{\frac{t_1}{t_2}}T_\odot \tag{15.42}$$

14. The mass of three helium nuclei $= 3 \times 4.002603$ amu $= 12.007809$ amu. The mass converted to energy is the difference between the sum of the masses of three helium nuclei and the mass of the resulting carbon nucleus:

$$12.007809 \text{ amu} - 12.000000 \text{ amu} = 7.809 \times 10^{-3} \text{ amu}$$

This represents a fractional loss of mass of the original mass.

$$m_{frac} = \frac{7.809 \times 10^{-3}}{12.007809} = 6.503 \times 10^{-4} \tag{15.43}$$

Let the stellar mass be M, luminosity L and helium-burning time t.

$$t = \frac{E}{0.3L} = \frac{\Delta mc^2}{0.3 \times 100 L_\odot} = \frac{M_{He} m_{frac} c^2}{30 L_\odot} \tag{15.44}$$

$$= \frac{0.2 M m_{frac} c^2}{30 L_\odot} = \frac{0.2 \times 20 M_\odot m_{frac} c^2}{30 L_\odot}$$

$$= \frac{0.2 \times 20 \times 1.9891 \times 10^{30} \times 6.503 \times 10^{-4} \times (3 \times 10^8)^2}{0.3 \times 100 \times 3.826 \times 10^{26}}$$

$$= 4.05 \times 10^{16} \text{ seconds}$$

$$= 1.28 \times 10^9 \text{ years} \tag{15.45}$$

Thus, it will take 1.3 billion years for the star to burn all that helium. However, in real stars, not all the helium is available for burning and the luminosity of a massive star in the helium-burning phase would be much higher. Thus, helium-burning time scales are much shorter.

15. To retain the same brightness, the flux of the star should remain the same. Using the radius−luminosity−temperature relation

$$L \propto R^2 T^4 \tag{15.46}$$

$$\frac{L_G}{L_{MS}} = \frac{R_G^2 T_G^4}{R_{MS}^2 T_{MS}^4}$$

$$= \left(\frac{R_G}{R_{MS}}\right)^2 \left(\frac{T}{T_{MS}}\right)^4 \tag{15.47}$$

$$= (100)^2 \left(\frac{1}{3}\right)^4 \approx \left(\frac{100}{9}\right)^2 = 123.5 \tag{15.48}$$

Now

$$F = \frac{L}{4\pi d^2}$$

$$\frac{F_G}{F_{MS}} = \frac{L_G}{L_{MS}} \left(\frac{d_{MS}}{d_G}\right)^2 = 1 \tag{15.49}$$

$$d_G = \sqrt{\frac{L_G}{L_{MS}}} \times 20 \text{ pc} \tag{15.50}$$

$$\approx \left(\frac{100}{9}\right) \times 20 \text{ pc}$$

$$\approx 220 \text{ pc} \tag{15.51}$$

Thus, at 220 pc it would be barely visible.

16. We can compare the energy of each fusion reaction to the solar constant.

$$N_{neutrino} = 2N_{fusion}$$

$$= 2\frac{S}{E_{fusion}} = \frac{2 \times 1366}{26.8 \times 1.602 \times 10^{-3}}$$

$$N_{neutrino} = 6.36 \times 10^{14} \text{ neutrinos/s/m}^2 \tag{15.52}$$

17. We find total energy available and calculate the time for which it can sustain current solar luminosity.

$$E = mc^2 = 0.008M_\odot c^2 \tag{15.53}$$

$$E = L_\odot t \tag{15.54}$$

$$\therefore \qquad t = \frac{0.008M_\odot c^2}{L_\odot} \tag{15.55}$$

$$= \frac{0.008 \times 1.9891 \times 10^{30} \times (2.9979 \times 10^8)^2}{3.826 \times 10^{26}}$$

$$= 3.74 \times 10^{18} \text{ sec}$$

$$\approx 1.2 \times 10^{11} \text{ years} \tag{15.56}$$

18. As the charged particle moves through and enters a uniform magnetic field, it will start gaining a velocity component perpendicular to both the initial velocity and to the magnetic field. The motion of this particle is similar to the motion in a cyclotron. If the thickness of the magnetic field is too large, then eventually the particle will turn back. Let τ be the thickness of the magnetic field.

$$\frac{mv^2}{r} = q\left|\vec{v} \times \vec{B}\right|$$

$$\therefore \qquad r = \frac{mv}{qB} = \frac{E}{cqB} \tag{15.57}$$

Now $\qquad r \geq \tau$

$$E \geq \tau cq B \tag{15.58}$$

$$E_{min} = 10^7 \times 2.998 \times 10^8 \times 1.602 \times 10^{-19} \times 30 \times 10^{-6}$$

$$= 1.4 \times 10^{-8} \text{ J} \tag{15.59}$$

19. Note that when the star will collapse into a neutron star, the magnetic field lines on the surface of the star will remain trapped and hence magnetic flux will be conserved.

$$4\pi R^2 B = 4\pi R_n^2 B_n \tag{15.60}$$

$$B_n = \left(\frac{R}{R_n}\right)^2 B \tag{15.61}$$

$$= \left(\frac{4 \times 6.955 \times 10^5}{20}\right)^2 \times 10^{-4}$$

$$B_n = 2 \times 10^6 \, T \tag{15.62}$$

20. The case of maximum and minimum energy photons being emitted will occur when one photon is along the intial momentum vector of π^0 meson $(\vec{p})$ and other photon is opposite $\vec{p}$. By conservation of momentum

$$\frac{E_{max} - E_{min}}{c} = p \tag{15.63}$$

$$\therefore \quad \frac{E_{max} - E_{min}}{c} = \frac{m_0 v}{\sqrt{1 - \dfrac{v^2}{c^2}}}$$

$$\left(\frac{E_{max} - E_{min}}{m_0 c}\right)^2 \left(1 - \frac{v^2}{c^2}\right) = v^2$$

$$\left(\frac{E_{max} - E_{min}}{m_0 c}\right)^2 = v^2 \left[1 + \left(\frac{E_{max} - E_{min}}{m_0 c^2}\right)^2\right]$$

$$\therefore \quad c^2 \left(E_{max} - E_{min}\right)^2 = v^2 \left[m_0^2 c^4 + \left(E_{max} - E_{min}\right)^2\right]$$

$$= v^2 \left[E^2 - p^2 c^2 + (E_{max} - E_{min})^2\right] \tag{15.64}$$

$$= v^2 \left[(E_{max} + E_{min})^2 - p^2 c^2 + p^2 c^2\right]$$

$$= v^2 (E_{max} + E_{min})^2$$

$$c(E_{max} - E_{min}) = v\,(E_{max} + E_{min})$$

$$v = \left(\frac{E_{max} - E_{min}}{E_{max} + E_{min}}\right) c \tag{15.65}$$

21. (a) Radiation flux of the star at the planet's surface is given by

$$F = \frac{L}{4\pi d^2} \tag{15.66}$$

   (b) We assume that out of the total flux incident, fraction α is reflected and the rest of the flux is absorbed. Thus, absorption rate of the planet is given by

$$A = (1 - \alpha)\pi R^2 F = (1 - \alpha)\frac{LR^2}{4d^2} \tag{15.67}$$

   (c) Energy reflected by the planet per unit time is

$$L_{pl-refl} = \alpha \pi R^2 F = \frac{\alpha L R^2}{4d^2} \tag{15.68}$$

   (d) Here, we will ignore the planet's internal source of energy, if any. Let T be the black-body temperature of the planet's surface in Kelvins. Since the planet is rotating fast, we may assume that its surface is being heated up uniformly to approximately the same temperature T. At equilibrium, the total amount of black-body radiation emitted by the planet's surface (given by Stefan's law) must be equal to the absorption rate in Equation 15.67.

$$4\pi R^2 \sigma T^4 = (1-\alpha)\frac{LR^2}{4d^2} \tag{15.69}$$

$$\therefore \qquad T = \sqrt[4]{\frac{(1-\alpha)L}{16\pi\sigma d^2}} \tag{15.70}$$

(e) In this case, only one side of the planet will act like an ideal black body. The emitted blackbody radiation is mostly from the planet's surface that faces the star. The emitting surface area is now only $2\pi R^2$ and not $4\pi R^2$. Hence, the surface temperature is given by T', where

$$2\pi R^2 \sigma (T')^4 = (1-\alpha)\frac{LR^2}{4d^2}$$

$$T' = \sqrt[4]{(1-\alpha)\frac{L}{8\pi\sigma d^2}} \tag{15.71}$$

$$= \sqrt[4]{2}T \approx (1.19)T \tag{15.72}$$

(f) Using Equation 15.70

$$T = \sqrt[4]{\frac{(1-\alpha)L}{16\pi\sigma d^2}}$$

$$T = \sqrt[4]{\frac{(1-0.25)\times 3.826\times 10^{26}}{16\pi\times 5.67\times 10^{-8}\times(1.523\times 1.496\times 10^{11})^2}}$$

$$= 209.9 \simeq 210 \text{ K} \tag{15.73}$$

22. From the graph, we estimate that

$$\log\left(\frac{L}{L_\odot}\right) = 4\log\left(\frac{M}{M_\odot}\right) \tag{15.74}$$

$$\therefore \qquad L \propto M^4 \tag{15.75}$$

As total energy produced by the star would roughly scale in the same proportion as its mass ($E \propto M$), the amount of time the star would spend on the main sequence would be given by

$$t = \frac{E}{L} \propto \frac{M}{M^4} = M^{-3} \tag{15.76}$$

$$\therefore \qquad t = t_\odot \times \left(\frac{5M_\odot}{M_\odot}\right)^{-3}$$

$$= 1\times 10^{10}/125$$

$$= 80 \text{ million years} \tag{15.77}$$

EA: We should estimate the ratio of the lifetime between one and two solar mass stars and then between two and five solar mass stars.

$$t_2 = t_\odot \times \left(\frac{2M_\odot}{M_\odot}\right)^{-3} = t_\odot/8 \tag{15.78}$$

$$t_5 = t_2 \times \left(\frac{5M_\odot}{2M_\odot}\right)^{-2.5} \tag{15.79}$$

$$= \frac{t_\odot}{8 \times 2.5^{2.5}} = \frac{1 \times 10^{10}}{79} \tag{15.80}$$

$$\approx 130 \text{ million years} \tag{15.81}$$

23. From Equation 15.74

$$\log\left(\frac{L}{L_\odot}\right) = 4\log\left(\frac{M}{M_\odot}\right)$$

$$\frac{L}{L_\odot} = \left(\frac{M}{M_\odot}\right)^4 \tag{15.82}$$

$$\tau = \frac{\eta M c^2}{L} = \frac{\eta M L_\odot c^2}{L M_\odot} \times \frac{M_\odot}{L_\odot}$$

$$= \frac{\eta M}{\eta_\odot M_\odot} \times \left(\frac{M}{M_\odot}\right)^{-4} \times \frac{\eta_\odot M_\odot c^2}{L_\odot}$$

$$\tau = \frac{\tau_\odot \eta}{\eta_\odot} \left(\frac{M}{M_\odot}\right)^{-3} \tag{15.83}$$

24. As the can is not completely filled with ice, it is natural that the volume not occupied by the ice would be occupied by the water vapours formed by sublimation of ice. If the can is sealed for a long time, the sublimation–solidification process will reach an equilibrium and water vapour density will reach saturation. At this stage, pressure inside the can is the saturated vapour pressure at that temperature.

This pressure at the boundary of ice and vapour is caused by mass-flux of ice molecules sublimating to vapour and mass-flux of vapour molecules solidifying to ice. As both the rates are the same at equilibrium, the contribution of either process is $p_s/2$. Now, if the can is suddenly opened, all vapour will escape and no molecule will solidify again. Thus, pressure exerted by molecules escaping from the can is $p = p_s/2$.

Now mass-flux of the molecules with molar mass $\mu = 18$ and temperature $T = 272$ can be calculated as

$$\varphi = \frac{\delta m}{\delta t} = \frac{m_0 \delta N}{\delta t}$$

$$= \frac{m_0 N / 6}{l / v} \qquad (\because \text{ 6 degrees of freedom})$$

$$= \frac{m_0 N v}{6l} = \frac{(m_0 . N) S v}{6 (S.l)}$$

$$= \frac{mS}{6V}\sqrt{\frac{3RT}{\mu}}$$

$$= \frac{\rho S}{6}\sqrt{\frac{3RT}{\mu}}$$

$$\varphi = \frac{pS}{6}\sqrt{\frac{3\mu}{RT}} \qquad\qquad \left(\because \rho = \frac{\mu p}{RT}\right) \quad (15.84)$$

Now, we can use this mass-flux to calculate the time taken for the entire ice to sublimate. For this duration, pressure (and hence force) will be exerted on the can.

$$\tau = \frac{m}{\varphi} = \frac{m}{\dfrac{pS}{6}\sqrt{\dfrac{3\mu}{RT}}}$$

$$= \frac{6m}{pS}\sqrt{\frac{RT}{3\mu}}$$

$$= \frac{6 \times 0.2}{550 \times 0.003}\sqrt{\frac{8314 \times 272}{3 \times 18}}$$

$$\tau \approx 149 \text{ s} \quad (15.85)$$

$$d = \frac{1}{2}a\tau^2 = \frac{F}{2M}\tau^2$$

$$= \frac{p \cdot S}{2M}\tau^2 = \frac{p_s \cdot S}{4M}\tau^2$$

$$\approx \frac{550 \times 0.003}{4 \times 100}(149)^2$$

$$d = 91.4 \text{ m} \quad (15.86)$$

Thus, the astronaut can cover more than 90 metres in just 2.5 minutes, which is sufficient for saving him/her.

25. The mass loss of the Sun can be calculated from the energy required for the Sun to sustain solar luminosity

$$L_\odot = -\frac{\Delta E}{\Delta t} = -\frac{\Delta M c^2}{\Delta t} \quad (15.87)$$

$$\Delta M = -\frac{L_\odot \Delta t}{c^2} \quad (15.88)$$

We have assumed that the mass loss rate has remained constant for $t = 100$ years. Note that angular momentum of radiation is zero. From conservation of angular momentum

$$M_\oplus v_1 r_1 = M_\oplus v_2 r_2 \quad (15.89)$$

$$\sqrt{\frac{GM_{\odot,1}}{r_1}}\,r_1 = \sqrt{\frac{GM_{\odot,2}}{r_2}}\,r_2$$

$$\therefore \qquad M_{\odot,1}r_1 = M_{\odot,2}r_2 \qquad (15.90)$$

$$M_{\odot,1}(r_2 - \Delta r) = (M_{\odot,1} - \Delta M)r_2 \qquad (15.91)$$

$$1 - \frac{\Delta M}{M_\odot} = 1 - \frac{\Delta r}{a_\oplus}$$

$$\Delta r = \frac{\Delta M a_\oplus}{M_\odot} = \frac{a_\oplus}{M_\odot} \times \frac{L_\odot \Delta t}{c^2} \qquad (15.92)$$

$$= \frac{1.496 \times 10^{11} \times 3.826 \times 10^{26} \times 100 \times 3.1557 \times 10^7}{\left(2.998 \times 10^8\right)^2 \times 1.9891 \times 10^{30}}$$

$$= 1.01 \text{ m} \qquad (15.93)$$

Thus, the radius increases by about 1 metre.

26. We need to be along the direction of the shaded region in Fig. 15.1 to be able to detect the beam. For each of the two strips

$$A_{shaded} = R \sin \theta_1 \times 2\pi \times R d\theta_2 \qquad (15.94)$$

Here, θ_1 is the angle between the rotation axis and the emission axis and $d\theta_2$ is the opening angle. Remember there are two such strips. As the pulsar distribution is random, the probability will be

$$p = \frac{2A_{shaded}}{A_{total}} = \frac{4\pi R^2 \sin \theta_1 d\theta_2}{4\pi R^2} \qquad (15.95)$$

$$= \sin \theta_1 d\theta_2 \qquad (15.96)$$

$$= 4° \times \frac{\pi}{180°} \times \sin\left(30°\right) = \frac{\pi}{90}$$

$$p = 0.035 \qquad (15.97)$$

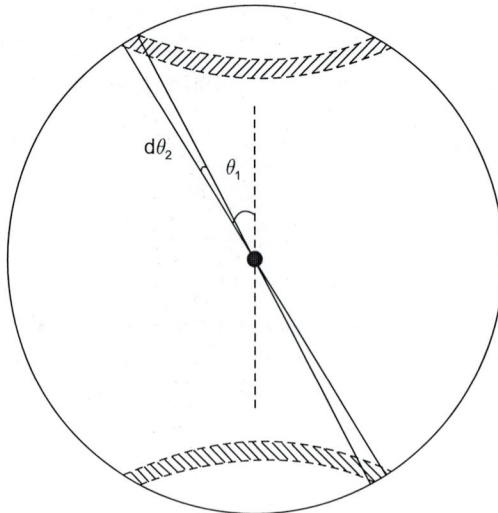

Fig. 15.1 *Variation in asteroid brightness for the three nights*

Now let us assume we are along this shaded region. Emission is not isotropic, but it is only along two small regions, each of $d\theta_2/2$ radius. Thus, solid angle is given by

$$\alpha = 4\pi(1 - \cos 2°) \tag{15.98}$$

$$= 4\pi \times 6.09 \times 10^{-4} \tag{15.99}$$

$$I_{pulsar} = \frac{L}{4\pi\left(1 - \cos 2°\right)d^2} \tag{15.100}$$

$$I_\odot = \frac{L_\odot}{4\pi d_0^2} \tag{15.101}$$

$$M_{bol} - M_{Sun} = -2.5 \log\left(\frac{I_{pulsar}}{I_\odot}\right) \tag{15.102}$$

$$= -2.5 \log\left(\frac{L}{4\pi\left(1 - \cos 2°\right)d^2} \times \frac{4\pi d_0^2}{L_\odot}\right)$$

$$= -2.5 \log\left(\frac{10000\,L_\odot}{6.09\times10^{-4}\times1000^2} \times \frac{10^2}{L_\odot}\right)$$

$$= -2.5 \log\left(\frac{1}{6.09\times10^{-4}}\right)$$

$$= -8.04 \tag{15.103}$$

$$M_{bol} = M_{Sun} - 8.04$$

$$= 4.72 - 8.04$$

$$M_{bol} = -3.32 \tag{15.104}$$

15.2   Data Analysis

1. (a) In Fig. 15.2, square symbols represent night A, diamond-shaped ones night B and triangular ones night C.

   (b) The graph of magnitude v/s airmass is a straight line for each line, the resulting equations are shown in Fig. 15.2. One can calculate β manually using Equation 5.6.

Night	$\sum_{i=1}^{n} x_i$	$\sum_{i=1}^{n} x_i^2$	$\sum_{i=1}^{n} y_i$	$\sum_{i=1}^{n} x_i y_i$	β
A	25.96	45.83	156.88	229.19	0.349 mag/airmass
B	25.96	45.83	156.56	229.39	0.428 mag/airmass
C	25.96	45.83	151.41	220.09	0.206 mag/airmass

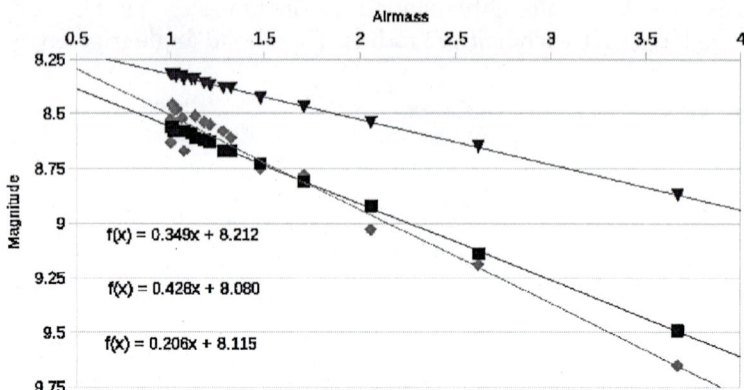

Fig. 15.2   *Extinction coefficient determination for the three nights*

One can see that a small change in the numbers will lead to a significantly different extinction coefficient.

(c)   As the plotted data for night B is very noisy at the left end of the graph (near airmass 1) as compared to other nights, clearly night B was affected by clouds.

(d)   Using Equations 5.4 and 5.7

$$M_{ast} = \mu_{ast} + A - \beta X \tag{15.105}$$

Corrected values for the asteroid are shown in Table 15.1. Fig. 15.3 shows the variation in the corrected asteroid magnitude with time on different nights.

(e)   The table below lists the rotation period as measured on the three nights.

Night	Time between Maxima	Minima	Average Semi-period	Average Period	Amplitude
A	3.6 hrs	2.4 hrs	3.0 hrs	6.0 hrs	0.10 mag
B	3.2 hrs	2.9 hrs	3.05 hrs	6.1 hrs	0.21 mag
C	3.1 hrs	3.2 hrs	3.15 hrs	6.3 hrs	0.10 mag

(f) Peak-to-peak amplitude as determined from the curves is mentioned in the table above.

Δt (hr)	Air Mass	M_{ast} Night A	Night B	Night C
0	1.28	6.98	10.98	13.00
0.44	1.18	6.98	10.91	12.99
0.89	1.11	6.94	10.97	12.92
1.33	1.06	6.90	10.92	12.91
1.77	1.02	6.95	11.03	12.92
2.21	1	6.97	11.25	12.96

Δt (hr)	Air Mass	M_{ast} Night A	Night B	Night C
2.26	1	6.97	11.13	12.98
3.1	1.01	6.94	10.98	12.98
3.54	1.03	6.90	10.91	12.94
3.99	1.07	6.88	11.06	12.95
4.43	1.13	6.90	10.91	12.93
4.87	1.21	6.94	11.02	12.91
5.31	1.32	6.95	11.09	12.96
5.76	1.48	6.96	11.13	13.02
6.2	1.71	6.98	11.01	13.01
6.64	2.06	6.96	11.03	12.99
7.09	2.62	6.94	10.90	12.92
7.53	3.67	6.92	10.94	12.93

Table 15.1 *Corrected magnitudes of the asteroid for three nights at different times*

Night	D	R	$\langle M \rangle$	m_r	φ
A	0.36	1.35	6.94	8.51	0.00
B	1.15	2.13	11.15	9.20	8.6
C	2.70	1.89	12.82	9.28	15.6

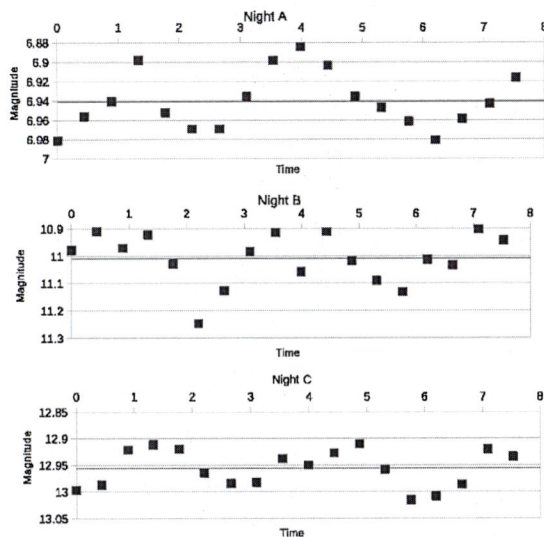

Fig. 15.3 *Variation in asteroid brightness for the three nights*

(g) The plot can be seen in Fig. 15.4.

(h) If you take two points of a non-zero phase angle, the angular coefficient will be

$$\text{Slope} = \frac{(9.28 - 9.20)}{(15.6 - 8.6)} = 0.011 \quad \text{mag/degree} \tag{15.106}$$

(i) As per the angular coefficient, without regoliths one would expect the asteroid to brighten up to a magnitude of 9.11, when the phase angle is zero. However, in reality, it is much brighter (magnitude = 8.51). Thus, it is clearly a regolith-covered asteroid.

2. (a) As $D(t) = N_0 - N(t)$, we have

$$N(t) = N_0 e^{-\lambda t}$$

$\therefore$

$$N_0 = N(t) e^{\lambda t}$$

$$D(t) = N_0 - N(t)$$

$$D(t) = N(t) e^{\lambda t} - N(t)$$

$$= N(t)(e^{\lambda t} - 1) \tag{15.107}$$

$$\frac{D(t)}{N(t)} = e^{\lambda t} - 1$$

$$\lambda t = \ln\left[\frac{D(t)}{N(t)} + 1\right] \text{and}$$

$$t = \frac{1}{\lambda} \ln\left[\frac{D(t)}{N(t)} + 1\right] \tag{15.108}$$

(b) After one half-life, half the parent nuclides will turn into daughter nuclides. Thus, from Equation. 15.108

$$D(t) = N(t)$$

$$T_{1/2} = \frac{\ln 2}{\lambda} = \frac{\ln 2}{1.42 \times 10^{-11}} \tag{15.109}$$

$$T_{1/2} = 48.81 \text{ Gyr} \tag{15.110}$$

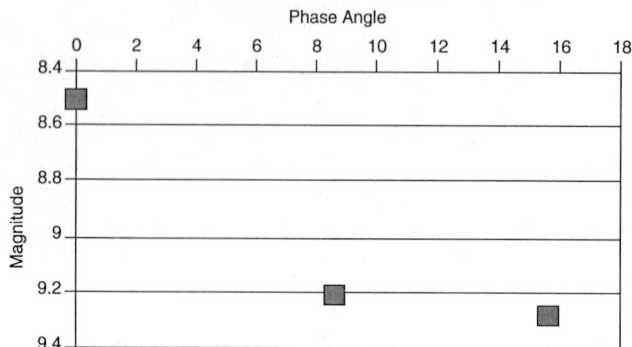

Fig. 15.4 *Magnitude of the asteroid at different phase angles*

(c) As it is possible that some ^{87}Sr was present in the meteorite from the beginning, we can use a simple linear regression equation

$$D(t) = D_0 + (e^{\lambda t} - 1)N(t) \tag{15.111}$$

$$^{87}Sr = {}^{87}Sr_0 + (e^{\lambda t} - 1)^{87} Rb$$

$$\frac{^{87}Sr}{^{86}Sr} = \left(\frac{^{87}Sr}{^{86}Sr}\right)_0 + \left(e^{\lambda t} - 1\right)\frac{^{87}Rb}{^{86}Sr} \tag{15.112}$$

$$\therefore \qquad a = \left(\frac{^{87}Sr}{^{86}Sr}\right)_0 \tag{15.113}$$

$$\& \qquad \beta = (e^{\lambda t} - 1) \tag{15.114}$$

Now, to find the regression coefficients for each type of meteorite, we separate samples of type A and type B. The calculation table for type A is shown below.

Sample	$\frac{^{87}Rb}{^{86}Sr}(X_i)$	$\frac{^{87}Sr}{^{86}Sr}(Y_i)$	X_i^2	Y_i^2	$X_i \cdot Y_i$
1	0.0101351	0.6993243	0.0001027	0.4890545	0.0070877
4	0.1741294	0.7114428	0.0303210	0.5061508	0.1238831
5	0.0203046	0.7005076	0.0004123	0.4907109	0.0142235
7	0.1197605	0.7065868	0.0143426	0.4992649	0.0846212
9	0.0816327	0.7040816	0.0066639	0.4957309	0.0574761
Total	0.4059622	3.5219432	0.0518425	2.4809122	0.2872916

Using these totals

$$S_{xx} = \sum_{i=1}^{n} X_i^2 - \frac{1}{n}\left(\sum_{i=1}^{n} X_i\right)^2$$

$$= 0.0518425 - \frac{0.4059622^2}{5}$$

$$S_{xx} = 0.0188814 \tag{15.115}$$

$$S_{yy} = \sum_{i=1}^{n} Y_i^2 - \frac{1}{n}\left(\sum_{i=1}^{n} Y_i\right)^2 \tag{15.116}$$

$$= 2.4809122 - \frac{3.5219432^2}{5}$$

$$S_{yy} = 0.0000954 \tag{15.117}$$

$$S_{xy} = \sum_{i=1}^{n} X_i Y_i - \frac{1}{n}\left(\sum_{i=1}^{n} X_i\right)\left(\sum_{i=1}^{n} Y_i\right)$$

$$= 0.2872916 - \frac{0.4059622 \times 3.5219432}{5}$$

$$S_{xy} = 0.0013364 \tag{15.118}$$

$$b = \frac{S_{xy}}{S_{xx}} = \frac{0.0013364}{0.0188814}$$

$$b = 0.0707786 \tag{15.119}$$

$$a = \bar{y} - b\bar{x}$$

$$= 0.6986419 \tag{15.120}$$

Thus, linear regression equation for type A meteorite is

$$\frac{^{87}Sr}{^{86}Sr} = 0.6986419 + 0.0707786\frac{^{87}Rb}{^{86}Sr} \tag{15.121}$$

Performing a similar analysis for type B

Sample	$\frac{^{87}Rb}{^{86}Sr}(X_i)$	$\frac{^{87}Sr}{^{86}Sr}(Y_i)$	X_i^2	Y_i^2	$X_i \cdot Y_i$
2	1.1669506	0.7614991	1.3617737	0.5798810	0.8886319
3	0.1940701	0.7129380	0.0376632	0.5082806	0.1383599
6	0.8337731	0.7493404	0.6951776	0.5615110	0.6247798
8	3.5234899	0.8859060	12.4149813	0.7848295	3.1214810
10	2.3783784	0.8324324	5.6566837	0.6929438	1.9798393
Total	8.0966621	3.9421160	20.1662795	3.1274458	6.7530920

$$S_{xx} = 20.1662795 - \frac{8.0966621^2}{5}$$

$$S_{xx} = 7.0550921 \tag{15.122}$$

$$S_{yy} = 3.1274458 - \frac{3.9421160^2}{5}$$

$$S_{yy} = 0.0193901 \tag{15.123}$$

$$S_{xy} = 6.7530920 - \frac{8.0966621 \times 3.9421160}{5}$$

$$S_{xy} = 0.3694958 \tag{15.124}$$

$$b = \frac{0.3694958}{7.0550921}$$

$$= 0.0523729 \tag{15.125}$$

$$a = 0.7039330 \tag{15.126}$$

Thus, the linear regression equation for the type B meteorite is

$$\frac{^{87}Sr}{^{86}Sr} = 0.7039330 + 0.0523729\frac{^{87}Rb}{^{86}Sr} \tag{15.127}$$

(d) Plots for each type of meteorite are shown in Fig. 15.5.

(e) For the type A meteorite

$$b = (\varepsilon^{\lambda t} - 1)$$

$$t = \frac{\ln(b+1)}{\lambda} \tag{15.128}$$

$$= \frac{\ln(1+0.0707786)}{1.42 \times 10^{-11}}$$

$$t_A = 4.815\,919 \text{ Gyr} \tag{15.129}$$

Next, we find errors in the estimations.

$$S_b = \sqrt{\frac{S_{yy} - \dfrac{S_{xy}^2}{S_{xx}}}{(n-2)S_{xx}}}$$

$$= \sqrt{\frac{0.0000954 - \dfrac{0.0013364^2}{0.0188814}}{3 \times 0.0188814}}$$

$$= 0.0037848 \tag{15.130}$$

$$S_a = S_b \sqrt{\sum_{i=1}^{n} X_i^2}$$

$$= S_b \sqrt{0.0518425}$$

$$= 0.0008618 \tag{15.131}$$

$$\frac{S_t}{t} = \frac{\partial t}{\partial b} \times \frac{S_b}{t} \tag{15.132}$$

$$S_t = \frac{S_b t}{(b+1)\ln(b+1)} \tag{15.133}$$

$$= \frac{0.0037848 \times 4.815919}{1.0707786 \ln 1.0707786}$$

$$= 0.25 \text{ Gyr} \tag{15.134}$$

For a type B meteorite

$$t = \frac{\ln(1+0.0523729)}{1.42 \times 10^{-11}} \tag{15.135}$$

$$t_B = 3.594896 \text{ Gyr} \tag{15.136}$$

$$S_b = \sqrt{\frac{S_{yy} - \dfrac{S_{xy}^2}{S_{xx}}}{(n-2)S_{xx}}}$$

$$= \sqrt{\frac{0.0193901 - \dfrac{0.3694958^2}{7.0550921}}{3 \times 7.0550921}}$$

$$= 0.0013491 \tag{15.137}$$

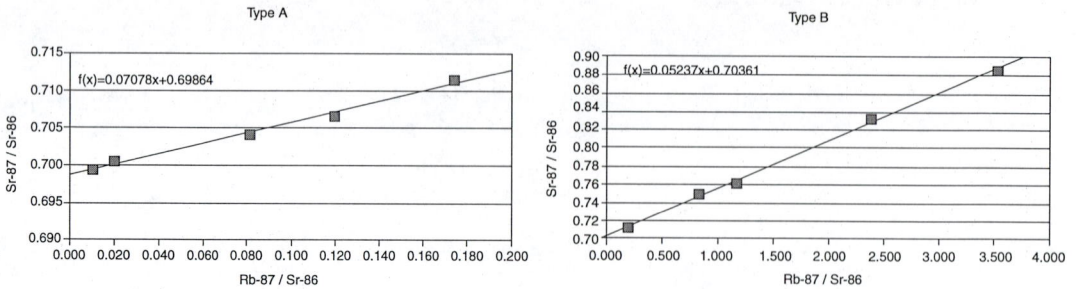

Fig. 15.5 *Regression plots for meteorite A (left) and B (right)*

$$S_a = S_b \sqrt{\sum_{i=1}^{n} X_i^2}$$

$$= 0.0013491 \times \sqrt{20.1662795}$$

$$= 0.0060586 \tag{15.138}$$

$$S_t = \frac{S_b t}{(b+1)\ln(b+1)} \tag{15.139}$$

$$= \frac{0.0013491 \times 3.594896}{1.0523729 \ln 1.0523729}$$

$$= 0.09 \text{ Gyr} \tag{15.140}$$

(f) Answers already found above.

Final Answers:

- For meteorite type A:

$$\frac{^{87}Sr}{^{86}Sr} = (0.699 \pm 0.001) + (0.071 \pm 0.004)\frac{^{87}Rb}{^{86}Sr} \tag{15.141}$$

$$\left(\frac{^{87}Sr}{^{86}Sr}\right) = (0.699 \pm 0.001) \tag{15.142}$$

$$t = (4.8 \pm 0.3) \; Gyr \tag{15.143}$$

- For meteorite type B:

$$\frac{^{87}Sr}{^{86}Sr} = (0.704 \pm 0.006) + (0.052 \pm 0.001)\frac{^{87}Rb}{^{86}Sr} \tag{15.144}$$

$$\left(\frac{^{87}Sr}{^{86}Sr}\right) = (0.704 \pm 0.006) \tag{15.145}$$

$$t = (3.59 \pm 0.09) \text{ Gyr} \tag{15.146}$$

3. Let us model the layers of the atmosphere with thick spherical shells. Take one such shell at height h from the planet's surface and with thickness Δh. The pressure, temperature and density at that height are given by $P(h), T(h)$ and $\rho(h)$, respectively. Assume the gravitational acceleration to be constant and that this shell lies within the region of the uniform descent of the probe. For equilibrium, the force due to pressure and gravitational force must be equal.

$$\Delta P.A = V\rho g$$

$$[P(h) - P(h+dh)](4\pi h^2) = (4\pi h^2)(\Delta h)\rho(h)(g)$$

$$\frac{\Delta P}{\Delta h} = -\rho g \tag{15.147}$$

$$\rho = \frac{P\mu}{RT} \qquad (\because PV = nRT)$$

$$\therefore \qquad \frac{dP}{dh} = \frac{-P\mu g}{RT} \tag{15.148}$$

$$h = h_0 - vt \qquad (\because \text{ acceleration} = 0)$$

$$\therefore \qquad \Delta h = -v\Delta t$$

$$\frac{\Delta P}{v\Delta t} = \frac{P\mu g}{RT} \tag{15.149}$$

Here, h_0 is the height from which the probe starts sending values.

(a) From Fig. 5.2 (left) for planet P_1, we estimate the value of $\dfrac{\Delta P}{\Delta t}$. This is the slope of the graph obtained by drawing a tangent towards the end of the probe's journey.

$$\frac{\Delta P}{\Delta t} = 0.06\,\text{units/s} \tag{15.150}$$

Thus, near the surface, we have

$$v = \frac{\Delta P}{\Delta t} \times \frac{RT_0}{P\mu g} \tag{15.151}$$

$$= 0.06 \times \frac{8.314 \times 700}{55 \times 0.044 \times 10}$$

$$v = 14.4\ \text{m s}^{-1}$$

$$h_0 = vt_{total}$$

$$= 14.4 \times 3750$$

$$h_0 = 54.1\ \text{km} \tag{15.152}$$

(b) Time taken for the probe to descend to this height will be

$$t = \frac{\Delta h}{v} = \frac{(54100 - 39600)}{14.4} = 1008\,\text{s} \tag{15.153}$$

From Fig. 5.2 (left), we take the corresponding $P = 4$ units and then find the slope of the tangent at this point.

$$\frac{\Delta P}{\Delta t} = 0.006\,\text{units/s} \tag{15.154}$$

$$\therefore \qquad T = \frac{P\mu g v}{\dfrac{\Delta P}{\Delta t} R}$$

$$= \frac{4 \times 0.044 \times 10.4}{.006 \times 8.314}$$

$$= 508 \text{ K} \tag{15.155}$$

(c) On this planet, as per Fig. 5.2 (right)

$$\frac{\Delta P}{\Delta t} = \frac{40}{2000} = 0.02 \text{ units/s} \tag{15.156}$$

$$P_{surface} = 50 \text{ units} \tag{15.157}$$

$$v = \frac{\Delta P}{\Delta t} \times \frac{RT_2}{\mu g_2 P_{surface}}$$

$$= 0.02 \times \frac{8.314 \times 750}{50 \times 0.044 \times 8}$$

$$v = 7.09 \text{ m s}^{-1}$$

$$h_0 = v t_{total}$$

$$= 7.09 \times 2000$$

$$h_0 = 14.2 \text{ km} \tag{15.158}$$

As the p vs. t graph has constant slope, p will also vary linearly with h.

$$P = 50 - \frac{\Delta P}{\Delta t} \times \left(\frac{h}{v}\right)$$

$$P = 50 - (0.00282)h \tag{15.159}$$

$$\therefore \qquad T = \frac{P \mu g v}{\frac{\Delta P}{\Delta t} R}$$

$$= \frac{0.044 \times 8 \times 7.09}{0.02 \times 8.314}(50 - (0.00282)h)$$

$$= 15 \times (50 - (0.00282)h)$$

$$T = 750 - 0.0423h \tag{15.160}$$

The plots are straight lines with the respective slopes, as shown in Fig. 15.6.

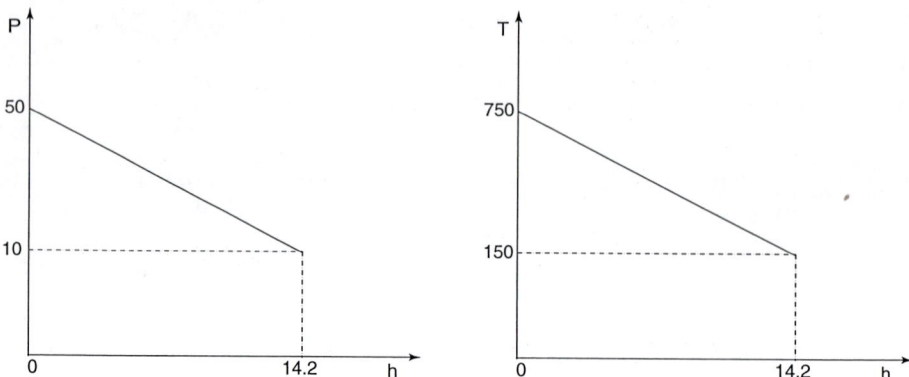

Fig. 15.6 *Variation in pressure and temperature as a function of height on planet P_2*

16

Solutions: Stellar Observations

16.1 Theory

1. Let F_1, F_2 and F_c be the flux of the first star, the second star and the combined flux, respectively.

$$m_1 - m_2 = -2.5 \log\left(\frac{F_1}{F_2}\right) \tag{16.1}$$

$$\frac{F_1}{F_2} = 10^{\left(\frac{2-1}{2.5}\right)}$$

$$= 10^{0.4} \tag{16.2}$$

$$F_c = F_1 + F_2 \tag{16.3}$$

$$m_c - m_2 = -2.5 \log\left(\frac{F_1 + F_2}{F_2}\right) \tag{16.4}$$

$$= 2 - 2.5 \log\left(1 + \frac{F_1}{F_2}\right)$$

$$= 2 - 2.5 \log(1 + 10^{0.4})$$

$$= 2.0 - 1.36$$

$$m_c = 0.64 \text{ mag} \tag{16.5}$$

2. Let d be the distance to that supernova. Then, the flux density on the Earth would be

$$F = \frac{10^{10} L_\odot}{4\pi d^2} = \frac{L_\odot}{4\pi d_{\oplus-\odot}^2} \tag{16.6}$$

$$\frac{10^{10}}{d^2} = \frac{1}{(1 \text{ AU})^2}$$

$$\therefore \quad d = 10^{\frac{10}{2}} \text{ AU} = 10^5 \text{ AU}$$

$$= 1.496 \times 10^{16} \text{ m} = \frac{1.496}{3.0856} \text{ pc}$$

$$\approx 0.5 \text{ pc} \tag{16.7}$$

3. The flux ratio can be calculated as

$$m_1 - m_2 = -2.5 \log \left(\frac{F_1}{F_2} \right) \tag{16.8}$$

$$\therefore \quad \frac{F_1}{F_2} = 10^{\frac{(m_2 - m_1)}{2.5}}$$

$$\frac{F_{min}}{F_{max}} = 10^{\frac{6.0 - (-1.5)}{2.5}} = 10^{\frac{7.5}{2.5}}$$

$$= 1000 \tag{16.9}$$

Thus, the brightest star is 1000 times brighter than the faintest star visible to the naked eye.

4. Let the magnitude of the full moon for current albedo (α_0) be m_0 and for the Moon with albedo $(\alpha_1) = 1$ be m_1, and let F be the total flux incident on the Moon's surface.

$$m_1 - m_0 = -2.5 \log \left(\frac{\alpha_0 F}{\alpha_1 F} \right) \tag{16.10}$$

$$m_1 = m_0 - 2.5 \log \left(\frac{1}{0.14} \right)$$

$$= -12.74 - 2.5 \log(7.14)$$

$$m_1 = -14.87 \tag{16.11}$$

5. Assuming the radiation of the star is isotropic

$$\text{Flux density} = \frac{\text{Luminosity}}{4\pi D^2} \tag{16.12}$$

$$\therefore \quad D = \sqrt{\frac{0.4 \times L_\odot}{4\pi \, (\text{flux density})}}$$

$$= \sqrt{\frac{0.4 \times 3.826 \times 10^{26}}{4\pi \times 6.23 \times 10^{-14}}}$$

$$= 1.4 \times 10^{19} \, \text{m} = \frac{1.4 \times 10^{19}}{3.0856 \times 10^{16}} \, \text{pc}$$

$$D \approx 450 \, \text{pc} \tag{16.13}$$

6. We take the Sun as a G2 star. Let E_{st} be the energy of the star collected by our eye every second and F_{st} and $F_\odot$ be the fluxes at the Earth from the star and the Sun, respectively. If N photons reach our eye per second from this star, then

$$m_{st} - m_\odot = -2.5 \log \frac{F_{st}}{F_\odot} \tag{16.14}$$

$$6 - (-26.72) = -2.5 \log \frac{F_{st}}{1366}$$

$$F_{st} = 1.12 \times 10^{-10} \, \text{W} / \text{m}^2 \tag{16.15}$$

$$E_{st} = F_{st} D_{eye}^2 \tag{16.16}$$

$$= 1.12 \times 10^{-10} \times 0.006^2$$

$$E_{st} = 4.02 \times 10^{-15} \text{ W} \tag{16.17}$$

$$N = \frac{E_{st}}{E_{photon}} = \frac{E_{st}\lambda}{hc} \tag{16.18}$$

$$= \frac{4.02 \times 10^{-15} \times 550 \times 10^{-9}}{6.62 \times 10^{-34} \times 2.998 \times 10^{8}} \tag{16.19}$$

$$\approx 1 \times 10^4 \tag{16.20}$$

Thus, we receive about 10,000 photons from such a star every second.

7. Radiation from stars is spherically symmetric. Let ΔE be the energy in the infinitesimally thin (thickness Δr) shell at distance r. $\Delta V = 4\pi r^2 \Delta r$. If light takes Δt time to travel Δr distance, then $\Delta r = c\Delta t$. The radiation pressure is the same as energy density of the electromagnetic radiation.

$$p_{rad} = \frac{\Delta E}{\Delta V} = \frac{L\Delta t}{4\pi r^2 \Delta r}$$

$$= \frac{L\cancel{\Delta t}}{4\pi r^2 c \cancel{\Delta t}}$$

$$\therefore \qquad p_{rad} = \frac{f}{c} \tag{16.22}$$

$$m_\Sigma - m_\odot = -2.5 \log\left(\frac{f_\Sigma}{f_\odot}\right)$$

$$m_\Sigma = m_\odot - 2.5 \log\left(\frac{p_{rad,\Sigma^c}}{p_{rad,\odot^c}}\right)$$

$$m_\Sigma = m_\odot + 2.5 \log\left(\frac{p_{rad,\odot}}{p_{rad,\Sigma}}\right) \tag{16.23}$$

8. Let f be the flux emitted per unit area by the Sun's disk. When the Earth passes in front, it blocks a small area as seen from a distance. As the star and exoplanet are very far from the observer, their mutual physical separation does not matter and their angular size is proportional to their cross-sectional area.

$$B_{max} = \pi R_\odot^2 F \tag{16.24}$$

$$B_{min} = \pi(R_\odot^2 - R_\oplus^2)F \tag{16.25}$$

$$\frac{B_{max}}{B_{min}} = \frac{\pi R_\odot^2 F}{\pi(R_\odot^2 - R_\oplus^2)F}$$

$$= \frac{R_\odot^2}{R_\odot^2 - R_\oplus^2}$$

$$= \frac{(695.5 \times 10^6)^2}{(695.5 \times 10^6)^2 - (6.3708 \times 10^6)^2}$$

$$\frac{B_{max}}{B_{min}} = 1.000084 \tag{16.26}$$

9. The amount of absorption due to the fog in London is

$$\Delta m = -26.72 - (-12.47) = -13.98 \, \text{mag}$$

$$I_v(r) = I_v(0) \times e^{-\tau} \tag{16.27}$$

$\therefore$

$$\frac{I_v(0)}{I_v(r)} = e^{\tau}$$

Now

$$\Delta m = -2.5 \log \left(\frac{I_v(0)}{I_v(r)} \right)$$

$$= -2.5 \log(e^{\tau})$$

$$= -2.5 \tau \, \log(e) \tag{16.28}$$

$$\tau = \frac{-\Delta m}{2.5 \times \log e} = \frac{13.98}{2.5 \times 0.434}$$

$$\tau = 12.9 \tag{16.29}$$

10.

$$m_{star} - m_{Vega} = -2.5 \log \left(\frac{F_{star}}{F_{Vega}} \right) \tag{16.30}$$

$$22 - 0 = -2.5 \log \left(\frac{F_{star}}{8.3 \times 10^{-12}} \right)$$

$\therefore$

$$F_{star} = 8.3 \times 10^{-12} \times 10^{-\frac{22}{2.5}}$$

$$= 1.32 \times 10^{-20} \text{W/m}^2/\text{nm} \tag{16.31}$$

For the star, the number of photons detected per unit wavelength per unit area is the flux divided by the energy of a photon with the effective wavelength.

$$N_{star} = \frac{F_{star}}{E_{photon}} \times (Area) \times QE \times \Delta\lambda \tag{16.32}$$

$$= \frac{F_{star}}{hc/\lambda_{eff}} \times \pi \frac{D^2}{4} \times QE \times \Delta\lambda \tag{16.33}$$

$$= \frac{1.32 \times 10^{-20} \times 8 \times 10^{-7}}{6.6261 \times 10^{-34} \times 2.9979 \times 10^8} \times \pi \frac{8^2}{4} \times 0.4 \times 24$$

$$= 25.7$$

$$N_{star} \approx 30 \text{ photons / s} \tag{16.34}$$

11. The oscillatory motion of the Sun will primarily be due to Jupiter, as the centre of mass of this system will not coincide with the centre of the Sun. We can ignore the contribution of all other planets. The magnitude of the Sun's oscillation will be given by the distance between the centre of the Sun and the centre of mass of the Sun–Jupiter system.

$$d_\odot = \frac{d_J M_J}{(M_\odot + M_J)} \tag{16.35}$$

$$= \frac{5.204 \times 1.898 \times 10^{27}}{(1.989 \times 10^{30} + 1.898 \times 10^{27})} \text{AU}$$

$$= 4.961 \times 10^{-3} \text{ AU} \tag{16.36}$$

$$d_\odot = 2.045 \times 10^{-8} \text{ pc}$$

$$\alpha = \frac{2d_\odot}{d_{Barnard}} = \frac{2 \times 2.405 \times 10^{-8}}{1.83} \tag{16.37}$$

$$= 2.628 \times 10^{-8} \text{ rad}$$

$$\alpha = 0.00542'' \tag{16.38}$$

Period of oscillation will be the same as the period of revolution of Jupiter.

$$T = 2\pi \sqrt{\frac{a_J^3}{G(M_\odot + M_J)}} \tag{16.39}$$

$$= 2\pi \sqrt{\frac{(5.024 \times 1.4960 \times 10^{11})^3}{6.6726 \times 10^{-11} \times (1.9891 \times 10^{30} + 1.898 \times 10^{27})}}$$

$$= 3.744 \times 10^8 \text{ s}$$

$$T = 11.87 \text{ years} \tag{16.40}$$

12. We first estimate the star's distance from its apparent and absolute magnitudes. We can find its luminosity by its absolute magnitude and then use it to find its radius using Stefan's law.

$$m - M = 5 \log d - 5 \tag{16.41}$$

$$\therefore \qquad \log d = \frac{m - M + 5}{5} = \frac{7.2 - 1.6 + 5}{5}$$

$$= 2.12$$

$$\therefore \qquad d = 132 \text{ pc} \tag{16.42}$$

$$M_\odot - M = 2.5 \log \left(\frac{L}{L_\odot} \right) \tag{16.43}$$

$$\log \left(\frac{L}{L_\odot} \right) = \frac{M_\odot - M}{2.5} = \frac{4.72 - 1.6}{2.5}$$

$$= 1.248$$

$$\therefore \qquad L = 17.7 \, L_\odot \tag{16.44}$$

$$= 17.70 \times 3.826 \times 10^{26}$$

$$L = 6.77 \times 10^{27} \text{ W} \tag{16.45}$$

$$L = 4\pi\sigma R^2 \, T_{eff}^4 \tag{16.46}$$

$$\therefore \qquad R = \frac{1}{T_{eff}^{2}}\sqrt{\frac{L}{4\pi\sigma}}$$

$$= \frac{1}{8700^2}\sqrt{\frac{6.77\times10^{27}}{4\pi\times5.67\times10^{-8}}}$$

$$R = 1.29\times10^{9}\text{ m} \tag{16.47}$$

13. We first calculate its absolute magnitude and correct it to bolometric magnitude. Then, bolometric magnitude is used to calculate its luminosity.

$$m_v - M_V = 5\log d - 5 \tag{16.48}$$

$$M_V - m_v = 5 + 5\log p \qquad\qquad (\because d = 1/p)$$

$$M_V = 12.2 + 5 + 5\log(0.001)$$

$$= 12.2 + 5 - 15 = 2.2\text{ mag} \tag{16.49}$$

$$\text{B.C.} = M_{bol} - M_V$$

$$M_{bol} = BC + M_V \tag{16.50}$$

$$M_{bol} = -0.6 + 2.2$$

$$M_{bol} = 1.6\text{ mag} \tag{16.51}$$

Now, as we have already seen in Equation 16.44, a star with a bolometric magnitude of 1.6 would be 17.7 times more luminous than the Sun. Thus, $L = 17.7L_\odot$.

(b) The star is more luminous than the Sun but is much cooler than the Sun. Therefore, it must be a red giant star.

14. Let B_0, V_0 and U_0 be the intrinsic absolute magnitudes of the white dwarf. Let A_B, A_V and A_U be the interstellar extinction coefficients per kpc. Let A_{neb_B}, A_{neb_V} and A_{neb_U} be the total extinction for the planetary nebula around the first WD, for light travelling from the centre of the nebula to the edge.

$$(U - B)_0 = (U - V)_0 - (B - V)_0 \tag{16.52}$$

$$= 0.330 - 0.300$$

$$(U - B)_0 = 0.030 \tag{16.53}$$

$$(U - V)_1 = (U - B)_1 + (B - V)_1 \tag{16.54}$$

$$= 0.038 + 0.327$$

$$(U - V)_1 = 0.365 \tag{16.55}$$

For WD inside the nebula

$$(B - V)_1 = (B - V)_0 + (A_B - A_V)d + \left(A_{neb_B} - A_{neb_V}\right) \tag{16.56}$$

$$\left(A_{neb_B} - A_{neb_V}\right) = (B - V)_1 - (B - V)_0 - (A_B - A_V)d$$

$$= 0.327 - 0.300 - (1.23 - 1.00)\times0.05$$

$$\left(A_{neb_B} - A_{neb_V}\right) = 0.0155 \tag{16.57}$$

$$\left(A_{neb_U} - A_{neb_V}\right) = (U - V)_1 - (U - V)_0 - \left(A_U - A_V\right)d \tag{16.58}$$

$$= 0.365 - 0.330 - (1.50 - 1.00) \times 0.05$$

$$\left(A_{neb_U} - A_{neb_V}\right) = 0.0100 \tag{16.59}$$

$$\left(A_{neb_U} - A_{neb_B}\right) = (U - B)_1 - (U - B)_0 - \left(A_U - A_B\right)d \tag{16.60}$$

$$= 0.038 - 0.030 - (1.50 - 1.23) \times 0.05$$

$$\left(A_{neb_U} - A_{neb_B}\right) = -0.0055 \tag{16.61}$$

Light from the second white dwarf has to travel the entire diameter of the planetary nebula and not just from its centre to the edge. Thus, for this white dwarf, the extinction of light from the planetary nebula would be double that of the first white dwarf. The overall distance of this pulsar is three times larger.

$$(B - V)_2 = (B - V)_0 + 3(A_B - A_V)d + 2(A_{neb_B} - A_{neb_V}) \tag{16.62}$$

$$= 0.300 + 3 \times (1.23 - 1.00) \times 0.05 + 2 \times 0.0155$$

$$(B - V)_2 = 0.3655 \approx 0.366 \tag{16.63}$$

$$(U - V)_2 = (U - V)_0 + 3(A_U - A_V)d + 2(A_{neb_U} - A_{neb_V}) \tag{16.64}$$

$$= 0.330 + 3 \times (1.50 - 1.00) \times 0.05 + 2 \times 0.0100$$

$$(U - V)_2 = 0.425 \tag{16.65}$$

$$(U - B)_2 = (U - B)_0 + 3(A_U - A_B)d + 2(A_{neb_U} - A_{neb_B}) \tag{16.66}$$

$$= 0.030 + 3 \times (1.50 - 1.23) \times 0.05 - 2 \times 0.0055$$

$$(U - B)_2 = 0.0595 \approx 0.060 \tag{16.67}$$

15. The physical radius of the cluster R will be given by

$$R = \frac{D\alpha}{2} \tag{16.68}$$

As the cluster contains N stars, its stellar number density will be

$$\rho = \frac{N}{V} = \frac{3N}{4\pi}\left(\frac{2}{D\alpha}\right)^3$$

$$\rho = \frac{6N}{\pi D^3 \alpha^3} \tag{16.69}$$

Now, for the astronomer, all the stars are roughly at the same distance but for the biologist, the stars are located in different shells around him. Let the luminosity of each star be L_0. Suppose we have a shell of thickness DR at a distance R' from the centre of the cluster, its flux will be given by

$$DV(R', DR) = 4\pi R'^2 DR$$

$$\Delta N(R', \Delta R) = \rho \Delta V = \frac{24NR'^2}{D^3 \alpha^3}\Delta R \tag{16.70}$$

$$F_B(R', \Delta R) = \frac{\Delta N L_0}{4\pi R'^2} \tag{16.71}$$

$$= \frac{24NR'^2}{D^3\alpha^3} \times \frac{L_0}{4\pi R'^2} \Delta R$$

$$F_B(R', \Delta R) = \frac{6NL_0}{\pi D^3\alpha^3} \Delta R \tag{16.72}$$

Note that this expression is independent of R'. Now, if we say

$$DR = R/n$$

$$F_B = nF_B(DR) \tag{16.73}$$

$$= \frac{D\alpha}{2\Delta R} \frac{6NL_0}{\pi D^3\alpha^3} \Delta R$$

$$\therefore \qquad F_B = \frac{3NL_0}{\pi D^2\alpha^2} \tag{16.74}$$

$$\text{For the astronomer } F_A = \frac{NL_0}{4\pi D^2} \tag{16.75}$$

(a) Difference in apparent magnitude will be

$$m_A - m_B = -2.5\log\left(\frac{F_A}{F_B}\right) \tag{16.76}$$

$$= -2.5\log\left(\frac{\pi D^2\alpha^2}{3NL_0} \frac{NL_0}{4\pi D^2}\right)$$

$$= -2.5\log\left(\frac{\alpha^2}{12}\right) \tag{16.77}$$

$$\therefore \qquad m_A - m_B = 2.5\log\left(\frac{12}{\alpha^2}\right) \tag{16.78}$$

(b) For the same brightness, the light-gathering power should be equal.

$$\therefore \qquad F_A \times \pi(D_A)^2 = F_B \times \pi(D_B)^2 \tag{16.79}$$

$$D_A = D_B\sqrt{\frac{F_B}{F_A}} = D_B\sqrt{\frac{12}{\alpha^2}}$$

$$= 6 \times \frac{2\sqrt{3}}{\alpha} \tag{16.80}$$

$$D_A \approx \frac{21}{\alpha}\text{mm} \tag{16.81}$$

(c) α is very small. As the field of view of the biologist is reduced, the flux will also be reduced. The solid angle seen will be

$$\omega = 2\pi\left(1 - \cos\frac{\alpha}{2}\right) \tag{16.82}$$

$$= 2\pi \frac{\alpha^2}{8} = \frac{\pi \alpha^2}{4} \tag{16.83}$$

$$\therefore \quad F'_B = \frac{F_B}{4\pi} \times \omega \tag{16.84}$$

$$= \frac{F_B}{4\pi} \times \frac{\pi \alpha^2}{4}$$

$$F'_B = \frac{\alpha^2}{16} F_B \tag{16.85}$$

$$m_A - m'_B = -2.5 \log \left(\frac{F_A}{F'_B} \right) \tag{16.86}$$

$$= -2.5 \log \left(\frac{F_A}{F_B} \times \frac{16}{\alpha^2} \right)$$

$$= -2.5 \log \left(\frac{\alpha^2}{12} \times \frac{16}{\alpha^2} \right) = -2.5 \log \left(\frac{4}{3} \right)$$

$$m_A - m'_B = -0.31 \tag{16.87}$$

16. (a) Let the intrinsic apparent magnitudes of the star be U_0, B_0 and V_0. Let E denote colour excess and let A denote the amount of extinction.

$$U - B = 8.15 - 8.50 = -0.35 \tag{16.88}$$

$$B - V = 8.50 - 8.14 = 0.36 \tag{16.89}$$

$$E(U - B) = (U - B) - (U - B)_0 \tag{16.90}$$

$$= -0.35 - (-0.45)$$

$$= 0.10 \tag{16.91}$$

$$E(U - B) = 0.72 E(B - V) \tag{16.92}$$

$$\therefore \quad E(B - V) = \frac{0.10}{0.72} = 0.14 \tag{16.93}$$

$$A_V = R_V E(B - V) \tag{16.94}$$

$$= 3.2 \times 0.14$$

$$A_V = 0.44 \tag{16.95}$$

$$V_0 = V - A_V = 8.14 - 0.44 = 7.70 \tag{16.96}$$

$$E(B - V) = (B - V) - (B - V)_0 \tag{16.97}$$

$$0.14 = 0.36 - (B_0 - V_0)$$

$$B_0 = 0.36 - 0.14 + 7.70$$

$$\therefore \quad B_0 = 7.92 \tag{16.98}$$

$$U_0 = B_0 + (U - B)_0 \tag{16.99}$$

$$= 7.92 - 0.44$$

$$\therefore \qquad U_0 = 7.47 \qquad (16.100)$$

Note that the numbers written here are rounded to the correct significant digits, while the actual calculations were carried out by retaining one additional digit in each number at every step. Thus, the answer in Equation 16.100 is correct although it is not obvious from the previous step.

(b) Star's absolute bolometric magnitude $= -0.25$
    Sun's absolute bolometric magnitude $= 4.72$

$$L = \sigma T^4 4\pi R^2$$

$$\frac{L}{L_\odot} = \left(\frac{T}{T_\odot}\right)^4 \left(\frac{R}{R_\odot}\right)^2 \qquad (16.101)$$

$$\log\left(\frac{L}{L_\odot}\right) = 4\log\left(\frac{T}{T_\odot}\right) + 2\log\left(\frac{R}{R_\odot}\right)$$

$$-2.5\log\left(\frac{L}{L_\odot}\right) = M - M_\odot \qquad (16.102)$$

$$4.72 - (-0.25) = 10\log\left(\frac{T}{T_\odot}\right) + 5\log 2.3$$

$$\log\left(\frac{T}{T_\odot}\right) = 0.1(4.97 - 1.8086) = 0.3161$$

$$T = 2.07 T_\odot$$

$$T \approx 12000K \qquad (16.103)$$

(c)

$$BC = -0.15$$

$$M_V = M_{bol} + BC \qquad (16.104)$$

$$= -0.25 - 0.15$$

$$= -0.4 \qquad (16.105)$$

$$m_v - M_V = 5\log\left(\frac{r}{10}\right) \qquad (16.106)$$

$$7.70 - (-0.4) = 5\log\left(\frac{r}{10}\right)$$

$$\log\left(\frac{r}{10}\right) = 1.619$$

$$r = 416 \text{ pc} \qquad (16.107)$$

16.2 Data Analysis

1. The human eye can easily recognise differences of the order of $Dm_V \sim 0.1-0.2$ mag, as denoted by size and intensity of black of different stars in the photograph. Note that the chart has a different scale and orientation as compared to the photograph, and we must first to align the two properly. Then, the magnitudes of the stars can easily be recognised. Stars 1, 2 and 12 are outside the boundaries of the photograph.

Star	3	4	5	6	7
m	7.3–7.9	5.3–5.9	5.2–5.8	4.6–5.2	5.2–5.8
Star	8	9	10	11	
m	4.5–5.1	4.3–4.9	4.9–5.5	5.3–5.9	

2. (a) This question specifically asks you to plot the magnitudes of KZ Hyd (Fig. 16.1) with respect to the comparison star and not simply plot DV and DR against HJD*. The plots will appear as shown in Fig. 16.2.

   (b) For the check star, the average of all 36 readings may be taken as the average magnitude.

   For KZ Hydrae, it is not correct to simply use the average of all the readings in each column. The readings contain one complete period and in addition some readings before

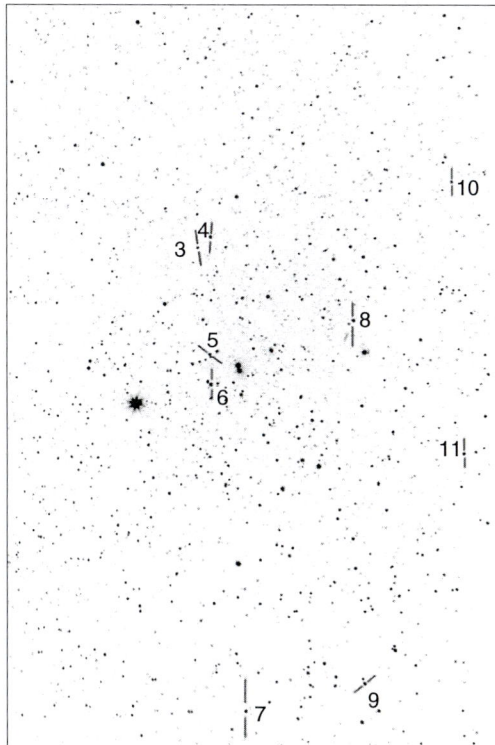

Fig. 16.1 *Astronomical chart with the stars of the Hyades cluster region marked*

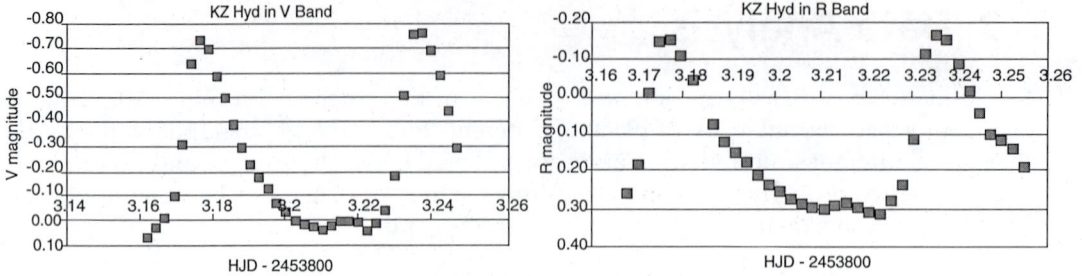

Fig. 16.2   *Light curves of KZ Hydrae*

and after that. Thus, if you take the average of all 36 readings, it will be biased. Also note that the light curve is not symmetric and the star's magnitude is close to minima for many readings. Thus, a simple average of maximum and minimum magnitude will also not be correct. To find a reasonably correct average, we should take the readings for one complete period (say maxima to maxima) and calculate the average for those reading.

$$DV_{av} = -0.208 \tag{16.108}$$

$$DR_{av} = 0.152 \tag{16.109}$$

$$DV_{ch-av} = 4.388 \tag{16.110}$$

$$DR_{ch-av} = 2.793 \tag{16.111}$$

EA: Even this average will be correct only if the readings are equispaced in time. Otherwise, ideally, we have to integrate the light curve and find the average magnitude such that the area bounded by the light curve and the horizontal line showing average magnitude is equal above and below the line. By doing so, we obtain values $DV_{av} = -0.205$ and $DR_{av} = 0.148$. However, this is not expected from students who compute the average magnitudes manually.

Further, the magnitudes are not additive, but the fluxes are. Thus, ideally, this procedure should be done with a flux curve to find the average flux and hence the exact average magnitude.

(c) Assuming that comparison and check stars do not have variable magnitudes, the standard deviation in each band will give the photometric precision in the respective band.

$$\sigma_V = \sqrt{\frac{\sum \left(\Delta V_{ch} - \Delta V_{ch-av}\right)^2}{N}} \tag{16.112}$$

$$= 0.083 \tag{16.113}$$

$$\sigma_R = \sqrt{\frac{\sum \left(\Delta R_{ch} - \Delta R_{ch-av}\right)^2}{N}} \tag{16.114}$$

$$= 0.011 \tag{16.115}$$

(d) From Fig. 16.2

Pulsation period in V band, $T_V = 0.058$ days $= 1.4$ hours

Pulsation period in R band, $T_R = 0.058$ days $= 1.4$ hours

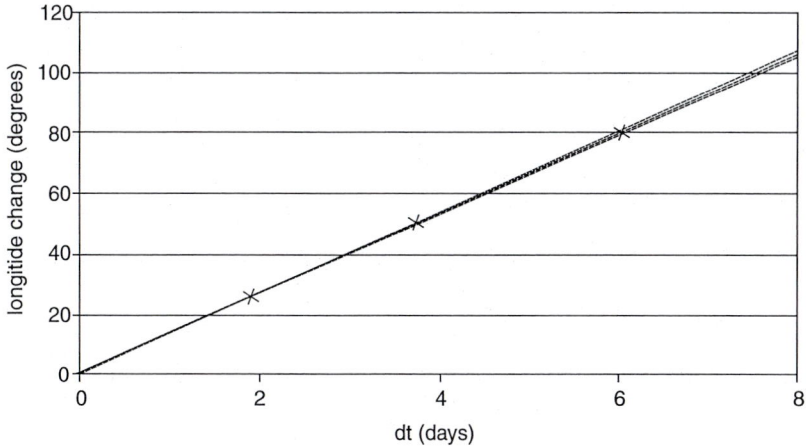

Fig. 16.3 *Graph showing sunspot rotation*

(e) From Fig. 16.2

   Pulsation amplitude in V band, $A_V = 0.83$ mag

   Pulsation amplitude in R band, $A_R = 0.48$ mag

(f) Within the uncertainities, there is no phase difference between the light curves in the two bands.

3. We should first correctly draw the axis of rotation of the Sun. This can be done by drawing a straight line at an angle of P_0 degrees anti-clockwise from the vertical for each photograph.

   Then, we must choose the correct Stonyhurst grid and place it on each photograph such that the solar axis on the grid coincides with the solar axis of the photograph. For the chosen three sunspots, we then estimate the heliocentric longitude ($\lambda_\odot$) and heliocentric latitude ($\beta_\odot$) with the help of the grid. The graph for sunspot rotation is shown in Fig. 16.3. In the graph, points for S1 are denoted by '+' symbols (continuous line), the points for S2 are denoted by diamond symbols (dotted line) and the points for S3 are denoted by 'x' symbols (dashed line). The slopes of these lines would be related to the rotation period of the Sun as

Date	Sunspot S1		Sunspot S2		Sunspot S3	
	$\lambda_\odot$	$\beta_\odot$	$\lambda_\odot$	$\beta_\odot$	$\lambda_\odot$	$\beta_\odot$
May 1	54	17.5	33	18.5	30.5	16
May 3	27	18	6	19	4	16
May 5	3	18.5	−19	18.5	−23	17
May 7	−24	18	−46	18	−49	16
May 9	−49.5	19	−72	18	−77	17

$$P_i = \frac{360}{(\text{slope})_i} \qquad (16.116)$$

$\therefore$

$$P_1 = \frac{360}{13.4} = 26.9\,\text{days}$$

$$P_2 = \frac{360}{13.1} = 27.5 \text{ days}$$

$$P_3 = \frac{360}{12.9} = 27.9 \text{ days}$$

$$\therefore \qquad P_\odot = (27.4 \pm 0.5) \text{ days} \tag{16.117}$$

4. For errors in each part, the approximate error in a function f will be given by

$$\frac{\Delta f}{f} = \sum_{i=1}^{n} \frac{\partial f}{\partial x_i} \frac{\Delta x_i}{f} \tag{16.118}$$

(a) For the observer A, the Sun is at distance $d_0 = 2.64$ pc

$$m_{\odot,0} - m_\odot = -5 \log\left(\frac{d_0}{a_\oplus}\right) \tag{16.119}$$

$$\therefore \qquad m_\odot = 5 \log\left(\frac{2.64 \times 206265}{1}\right) - 26.72$$

$$m_\odot = 1.96$$

$$\frac{\Delta m_\odot}{m_\odot} = \frac{\Delta m_{\odot,0}}{|m_{\odot,0}|} + \frac{\Delta d_0}{d_0 \log d_0} \tag{16.120}$$

$$\Delta m_\odot = \left[\frac{0.01}{26.72} + \frac{0.01}{2.64 \log 2.64}\right] \times 1.96$$

$$Dm_\odot = 0.02$$

$$\therefore \qquad m_\odot = (1.96 \pm 0.02) \tag{16.121}$$

(b) Magnitude of Sirius for observer A is calculated in the same way. In this, however, the error in measurement of the orbital radius of the host planet of observer A would have to be added to total error.

$$m_{Sr} = -5 \log\left(\frac{d_0}{10 a_\oplus}\right) + m_{Sr,\oplus}$$

$$= -5 \log\left(\frac{2.64 \times 206265}{10}\right) - 1.46$$

$$m_{Sr} = -25.14$$

$$\Delta m_{Sr} = \left[\frac{0.01}{1.46} + \frac{0.01}{2.64 \log 2.64} + \frac{1}{10 \log 10}\right] \times (-25.14)$$

$$Dm_{Sr} = -2.9$$

$$\therefore \qquad m_{Sr} = -(25 \pm 3) \tag{16.122}$$

(c) We find the intrinsic luminosity of each star and then add it together.

$$m_{\odot,0} - m = -2.5 \log \left(\frac{\frac{L_\odot}{a_\oplus^2}}{\frac{L}{d^2}} \right)$$

$$m_{\odot,0} - m = -2.5 \log \left(\frac{206265^2 L_\odot}{P^2 L} \right)$$

$$\therefore \qquad L = \frac{206265^2 L_\odot}{p^2} 10^{0.4(m_{\odot,0} - m)} \qquad (16.123)$$

$$L_{Al} = \left(\frac{10^{0.2(-26.72-3.99)} \times 206265}{0.03991} \right)^2 L_\odot$$

$$L_{Al} = 13.89 L_\odot \qquad (16.124)$$

$$\Delta L = \left[\frac{2 \times 0.13}{39.91} + 0.01 \ln(26.72) + 0.01 \ln(3.99) \right] \times 13.89 \qquad (16.125)$$

$$\Delta L = 0.74$$

$$L_{Al} = (13.9 \pm 0.7) L_\odot \qquad (16.126)$$

Similarly, we calculate the luminosity of other components.

$$L_{MA} = (77 \pm 10) L_\odot \qquad (16.127)$$

$$L_{MB} = (17 \pm 2) L_\odot \qquad (16.128)$$

$$L_{SL} = (13 \pm 2) L_\odot \qquad (16.129)$$

$$\therefore \qquad L_{tot} = L_{Al} + L_{MA} + L_{MB} + L_{SL}$$

$$= (13.9 + 77 + 17 + 13) L_\odot$$

$$L_{tot} = (121 \pm 15) L_\odot \qquad (16.130)$$

(d) Mizar A, Mizar B and Alcor are almost at the same distance from the Earth (almost same parallax). It is known that Alcor (which is itself a binary) is gravitationally bound to the Mizar (quadruple) system. The star Sidus Ludoviciana is, however, too far to be gravitationally bound to the other star. Thus, in all questions that refer to the gravitationally bound stars of the Mizar system, we should only consider the first three stars.

$$d_{av} = \frac{1}{3} \sum_{i=1}^{3} \frac{1}{p_i}$$

$$= \frac{1000}{3} \left[\frac{1}{39.91} + \frac{1}{38.01} + \frac{1}{38.01} \right]$$

$$d_{av} = 25.89 \text{ pc}$$

$$\Delta d_{av} = \left[\frac{0.13}{39.91} + \frac{1.71}{38.01} + \frac{1.71}{38.01} \right] \times 25.89$$

$$= 2.41 \text{ pc}$$

$$d_{av} = (26.0 \pm 0.2) \text{ pc} \tag{16.131}$$

(e) Let θ be the angular seperation.

$$\cos \theta = \sin \delta_1 \sin \delta_2 + \cos \delta_1 \cos \delta_2 \cos(\alpha_2 - \alpha_1) \tag{16.132}$$

$$= \sin(54°55'31'') \sin(-16°43') + \cos(54°55'31'') \cos(-16°43') \cos(99°43'53'')$$

$$= -0.3284$$

$$\theta = 109°10'25''$$

$$\frac{\Delta\theta}{\theta} = \frac{\Delta\delta_1}{\delta_1} + \frac{\Delta\delta_2}{\delta_2} + \frac{\Delta\alpha_1}{\alpha_1} + \frac{\Delta\alpha_2}{\alpha_2}$$

$$= \frac{1''}{54°55'31''} + \frac{1'}{16°43'} + \frac{0^h0^m0.1^s}{13^h23^m55.5^s} + \frac{0^h1^m}{6^h45^m}$$

$$\Delta\theta = 21'$$

$$\theta = (109°10' \pm 21') \tag{16.133}$$

(f) By the cosine rule

$$d^2 = (26)^2 + (2.64)^2 - 2 \times 26 \times 2.64 \times \cos(109°10')$$

$$\therefore \qquad d = 26.87 \text{ pc}$$

$$\delta d = \left[\frac{\Delta d_{av}}{d_{av}} + \frac{\Delta d_0}{d_0} + \frac{\Delta\theta}{\theta} \right] d$$

$$= \left[\frac{2}{26} + \frac{0.01}{2.64} + \frac{21'}{109°10'} \right] \times 26.87$$

$$\delta d = 2.3 \text{ pc}$$

$$d = (27.0 \pm 0.2)\text{p} \tag{16.134}$$

(g)

$$m_{\odot,0} - m_A = -2.5 \log \left(\frac{\dfrac{L_\odot}{a_\oplus^2}}{\dfrac{L_{tot}}{d^2}} \right)$$

$$\therefore \qquad m_A = m_{\odot,0} + 2.5 \log \left(\frac{L_\odot d^2}{L_{tot} a_\oplus^2} \right)$$

$$= -26.72 + 2.5 \log \left(\frac{(27 \times 206265)^2}{121} \right)$$

$$m_A = 1.80$$

$$\Delta m_A = \left| \frac{0.01}{26.72} + \frac{2}{27 \log 27} + \frac{15}{121 \log 121} \right| \times 1.80$$

$$\Delta m_A = 0.2$$

$$\therefore \qquad m_A = (1.8 \pm 0.2) \qquad\qquad (16.135)$$

5. First, import the ASCII data of the text file in the spreadsheet programme.

   (a) In order to calculate the angular distance (φ), all coordinates should be converted into decimal degrees and then into radians.

   (b) Using the cosine law

   $$\varphi = \cos^{-1}(\sin \delta_1 \sin \delta_2 + \cos \delta_1 \cos \delta_2 \cos(\alpha_1 - \alpha_2)) \qquad (16.136)$$

   the angular distance φ between each of the stars and the point of convergence can be calculated.

   (c) The proper motion of each star will be given by

   $$\mu = \sqrt{(\mu_a \cos d)^2 + (\mu_d)^2} \qquad\qquad (16.137)$$

   (d) Using Equation 6.1 (remember to divide the given values of μ by 1000 to obtain arcseconds), we should be able to calculate the distance r_μ of each star.

   (e) The trigonometric parallax distance is given by $r_\pi = \dfrac{1}{\pi \times 10^{-3}}$.

   The results are summarised in Table 16.1.

   (f)
   $$r_\mu = 39.81 \text{ pc}$$
   $$\sigma_\mu = 4.63 \text{ pc}$$
   $$r_\pi = 52.96 \text{ pc}$$
   $$\sigma_\pi = 12.96 \text{ pc}$$

   (g) The method with the smaller standard deviation (i.e., moving cluster method) is more accurate.

6. (a) A graph is drawn with $(B - V)_0$ on the x-axis and BC on the y-axis.

Table 16.1   *Moving cluster distances of the stars*

HIP	φ	μ	r_μ	d_{centre}	Cluster?	r_π
		arcsec/yr	pc	pc		pc
13834	47.676	236.91	27.4738	18.8662	NO	
14838	44.382	154.84	32.9328	13.4072	NO	
18170	34.254	147.05	34.1913	12.1487	NO	
18735	32.714	132.54	32.4085	13.9315	NO	
19554	28.775	146.95	28.8556	17.4844	NO	
20205	27.649	117.73	36.8706	9.4694	YES	47.237

HIP	φ	μ	r_μ	d_{centre}	Cluster?	r_π
		arcsec/yr	pc	pc		pc
20261	27.323	110.74	35.6283	10.7117	NO	
20400	26.742	116.03	34.6263	11.7137	NO	
20455	27.502	111.54	39.0391	7.3009	YES	46.970
20542	27.209	114.97	36.9781	9.3619	YES	44.723
20635	28.903	114.35	39.3132	7.0268	YES	47.015
20711	28.963	117.93	35.2453	11.0947	NO	
20713	26.129	119.40	35.3599	10.9801	NO	
20842	28.045	106.83	39.4468	6.8932	YES	47.962
20885	25.718	105.83	38.5670	7.7730	YES	48.403
20889	26.853	113.36	37.0929	9.2471	YES	47.529
20894	25.671	111.82	35.2721	11.0679	NO	
20901	24.913	106.25	36.7947	9.5453	YES	49.188
21029	25.338	107.95	37.9373	8.4027	YES	44.366
21036	24.638	109.84	34.1743	12.1657	NO	
21039	25.161	106.96	36.648	9.6920	YES	44.346
21137	24.932	112.36	31.4207	14.9193	NO	
21152	23.639	114.32	32.1464	14.1936	NO	
21459	27.238	122.45	38.3993	7.9407	YES	44.248
21589	22.578	102.82	38.1353	8.2047	YES	45.893
21683	23.271	84.68	38.1394	8.2006	YES	48.757
22044	20.809	99.78	31.8170	14.5230	NO	
22157	20.529	67.85	50.0608	3.7208	YES	81.699
22176	22.905	101.01	38.9200	7.4200	YES	92.507
22203	21.485	94.65	37.2117	9.1283	YES	51.493
22565	21.906	86.13	36.2419	10.0981	NO	
22850	21.525	69.40	46.0346	0.3054	YES	68.166
23497	21.282	80.13	38.9646	7.3754	YES	49.975
23983	14.553	64.03	37.7718	8.5682	YES	53.937
24019	25.072	82.40	53.7798	7.4398	YES	54.705

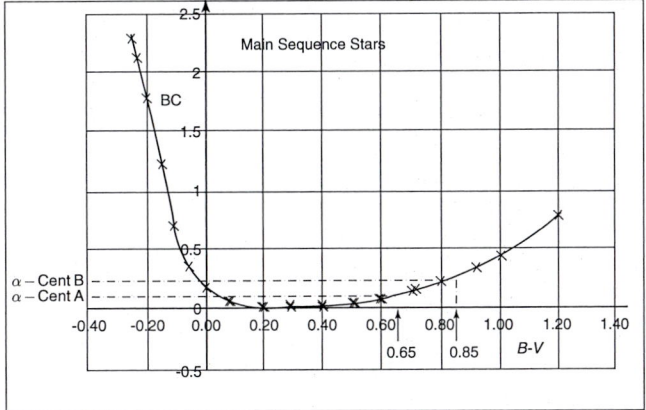

(b) From the graph

$$BC_A = 0.09$$

$$m_{bol-A} = m_v - BC = -0.01 - 0.09$$

$$= -0.1 \tag{16.138}$$

$$BC_B = 0.23$$

$$m_{bol_B} = m_v - BC = 1.34 - 0.23$$

$$= 1.11 \tag{16.139}$$

(c) Orbital period of α–Centauri is $T = 79.24$ years and its angular semi-major axis is $\alpha = 17.59''$. If d is the distance to the star in parsec, M_A and M_B are masses of two components in solar masses and a is their orbital radius in AU, using Kepler's third law, we get

$$T^2 = \frac{a^3}{(M_A + M_B)} \tag{16.140}$$

$$= \frac{(\alpha d)^3}{(M_A + M_B)}$$

$$d^3 = \frac{(M_A + M_B)T^2}{\alpha^3} \tag{16.141}$$

The implicit trick here is the fact that the Earth goes around one solar mass star in one year with orbital radius of 1 AU. So, taking quantities in those units will automatically eliminate $\frac{4\pi^2}{G}$.

From this, we can proceed using two methods:

i. We find the masses by the iterative method.

   1st *iteration:* We first assume

$$M_A + M_B = 2M_\varepsilon \tag{16.124}$$

$$d^3 = \frac{(M_A + M_B)T^2}{\alpha^3}$$

$$d = \sqrt[3]{\frac{2 \times 79.24^2}{17.59^3}}$$

$$= \sqrt[3]{2.3074}$$

$$d = 1.321 pc \tag{16.143}$$

We determine the absolute bolometric magnitude.

$$M_{bol} = m_{bol} + 5 - 5 \log d \tag{16.144}$$

$$M_{bol-A} = -0.1 + 5 - 5 \log(1.3214)$$

$$M_{bol-A} = 4.9 - 0.6052 = 4.29 \tag{16.145}$$

$$M_{bol-B} = 1.11 + 5 - 5 \log(1.3214)$$

$$M_{bol-B} = 6.11 - 0.6052 = 5.50 \tag{16.146}$$

Now, we determine the mass of both stars using the luminosity–mass relation.

$$M_{bol} = -10.2 \log\left(\frac{M}{M_\odot}\right) + 4.9$$

$$\therefore \qquad M = 10^{\frac{(4.9 - M_{bol})}{10.2}} M_\odot \tag{16.147}$$

$$M_A = 10^{\frac{(4.9 - 4.29)}{10.2}} M_\odot$$

$$= 10^{\frac{0.61}{10.2}} M_\odot$$

$$M_A = 1.1476 M_\odot \tag{16.148}$$

$$M_B = 10^{\frac{(4.9 - 5.50)}{10.2}} M_\odot$$

$$= 10^{\frac{-0.6}{10.2}} M_\odot$$

$$M_B = 0.8733 M_\odot \tag{16.149}$$

$$\therefore \qquad M_A + M_B = (1.1476 + 0.8733) M_\odot$$

$$M_A + M_B = 2.0209 M_\odot \tag{16.150}$$

2nd *iteration:* Repeating the steps above and using the previous resulting total mass from the first iteration

$$d = \sqrt[3]{\frac{2.0209 \times (79.24)^2}{(17.59)^3}}$$

$$d = 1.3260 pc \tag{16.151}$$

$$M_{bol-A} = -0.1 + 5 - 5 \log(1.3260)$$

$$M_{bol-A} = 4.29 \tag{16.152}$$

$$M_{bol-B} = 1.11 + 5 - 5 \log(1.3260)$$

$$M_{bol-B} = 5.50 \tag{16.153}$$

We can note that within the accuracy limits of magnitudes, the absolute bolometric magnitudes in the second iteration are exactly the same as the ones in the first iteration. Thus, the masses determined would again be exactly the same. Thus

$$\therefore \qquad M_A = 1.15 M_\odot \qquad (16.154)$$

$$\& \, M_B = 0.87 M_\odot \qquad (16.155)$$

ii. Alternatively, we can substitute d in terms of mass.

$$d^3 = \frac{(M_A + M_B)T^2}{\alpha^3}$$

$$\therefore \qquad \frac{(M_A + M_B)}{d^3} = \frac{\alpha^3}{T^2} = \frac{17.59^3}{79.24^2} \qquad (16.156)$$

$$= 0.8668 M_\odot/pc^3 \qquad (16.157)$$

$$M_{bol} = m_{bol} + 5 - 5 \log d$$

$$M_{bol} = -10.2 \log\left(\frac{M}{M_\odot}\right) + 4.9$$

$$\therefore \qquad 10.2 \log\left(\frac{M}{M_\odot}\right) = 5 \log d - m_{bol} - 5 + 4.9$$

$$\log M = \frac{5 \log d - m_{bol} - 0.1}{10.2} \qquad (16.158)$$

$$\log M_A = 0.49 \log d \qquad (16.159)$$

$$\log M_B = 0.49 \log d - \frac{1.21}{10.2} \qquad (16.160)$$

Combining the two equations, we get

$$\log M_B = \log M_A - \frac{1.21}{10.2}$$

$$\therefore \qquad M_B = 10^{\frac{-1.21}{10.2}} M_A$$

$$M_B = 0.7610 M_A \qquad (16.161)$$

$$M_A + M_B = 1.7610 M_A$$

$$\therefore \qquad 0.8668 d^3 = 1.7610 d^{0.49} \qquad (16.162)$$

$$d = \left(\frac{1.7610}{0.8668}\right)^{\frac{1}{2.51}}$$

$$d = 1.3260 pc \qquad (16.163)$$

$$M_A = d^{0.49}$$

$$= 1.15 M_\odot \qquad (16.164)$$

$$M_B = 0.7610 \times 1.1483 M_\odot$$

$$M_B = 0.87 M_\odot$$

17

Solutions: Binaries and Variables

17.1 Theory

1. As the orbital plane is perpendicular to the line of sight, the largest angular separation corresponds to the apastron position and the smallest angular separation corresponds to the periastron position. Thus

$$a = \frac{1}{2} \times (7'' + 1'') \times 10 \tag{17.1}$$

$$a = 40 \text{ AU} \tag{17.2}$$

$$M_\odot = \frac{4\pi^2}{G} \frac{(1\,\text{AU})^3}{(1\,\text{year})^2}$$

$$m_1 + m_2 = \frac{4\pi^2}{G} \frac{a^3}{T^2}$$

$$= \frac{40^3}{100^2} M_\odot$$

$$m_1 + m_2 = 6.4 M_\odot \tag{17.3}$$

$$a_2 = a - a_1 = 4.0'' - 3.0''$$

$$= 1.0'' \tag{17.4}$$

$$\because \quad \frac{m_1}{m_2} = \frac{a_2}{a_1} = \frac{1}{3} \tag{17.5}$$

$$\therefore \quad m_1 = 1.6 M_\odot \tag{17.6}$$

$$m_2 = 4.8 M_\odot \tag{17.7}$$

2. From the light curve, the period of the Cepheid is P $\sim$ 11 days and its average apparent magnitude is $\sim \frac{(14.8 + 14.1)}{2} = 14.45$ mag. In addition, you may note that the upper half and lower half of the light curve are not symmetrical. The star spends more time in the fainter part of the light curve. Thus, the average magnitude integrated over one cycle would be slightly fainter than a simple mathematical average of the maxima and the minima. For this reason, we choose $m_{av} = 14.5$ mag.

From the period–luminosity relation, we estimate that for a period of 11 days, the expected absolute magnitude of the Cepheid is $M \approx -4.2$.

$$m - M = -5 + 5 \log r \tag{17.8}$$

$$\log r = \frac{(14.5 + 4.2 + 5)}{5} = 4.74$$

$$r = 10^{4.74} \approx 55\ 000 \text{ pc}$$

$$r = 55.0 \text{ kpc} \tag{17.9}$$

If extinction in the direction of the Cepheid is $A = 0.25$ mag, then

$$\log r = \frac{(14.5 + 4.2 + 5 + 0.25)}{5} = 4.79$$

$$r = 10^{4.79} \approx 61\ 700 \text{ pc}$$

$$r = 61.7 \text{ kpc} \tag{17.10}$$

3. The apparent magnitude of star A is m_A, of star B is m_B and that of the system as a whole is m_C.

The corresponding apparent brightnesses are l_A, l_B and $l_C = l_A + l_B$.

For star A:

$$m_C - m_A = -2.5 \log \left(\frac{l_A + l_B}{l_A} \right) \tag{17.11}$$

$$m_A = m_C + 2.5 \log \left(1 + \frac{1}{2} \right) \qquad (\because l_A / l_B = 2)$$

$$= 5 + 2.5 \log 1.5$$

$$\therefore \qquad m_A = 5.44 \text{ mag} \tag{17.12}$$

Similarly, for star B:

$$m_C - m_B = -2.5 \log \left(\frac{l_A + l_B}{l_B} \right)$$

$$m_B = 5 + 2.5 \log 3$$

$$m_B = 6.19 \text{ mag} \tag{17.13}$$

4. The distance of both the stars from us is almost the same. Thus, their magnitude difference can be directly related to their luminosity ratio. As both the stars are of same spectral type, one can assume that they have the same effective temperature (T_{eff}).

$$\Delta m = m_B - m_A = 2.5 \log \frac{\frac{L_A}{4\pi r^2}}{\frac{L_B}{4\pi r^2}}$$

$$10 = 2.5 \log \frac{L_A}{L_B}$$

$$\therefore \qquad L_A = 10^4 L_B \tag{17.14}$$

$$\frac{L_A}{L_B} = \frac{4\pi R_A^2 \sigma T_{eff}^4}{4\pi R_B^2 \sigma T_{eff}^4}$$

$$10^4 = (R_A/R_B)^2 \tag{17.15}$$

$\therefore$
$$R_B = 0.01R_A = 0.01 \times 1.7 \times 6.955 \times 10^8$$

$$R_B = 1.2 \times 10^7 \text{ m} \tag{17.16}$$

5. Assuming brightness is proportional to the area of stars visible to us.

$$B_{max} \propto 2 \times \text{(area of elliptic cross-section)}$$

$\therefore$
$$B_{max} \propto 2\pi ab \tag{17.17}$$

$$B_{min} \propto 2 \text{ (area of circular cross-section)}$$

$$B_{min} \propto \pi b^2 \tag{17.18}$$

$$\frac{B_{max}}{B_{min}} = \frac{2\pi ab}{\pi b^2}$$

$$= \frac{2a}{b} = 4 \tag{17.19}$$

$$\Delta m = 2.5 \log\left(\frac{B_{max}}{B_{min}}\right) \tag{17.20}$$

$$= 2.5 \log 4 \tag{17.21}$$

$$\Delta m = 1.5 \tag{17.22}$$

6. (a) From conservation of angular momentum

$$\omega r^2 = \text{constant} \tag{17.23}$$

$$\omega r^2 = \langle \omega \rangle \, ab \tag{17.24}$$

Thus, when $\omega < \langle \omega \rangle$, clearly $r > \sqrt{ab}$. From the image

$$2a = 6.2 \, cm \tag{17.25}$$

$$2b = 5.0 \, cm \tag{17.26}$$

$$\sqrt{ab} \approx 2.8 \, cm < r \tag{17.27}$$

We can measure r from M at various points to mark the regions.

(b) Let V_t be the tangential velocity at distance r. Now, at periastron, the total velocity of m is maximum and is purely tangential. Hence, that is the point where $v_t = v_{tmax}$. Similarly, at apastron, $v_t = v_{tmin}$.

(c) For maximum radial velocity, one can note that radial accelaration changes sign at the end points of the latus rectum. Thus, they are the points where radial velocity will be maximum (when receding from the observer) or minimum (when approaching the observer).

7. Remember that apparent magnitude of Vega is zero.

$$L_{cep} = \sigma 4\pi R^2 T^4$$

$$M_{Vega} - M_\odot = -2.5 \log\left(\frac{L_{Vega}}{L_\odot}\right)$$

$$\therefore \qquad L_{Vega} = 10^{0.4M\odot}L_{\odot} \qquad\qquad (17.28)$$

$$M_{cep} - M_{Vega} = -2.5\log\left(\frac{L_{cep}}{L_{Vega}}\right) \qquad\qquad (17.29)$$

$$\therefore \qquad M_{cep} = -2.5\log\left(\frac{\sigma 4\pi R^2 T^4}{10^{0.4M\odot}L_{\odot}}\right)$$

Now, as $P = 2\pi R\sqrt{\dfrac{R}{GM}}$

$$M_{cep} = -2.5\log\left[\frac{\sigma 4\pi T^4}{10^{0.4M_{\odot}}L_{\odot}}\times\left(GM\frac{R}{4\pi^2}\right)^{\frac{2}{3}}\right]$$

$$= -2.5\log\left[\frac{2\sigma T^4}{10^{0.4M_{\odot}}L_{\odot}}\times\left(\frac{G^2M^2}{2\pi}\right)^{\frac{1}{3}}\right] - 2.5\log P\frac{4}{3}$$

$$= -2.5\log\left[\frac{2\sigma T^4}{10^{0.4M\odot}L_{\odot}}\times\left(\frac{G^2M^2}{2\pi}\right)^{\frac{1}{3}}\right] - 2.5\times\frac{4}{3}\log P$$

$$\therefore \qquad M_{cep} = -2.5\log k - \frac{10}{3}\log P \qquad\qquad (17.30)$$

8. During the secondary minimum, the brighter (and larger) star eclipses the fainter (and smaller) star. Therefore, during the primary minimum, we will have an annular eclipse; the cooler and smaller component is visible against the larger one, only obscuring it partially.

We use subscripts:

0 - data concerning the sum of both components (when there is no eclipse)

1 - data concerning the brighter component

2 - data concerning the fainter component

p - data concerning the primary minimum

s - data concerning the secondary minimum

Let R_is be radii, T_is be the effective temperatures, L_is be the luminosities and f_is be the luminosities per unit surface area of the star.

Remember that the eclipse starts (first contact) when two stars' edges are seen to be touching from the outside. At the start of the totality phase (second contact), the edges touch from the inside. At the end of totality (third contact), the edges again touch from the inside and at the end of the eclipse (fourth contact), the edges again touch from the outside.

Thus, between the first and second contact, the fainter star moves a distance of $2R_2$.

Between the first and fourth contact (corresponding to D), the fainter star moves a distance of $2(R_1 + R_2)$.

Between the second and third contact (corresponding to d), the fainter star moves a distance of $2(R_1 - R_2)$.

From the graph

$$\frac{2(R_1 + R_2)}{2(R_1 - R_2)} = \frac{D}{d} = 9 \tag{17.31}$$

$$\therefore \qquad \frac{R_2}{R_1} = \frac{4}{5} \tag{17.32}$$

$$L_0 = L_1 + L_2 = R_1^2 f_1 + R_2^2 f_2 \tag{17.33}$$

$$L_s = L_1 = R_1^2 f_1 \tag{17.34}$$

$$L_p = R_2^2 f_2 + \left(R_1^2 - R_2^2\right) f_1 \tag{17.35}$$

$$m_0 - m_s = -2.5 \log\left(\frac{L_0}{L_s}\right) = -2.5 \log\left(\frac{R_1^2 f_1 + R_2^2 f_2}{R_1^2 f_1}\right) \tag{17.36}$$

$$= -2.5 \log\left(1 + \frac{R_2^2 f_2}{R_1^2 f_1}\right) \tag{17.37}$$

Let the bracket be $(1 + x)$

$$-0.33 = -2.5 \log(1 + x)$$

$$\therefore \qquad 1 + x = 10^{\frac{0.33}{2.5}}$$

$$1 + x = 1 + \frac{R_2^2 f_2}{R_1^2 f_1} = 1.3552 \tag{17.38}$$

$$m_p - m_0 = -2.5 \log\left(\frac{L_p}{L_0}\right) = -2.5 \log\left(\frac{R_2^2 f_2 + \left(R_1^2 - R_2^2\right) f_1}{R_1^2 f_1 + R_2^2 f_2}\right) \tag{17.39}$$

$$= -2.5 \log\left(\frac{\dfrac{R_2^2 f_2}{R_2^1 f_1} + 1 - \dfrac{R_2^2}{R_2^1}}{1 + \dfrac{R_2^2 f_2}{R_2^1 f_1}}\right)$$

$$= -2.5 \log\left(\frac{1 + x - \dfrac{R_2^2}{R_1^2}}{1 + x}\right)$$

$$= -2.5 \log\left(1 - \frac{1}{1 + x}\left(\frac{R_2}{R_1}\right)^2\right) \tag{17.40}$$

$$= -2.5 \log\left(1 - \frac{1}{1.3552}\left(\frac{4}{5}\right)^2\right)$$

$$m_p - m_0 = 0.694 \tag{17.41}$$

This is 2.1 times the magnitude difference between m_0 and m_s. Hence, we can draw the light curve at primary minima.

9. (a) The total angular momentum of the system is

$$L = I\omega = \left(M_1 r_1^2 + M_2 r_2^2\right)\omega \tag{17.42}$$

As there is quasi-static equilibrium, $M_1 r_1 = M_2 r_2$ and $D = r_1 + r_2$, which yields

$$r_1 = \frac{M_2 D}{M_1 + M_2} \tag{17.43}$$

$\therefore$

$$L = \frac{M_1 M_2}{M_1 + M_2} D^2 \omega \tag{17.44}$$

The kinetic energy of the system is

$$KE = \frac{1}{2} M_1 \left(r_1 \omega\right)^2 + \frac{1}{2} M_2 \left(r_2 \omega\right)^2$$

$$\frac{1}{2}\left(M_1 r_1^2 + M_2 r_2^2\right)\omega^2 = \frac{1}{2} L\omega$$

$$= \frac{1}{2} \frac{M_1 M_2}{M_1 + M_2} D^2 \omega^2 \tag{17.45}$$

(b) Equating the centripetal acceleration to the gravitational acceleration

$$M_1 \omega^2 r_1 = \frac{GM_1 M_2}{D^2} \tag{17.46}$$

Equations 17.43 and 17.46 together yield

$$\omega^2 = \frac{G\left(M_1 + M_2\right)}{D^3} \tag{17.47}$$

(c) As the system is isolated

$$M_1 + M_2 = \text{constant}$$

Since there is no external torque acting on the system, the total angular momentum must be conserved.

$$L = \frac{M_1 M_2}{M_1 + M_2} D^2 \omega = \text{constant}$$

$\therefore$

$$M_1 M_2 D^2 \omega = \text{constant} \tag{17.48}$$

Now, after the mass transfer

$$\omega \to \omega + \Delta\omega$$

$$M_1 \to M_1 + \Delta M_1 \tag{17.49}$$

$$M_2 \to M_2 - \Delta M_1 \tag{17.50}$$

$$D \to D + \Delta D$$

$\therefore$

$$M_1 M_2 D^2 \omega = (M_1 + \Delta M_1)(M_2 - \Delta M_1)(D + \Delta D)^2(\omega + \Delta\omega) \tag{17.51}$$

$$1 = \left(1 + \frac{\Delta M_1}{M_1}\right)\left(1 - \frac{\Delta M_1}{M_2}\right)\left(1 + \frac{\Delta D}{D}\right)^2\left(1 + \frac{\Delta \omega}{\omega}\right)$$

After using the approximation $(1+x)^n \sim (1+nx)$ and rearranging, we get

$$1 = 1 + \frac{\Delta M_1}{M_1} - \frac{\Delta M_1}{M_2} + \frac{2\Delta D}{D}\frac{\Delta \omega}{\omega}$$

$$\frac{\Delta \omega}{\omega} + 2\frac{\Delta D}{D} = \left(\frac{M_1 - M_2}{M_1 M_2}\right)\Delta M_1 \tag{17.52}$$

From Equation 17.47, $\omega^2 D^3$ is also constant. That is

$$\omega^2 D^3 = (\omega + \Delta\omega)^2(D + \Delta D)^3$$

$$\frac{\Delta D}{D} = -\frac{2}{3}\frac{\Delta \omega}{\omega} \tag{17.53}$$

$$\therefore \qquad \Delta\omega = -\left(\frac{3(M_1 - M_2)}{M_1 M_2}\right)\omega\Delta M_1 \tag{17.54}$$

(d) We first find $\Delta\omega$ by

$$\Delta\omega = \omega_2 - \omega_1 = \frac{2\pi}{T_2} - \frac{2\pi}{T_1}$$

$$\approx \frac{2\pi(T_1 - T_2)}{T^2} = \frac{-\omega}{T}\Delta T \tag{17.55}$$

$$\therefore \qquad \Delta M_1 = -\left(\frac{M_1 M_2}{3(M_1 - M_2)}\right)\frac{\Delta \omega}{\omega}$$

$$\Delta M_1 = -\left(\frac{M_1 M_2}{3(M_1 - M_2)}\right)\frac{\Delta T}{T} \tag{17.56}$$

$$\frac{\Delta M_1}{M_1 \Delta t} = \frac{1.4 \times 20}{3 \times (2.9 - 1.4) \times 2.49 \times 86400 \times 100}$$

$$\approx 2.9 \times 10^{-7} \text{ per year} \tag{17.57}$$

(e) In Equation 17.49 above, we added ΔM_1 to M_1. As the final sign of ΔM_1 is positive, mass is flowing from M_2 to M_1.

(f) From Equations 17.53 and 17.55:

$$\frac{\Delta D}{D} = -\frac{2}{3}\frac{\Delta \omega}{\omega} = +\frac{2}{3}\frac{\Delta T}{T}$$

$$\therefore \qquad \frac{\Delta D}{D\Delta t} = +\frac{2}{3}\frac{\Delta T}{T\Delta t}$$

$$= \frac{2 \times 20}{3 \times 2.49 \times 86400 \times 100}$$

$$= 6.2 \times 10^{-7} \text{ per year} \tag{17.58}$$

10. We first calculate angular separation between the stars.

$$\Delta\alpha = 14^h39^m39.39^s - 14^h29^m44.95^s$$

$$= 9^m54.44^s = 2.4768° \tag{17.59}$$

$$\Delta\delta = -60°50'22.10'' - (-62°40'46.14'')$$

$$= 1°50'24.04'' = 1.87400° \tag{17.60}$$

$$\Delta\alpha \cos\delta_{av} = 2.4768° \times \cos(-61°45'34.12'')$$

$$= 1.17196° \tag{17.61}$$

$$\therefore \qquad \Delta\theta = \sqrt{\Delta\delta^2 + (\Delta\alpha\cos\delta)^2} \tag{17.62}$$

$$= \sqrt{1.8400^2 + 1.17196^2}$$

$$= 2.1815° \tag{17.63}$$

Next, we find the physical separation between the two stars.

$$a^2 = d_1^2 + d_2^2 - 2d_1d_2\cos\Delta\theta \tag{17.64}$$

$$a = \sqrt{1.2953^2 + 1.3475^2 - 2\times1.2953\times1.3475\cos2.1815°}$$

$$a = 0.07249 \text{ pc}$$

$$= 2.237 \times 10^{15} \text{ m} \tag{17.65}$$

Next, we find the relative velocity of one star with respect to another.

$$\Delta\mu\alpha = 0.176'' \tag{17.66}$$

$$\Delta\mu\delta = 0.18'' \tag{17.67}$$

$$V_{rel} = d_{av}\sqrt{(\Delta\mu_\delta)^2 + (\Delta\mu_\alpha)^2} \tag{17.68}$$

$$= 1.3214 \times \sqrt{\frac{(0.18^2 + 0.176^2)}{206265}} \times \frac{3.0856\times10^{16}}{3.1557\times10^7}$$

$$V_{rel} = 1.58 \text{ km/s} \tag{17.69}$$

The Keplerian orbital velocity for this orbital radius, where the central mass is about 1–2 solar masses is given by

$$V_{Kep} = \sqrt{\frac{GM_\odot}{a}} \tag{17.70}$$

$$= \sqrt{\frac{6.6726\times10^{-11}\times1.9891\times10^{30}}{2.237\times10^{15}}}$$

$$\approx 250 \text{ m/s} \tag{17.71}$$

Thus, clearly, $V_{rel} > V_{Kep}$, which means that the two stars are NOT gravitationally bound.

11. Refer to Fig. 17.1. As the planet is going around the star, there will be a component of its velocity along the line of sight of the terrestrial observer. As shown in Fig. 17.1, the difference in radial velocity of a planet between the begining and end of the transit is due

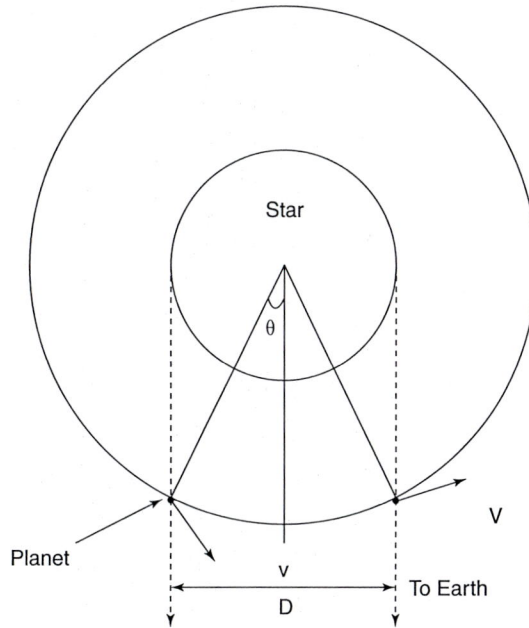

Fig. 17.1 *Transit of exoplanet*

to change in radial velocity of the planet due to revolution. Any velocity due to rotation of the planet will be cancelled.

$$2\theta = \frac{t_{transit}}{T} \times 360 \tag{17.72}$$

$$\theta = \frac{180}{2 \times 84 \times 60} \times 360$$

$$= 12.86° \tag{17.73}$$

$$V_{r1} = -V\sin\theta$$

$$V_{r2} = V\sin\theta$$

$$\Delta V_r = 2V\sin(\theta) \tag{17.74}$$

$$\therefore \qquad V = \frac{\Delta V_r}{2\sin\theta} = \frac{30}{2 \times \sin 12.85}$$

$$V = 134\text{ km/s} \tag{17.75}$$

This orbital velocity will allow us to calculate the orbital radius, assuming a circular orbit.

$$V = \frac{2\pi a}{T} \tag{17.76}$$

$$a = \frac{VT}{2\pi}$$

$$= \frac{134 \times 10^3 \times 84 \times 3600}{2\pi}$$

$$a = 6.45 \times 10^9 \text{ m} \tag{17.77}$$

$$M = \frac{4\pi^2 a^3}{GT^2} \tag{17.78}$$

$$= \frac{4\pi^2 \times \left(6.45 \times 10^9\right)^3}{6.6726 \times 10^{-11} \times \left(84 \times 3600\right)^2}$$

$$M = 1.74 \times 10^{30} \text{ kg} \tag{17.79}$$

$$R_{st} = a \sin \theta = \frac{a \Delta V_r}{2V} \tag{17.80}$$

$$= \frac{6.45 \times 10^9 \times 30}{2 \times 134} \tag{17.81}$$

$$R_{st} = 7.2 \times 10^8 \text{ m} \tag{17.82}$$

12. As the orbits are circular, the magnitude of velocity of the stars remains constant at any point in their orbit. Let $a_{1,2}$ indicate the orbital radii, $M_{1,2}$ the masses, $V_{1,2}$ the velocities and $R_{1,2}$ be the stellar radii.

$$T = 30 \text{ days} = 2.59 \times 10^6 \text{ s} \tag{17.83}$$

$$\omega = \frac{2 \times \pi}{T} = \frac{2 \times \pi}{2.59 \times 10^6}$$

$$= 2.424 \times 10^{-6} \text{ rad/s} \tag{17.84}$$

$$\therefore \qquad V = a\omega \tag{17.85}$$

$$a_1 = \frac{V_1}{\omega} = \frac{30 \times 10^3}{2.424 \times 10^{-6}} m$$

$$a = 1.24 \times 10^{10} \text{ m} \tag{17.86}$$

$$a_2 = \frac{V_2}{\omega} = 1.65 \times 10^{10} m \tag{17.87}$$

$$a = a_1 + a_2 \tag{17.88}$$

$$= (1.24 + 1.65) \times 10^{10} \text{ m}$$

$$a = 2.89 \times 10^{10} \text{ m} \tag{17.89}$$

This total separation between the two stars will be used in Kepler's third law. Next, we find the masses by noting that moments around the centre of mass of the system should be the same.

$$\therefore \qquad M_1 a_1 = M_2 a_2 \tag{17.90}$$

$$\frac{M_2}{M_1} = \frac{a_1}{a_2} = \frac{V_1}{V_2} = \frac{3}{4} \tag{17.91}$$

$$T = 2\pi \sqrt{\frac{a^3}{G\left(M_1 + M_2\right)}} \tag{17.92}$$

$$2.59 \times 10^6 = 2\pi \sqrt{\frac{\left(2.89 \times 10^{10}\right)^3}{6.6726 \times 10^{-11} \times \left(M_1 + M_2\right)}}$$

$$\therefore \qquad M_1 + M_2 = \frac{4\pi^2 \times \left(2.89 \times 10^{10}\right)^3}{6.6726 \times 10^{-11} \times \left(2.59 \times 10^6\right)^2}$$

$$= 2.13 \times 10^{30} \text{ kg} \tag{17.93}$$

$$M_1 + M_2 = 1.06 M_\odot \tag{17.94}$$

$$\therefore \qquad M_1 = \frac{4}{7}\left(M_1 + M_2\right) = \frac{4 \times 1.06}{7} M_\odot \tag{17.95}$$

$$M_1 = 0.67 M_\odot \tag{17.96}$$

$$M_2 = \frac{3}{7}\left(M_1 + M_2\right) \tag{17.97}$$

$$M_2 = 0.45 M_\odot \tag{17.98}$$

If we assume the primary star to be stationary, then the secondary star appears to move in front of it with a relative velocity of

$$V_r = V_1 + V_2 = 70 \text{ km/s} \tag{17.99}$$

During A to D, the distance covered is $2(R_1 + R_2)$ and during B to C, it is $2(R_1 - R_2)$. This assumes that the star is moving transverse to the line joining the stars to the Earth as time period of eclipse $\ll$ time period of orbit.

$$2(R_1 + R_2) = 70 \times 10^3 \times 8 \text{ hours} \tag{17.100}$$

$$= 70 \times 10^3 \times 2.88 \times 10^4$$

$$R_1 + R_2 = 1.008 \times 10^9 \text{ m} = 1.448 R_\odot \tag{17.101}$$

$$2(R_1 - R_2) = 70 \times 10^3 \times 78 \text{ min} \tag{17.102}$$

$$= 70 \times 10^{30} \times 4.68 \times 10^3$$

$$R_1 - R_2 = 1.638 \times 10^8 \text{ m} = 0.235 R_\odot \tag{17.103}$$

$$\therefore \qquad R_1 = 0.841 R_\odot \tag{17.104}$$

$$\& \qquad R_2 = 0.607 R_\odot \tag{17.105}$$

Thus, the bigger star has a mass of $0.61 M_\odot$ and radius of $0.841 R_\odot$. The smaller star has a mass of $0.45 M_\odot$ and radius of $0.607 R_\odot$.

17.2 Data Analysis

1. (a) The plot can be seen in Fig. 17.2.
   (b) The best fit can be found by

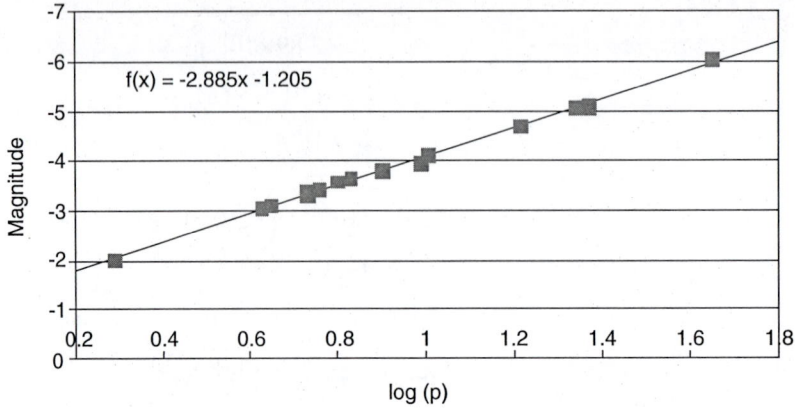

Fig. 17.2   *Period–Luminosity graph of Cepheids*

$$\sum_{i=1}^{n} x_i = 13.90 \tag{17.106}$$

$$\left(\sum_{i=1}^{n} x_i\right)^2 = 193.21$$

$$\sum_{i=1}^{n} x_i^2 = 14.57 \tag{17.107}$$

$$\sum_{i=1}^{n} y_i = -58.18 \tag{17.108}$$

$$\sum_{i=1}^{n} x_i y_i = -58.78 \tag{17.109}$$

$$\beta = \frac{\displaystyle\sum_{i=1}^{n} x_i y_i - \frac{1}{n}\sum_{i=1}^{n} x_i \sum_{i=1}^{n} y_i}{\displaystyle\sum_{i=1}^{n} x_i^2 - \frac{1}{n}\left(\sum_{i=1}^{n} x_i\right)^2}$$

$$= \frac{-58.78 - \dfrac{1}{15}\times(13.90)\times(-58.18)}{14.57 - \dfrac{1}{15}\times 193.21}$$

$$\beta = -2.88 \tag{17.110}$$

$$\langle M_v \rangle = -1.21 - 2.88(\log_{10} P_0) \tag{17.111}$$

(c) Approximate period of Cepheid 1 is (48 ± 1) days. Thus, as per Equation 17.111, it will have an absolute magnitude of about -6.06. Its observed mean magnitude and hence its distance (including uncertainty) is given by

$$\langle m \rangle = 25.30 \pm 0.1 \tag{17.112}$$

$$m = M + 5\log d - 5 \tag{17.113}$$

$$d = 10^{\frac{(m-M+5)}{5}} \tag{17.114}$$

$$d_1 = 10^{\frac{(25.30+6.06+5)}{5}}$$

$$= 1.86 \times 10^7 pc$$

$$d_1 = 18.7 \; Mpc \tag{17.115}$$

For a simplified calculation of uncertainty, we will assume that the coefficients determined in the previous question have high accuracy and the primary source of error is observations of these two distant Cepheids. Thus

$$\frac{\Delta d}{d} = \frac{\Delta P}{P^2} + \frac{\Delta m}{m} \tag{17.116}$$

$$\Delta d = 18.6 \times \left(\frac{1}{48^2} + \frac{0.1}{25.3} \right)$$

$$= 0.1 \; Mpc \tag{17.117}$$

Similarly, for the second Cepheid

$$P = 23 \pm 1 \text{ days} \tag{17.118}$$

$$\therefore \qquad M_2 = -5.11 \tag{17.119}$$

$$\langle m \rangle = 26.30 \pm 0.1 \tag{17.120}$$

$$d_2 = 10^{\frac{(26.30+5.11+5)}{5}}$$

$$d_2 = (19.1 \pm 0.1) \; Mpc \tag{17.121}$$

(d) Assuming both the Cepheids lie along the same of line of sight, we note even after including error margins that they are separated by at least 200 kpc. This distance is much bigger than the size of a typical spiral galaxy[1]. Thus, prima facie it is unlikely that both the Cepheids lie in the same galaxy.

EA: In reality, both the Cepheids used here are from the same galaxy in the Virgo cluster. Light from the second Cepheid is heavily extincted due to interstellar matter in that galaxy. That is the prime reason for variation in the distance estimate.

2. The errors in the last column of Table 7.2 are merely indicative of the fact that observations are not exact. Including them in the calculations will unnecessarily complicate the solution.

(a) The graph shows that the primary and secondary minima are almost similar. Thus, the reported minima can be either primary or secondary. Further, from the graph we note that the secondary minima happens exactly at the phase 0.5. Next, we note that there

---

1 Diameter of the Milky Way is 30 kpc.

are some pairs of minima which are reported for the same night. As observations in the same night are continuous, we can assume that they are consecutive minima. One should remember that JD changes at noon UT but civil date changes at midnight UT. Hence, consecutive minima during the same night may appear on different civil dates but will be on the same JD. We find five pairs of consecutive minima in Table 7.2.

Sr.	Between	Difference (days)
1	1 and 2	0.1367 ± 0.0006
2	3 and 4	0.1372 ± 0.0010
3	5 and 6	0.1364 ± 0.0020
4	10 and 11	0.1373 ± 0.0005
5	11 and 12	0.1359 ± 0.0005

The average of these values gives the initial estimate of the half-period of V 1107 CAS as 0.1367 days. Hence, the initial estimate of the period of V 1107 CAS is 0.2734 days.

Coincidentally, the difference between the first and second observations is the same as the average. However, this event is sheer chance and it is necessary to take the average of all five pairs. It is also important to include all five pairs in the average. If you miss one of the pairs, your average will be little farther from the true period. The small error in each period will keep accumulating and the final answers will be affected.

(b) We can assume the first reading to be M_0. Thus, $M_0 = 2454092.4111$. Now, given the initial period (P), we can count approximately how many periods have elapsed since the initial moment (E). This gives us the expected or calculated instance of the minima. We can then compare it with the observed instance of minima and find the difference (O–C). This difference should be plotted against the number of epochs to obtain the O–C graph (Fig. 17.3).

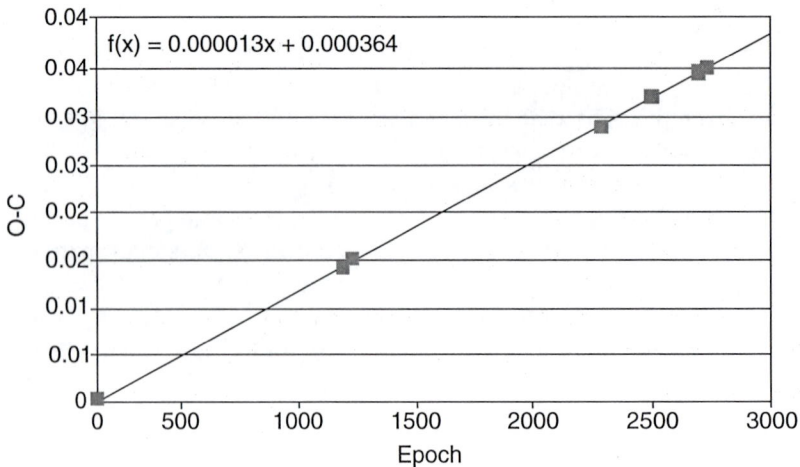

Fig. 17.3   *O–C diagram for V1107 Cas*

E	M_{cal}	M_{obs}	$M_{obs} - M_{cal}$
0	2454092.4111	2454092.4111	0.0000
0.5	2454092.5478	2454092.5478	0.0000
1005.5	2454367.3148	2454367.3284	0.0136
1006	2454367.4515	2454367.4656	0.0141
1083	2454388.5033	2454388.5175	0.0142
1083.5	2454388.6400	2454388.6539	0.0139
2240	2454704.8271	2454704.8561	0.0290
2502	2454776.4579	2454776.4901	0.0322
2717	2454835.2389	2454835.2734	0.0345
2761	2454847.2685	2454847.3039	0.0354
2761.5	2454847.4052	2454847.4412	0.0360
2762	2454847.5419	2454847.5771	0.0352

(c) The O–C diagram shows the difference between the observed and calculated moments of minima. The difference is non-zero because our initial estimate of P and M_0 may not be exact. The linear fit to all points in the graph will help us eliminate these errors. The y-intercept of this graph will give you the error in M_0. To obtain the error in the initial period, realise that slope of this graph is nothing but the average (per period) difference between the observed and calculated moments. This is exactly the error in the initial period.

From the graph, the slope is 0.000013 and y-intercept is 0.000364.

Thus, the corrected period and initial moments will be

$$P = 0.2734 + 0.000013$$

∴
$$P = 0.2734 \text{ days} \tag{17.122}$$

$$M_0 = 2454092.4111 + 0.000364$$

∴
$$M_0 = 2454092.4115 \text{ HJD} \tag{17.123}$$

However, we will retain the additional decimal digits for calculations in the next question.

(d) To jump to 1 September 2011, we use the fact that we know HJD for 23 September 2007. Each Julian year will be exactly 365.25 days long. Thus, the Julian date for 1–2 September 2011 midnight UT will be

$$JD_{obs} = 2454367.5 + 365.25 \times 4 - 22 \tag{17.124}$$

$$= 2455806.5 HJD \tag{17.125}$$

Thus, we are looking for minima between HJD 2455806.2917 and HJD 2455806.5833. Using corrected period ($P = 0.273413$) and initial moment ($M_0 = 2454092.411464$), we find that there are three instances of minima in this window.

1st minima = 2455806.3009 HJD = 19^h 13^m UT

2nd minima = 2455806.4376 HJD = 22^h 30^m UT

3rd minima = 2455806.5743 HJD = 1^h 47^m UT

18

Solutions: Galactic Astrophysics

18.1 Theory

1. The difference in frequencies is due to the relativistic Doppler shift. Since the observed frequency of emission from the gas cloud is higher than the laboratory frequency ν_0, the gas cloud must be approaching the observer.

$$v = v_0 \sqrt{\frac{c+v}{c-v}} \qquad (18.1)$$

$$\frac{v}{c} = \frac{\left(\dfrac{v}{v_0}\right)^2 - 1}{\left(\dfrac{v}{v_0}\right)^2 + 1}$$

$$= \frac{\left(1.000876\right)^2 - 1}{\left(1.000876\right)^2 + 1}$$

$$= \frac{0.001752379}{2.001752379} = 0.0008754224$$

$$v = 0.0008754224 \times 2.99792458 \times 10^8$$

$$= 2.62426 \times 10^5 \text{m}$$

$$v = 262.426 \text{ km s}^{-1} \qquad (18.2)$$

2. Detected frequency $\nu = 1421.23$ MHz. By performing calculations similar to those in the previous problem

$$v = -174 \text{ km/s} \qquad (18.3)$$

However, in both these problems, as the velocity of the cloud is much smaller than the velocity of light, we can approximate the relativistic expression as

$$Dv = v_{21} - v = 1420.406 - 1421.23 \qquad (18.4)$$

$$= -0.82 \text{ MHz} \qquad (18.5)$$

$$v = \frac{\Delta v}{v_{21}} c = \frac{-0.82}{1420.41} \times 3 \times 10^8 \qquad (18.6)$$

$$= -1.74 \times 10^5 \text{ m/s} \tag{18.7}$$

Since $v > v_{21}$, the cloud is moving towards us.

If M is the mass of the black hole, v is the speed of the cloud and R is the orbital radius of the cloud, then

$$v^2 = \frac{GM}{R}$$

$$\therefore \qquad M = \frac{v^2 R}{G} \tag{18.8}$$

$$= \frac{(1.74 \times 10^5)^2 \times 0.2 \times 3.0856 \times 10^{16}}{6.6726 \times 10^{-11}}$$

$$= 2.80 \times 10^{36} \text{ Kg} = \frac{2.80 \times 10^{36}}{1.9891 \times 10^{30}} M_\odot$$

$$= 1.4 \times 10^6 \, M_\odot \tag{18.9}$$

Thus, the mass of the black hole is 1.4 billion solar masses and the cloud is coming towards us at a velocity of 174 km/s.

3. By Kepler's third law

$$T^2 = \frac{4\pi^2}{GM} a^3 \tag{18.10}$$

$$\therefore \qquad \frac{4\pi^2}{G} = \frac{T_\oplus^2 M_\odot}{a_\oplus^3} = \frac{T_{st}^2 M_{BH}}{a_{st}^3}$$

$$a_{st} = \frac{0.12''}{206265} \times 8300 \times 3.0856 \times 10^{16}$$

$$= 1.490 \times 10^{14} \text{ m}$$

$$a_{st} = 966 \text{ AU} \tag{18.11}$$

$$\frac{M_{BH}}{M_\odot} = \frac{a_{st}^3}{T_{st}^2} \times \frac{T_\oplus^2}{a_\oplus^3} = \frac{(996)^3}{(15)^2} \times \frac{1}{1}$$

$$\therefore \qquad M_{BH} = 4.4 \times 10^6 \, M_\odot \tag{18.12}$$

4. The vertical density profile will be

$$\rho(h) = \rho_0 e^{-h/h_0} \tag{18.13}$$

where $\rho(h)$ = density at a distance h from the mid-plane and h_0 is the scale height.

$$\rho(h) = \rho_0 e^{-h/h_0} \tag{18.14}$$

$$\rho(0.5) = \rho_0 e^{-0.5/0.3}$$

$$= 0.189 \rho_0 \tag{18.15}$$

$$\rho(1.5) = \rho_0 e^{-1.5/0.3}$$

$$= 0.0064 \rho_0 \tag{18.16}$$

5. By Tully–Fischer Relation

$$M_B = -9.95 \log \upsilon_{max} + 3.15 \tag{18.17}$$

$$= -9.95 \log 324 + 3.15$$

$$M_B = -21.83 \tag{18.18}$$

$$\log R_{25} = -0.249 M_B - 4.00 \tag{18.19}$$

$$R_{25} = 27.27 \text{ kpc} \tag{18.20}$$

Thus, dynamic mass will be

$$\mu_{25} = \frac{R_{25} \upsilon_{max}^2}{G} \tag{18.21}$$

$$= \frac{27.27 \times 10^3 \times 3.0856 \times 10^{16} \times \left(3.24 \times 10^5\right)^2}{6.6726 \times 10^{-11}}$$

$$= 1.324 \times 10^{42} \text{ kg}$$

$$\mu_{25} = 6.65 \times 10^{11} \, M_\odot \tag{18.22}$$

Sun's absolute magnitude in B-band is

$$M_{B\odot} = M_{V\odot} + [B_\odot - V_\odot] \tag{18.23}$$

$$= 4.82 + 0.64$$

$$= 5.46 \tag{18.24}$$

and

$$M_B = -21.83 \tag{18.25}$$

$$M_B - M_{B\odot} = -2.5 \log\left(\frac{L}{L_\odot}\right) \tag{18.26}$$

$$= -21.83 - 5.46 = -27.29 \tag{18.27}$$

$$L = 10^{\frac{-27.29}{-2.5}} L_\odot \tag{18.28}$$

$$L = 8.24 \times 10^{10} \, L_\odot \tag{18.29}$$

6. In Fig. 18.1, S is the location of the Sun, C is the location of the galactic centre and P is the possible location of the star. Let R_0 be the distance of the Sun from the centre of the galaxy. Let the same for the star be denoted by R. Thus, the radial velocity of the star with respect to the Sun is

$$V_r = V_{st} \cos \alpha - V_\odot \sin l \tag{18.30}$$

$$= V_0(\cos \alpha - \sin l) \tag{18.31}$$

In the triangle $\triangle$ SCP

$$\angle CPS = 180 - (90 - \alpha) \tag{18.32}$$

$$= 90 + \alpha \tag{18.33}$$

$\therefore$

$$\frac{\sin l}{R} = \frac{\sin(90 + \alpha)}{R_0} \tag{18.34}$$

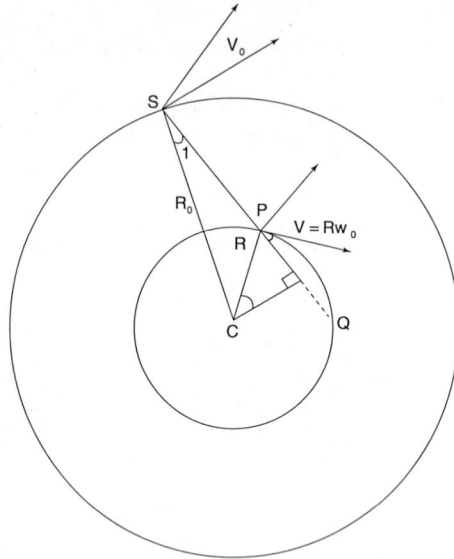

Fig. 18.1   *Galactic position of the star as seen from the galactic south pole*

$$\cos\alpha = \frac{R_0}{R}\sin l \tag{18.35}$$

$$V_r = V_0\left(\frac{R_0}{R} - 1\right)\sin l \tag{18.36}$$

$$V_r R = V_0 R_0 \sin l - V_0 R \sin l \tag{18.37}$$

$$R = \frac{V_0 \sin l}{V_r + V_0 \sin l} R_0 \tag{18.38}$$

$$R = \frac{250\sin 15°}{100 + 250\sin 15°} \times 8.3 \tag{18.39}$$

$$R = 3.1 \text{ kpc} \tag{18.40}$$

Note that this distance of 3.1 kpc is the distance to point P from the Sun. However, there is another possible solution, which is the star located at point Q. One may argue that the radial velocity given in the problem implicitly includes a positive sign and hence Q may be ignored.

7. (a) We find the maximum distance, as a relation between the apparent and absolute magnitude, is given by

$$m = M + 5\log d - 5 \tag{18.41}$$

$$18 = -0.2 + 5\log d - 5$$

∴ $$d = 10^{4.64}$$

$$= 4.37 \times 10^4 \text{ pc}$$

$$d = 43.7 \text{ kpc} \tag{18.42}$$

(b) Adding the term for extinction will make the stars dimmer. Let us say that our new limiting distance is x kpc. Thus, the new expression will be

$$m = M + 5\log\left(\frac{1000x}{10}\right) + 0.7x \tag{18.43}$$

$$= M + 10 + 5\log x + 0.7x \tag{18.44}$$

$$8.2 = 5\log x + 0.7\,x \tag{18.45}$$

$$\text{Let } e(x) = 5\log x + 0.7\,x - 8.2 \tag{18.46}$$

As it is not possible to solve this equation analytically, we try different values of x.

x	5.0	6.0	6.5	6.2	6.1
$e(x)$	−1.205	−0.109	0.415	0.102	−0.003

Thus, the distance reduces to approximately 6.1 kpc.

(c) For a solid angle Ω, the number of observed red giant stars at the distance in the range of d and $(d + Dd)$ is given by

$$DN = \text{Volume} \times \text{Number density} \times \text{Fraction of red giant stars}$$

$$= \Omega x^2 \Delta x\, f n\,(r) \tag{18.47}$$

$$\therefore \quad \frac{\Delta N}{\Delta x} = \Omega x^2\, fn(r) \tag{18.48}$$

$$m = M + 5\log x + 10$$

$$m + \Delta m = M + 5\log(x + \Delta x) + 10 \tag{18.49}$$

$$\therefore \quad \Delta m = 5\log\left(\frac{x + \Delta x}{x}\right) \tag{18.50}$$

$$= 5\log\left(1 + \frac{\Delta x}{x}\right)$$

$$\Delta m = \frac{5}{\ln(10)}\left(\frac{\Delta x}{x}\right) \tag{18.51}$$

$$\frac{\Delta x}{\Delta m} = \frac{x\ln(10)}{5} \tag{18.52}$$

Finally, combining Equations 18.48 and 18.52

$$\frac{\Delta N}{\Delta m} = \frac{\Delta N}{\Delta x} \times \frac{\Delta x}{\Delta m} \tag{18.53}$$

$$= \Omega x^2 f\, n(r) \times \frac{x\ln(10)}{5} \tag{18.54}$$

$$= \frac{n_0 f \ln(10)}{5}\Omega x^3 e^{-\left(\frac{r - R_0}{R_d}\right)} \tag{18.55}$$

We have two distance variables, x and r. They can be related to each other by

$$x = R_0 - r \quad \text{for } x < R_0$$
$$x = R_0 + r \quad \text{for } x > R_0$$

Finally, we write x in terms of apparent magnitude.

$$x = 10^{\frac{m-9.78}{5}} \tag{18.56}$$

For $x < R_0$

$$\frac{\Delta N}{\Delta m} = \frac{n_0 f \ln 10}{5} \Omega x^3 e^{\left(\frac{x}{R_d}\right)} \tag{18.57}$$

For $43.7 \text{kpc} > d > R_0$

$$\frac{\Delta N}{\Delta m} = \frac{n_0 f \ln 10}{5} \Omega x^3 e^{\left(\frac{(2R_0 - x)}{R_d}\right)} \tag{18.58}$$

8. Since the galaxy is edge-on, there will be no correction for inclination.

(a) We draw the first line going through points (0,0) and (16,214). The scale on the axes are kly and km/s, respectively. The second line can be drawn through (16,214) and (60, 200). Thus, the function becomes

$$V(D) = 13.375D \qquad 0 < D < 16$$
$$= 214 - \frac{14}{45}D \qquad D > 16 \tag{18.59}$$

where V is in km/s and D in kly.

(b) For the spiral arms to take one turn around the galaxy, we note that angular velocity of the spiral wave is the difference between the angular velocities of the fastest and lowest points of the pressure wave.

$$\omega_{wave}(D) = \frac{1}{2}\omega_{mass}(D) = \frac{V(D)}{2D} \tag{18.60}$$

$$\omega_{spiral} = \omega_{wave}^{max} - \omega_{wave}^{min} \tag{18.61}$$

$$\omega_{spiral} = \frac{1}{2}\left[\left(\frac{214}{16} - \frac{14}{5}\right) - \left(\frac{214}{80} - \frac{14}{45}\right)\right]$$
$$= 1.78 \times 10^{-8} \text{ rad/yr} \tag{18.62}$$

$$P_{spiral} = \frac{2\pi}{\omega_{rel}} \tag{18.63}$$

$$= 3.52 \times 10^8 \text{ years} \tag{18.64}$$

(c) The maximum velocity difference will be given by

$$\Delta V = 2V_{max}(D) = 2 \times 230 \text{ km/s} \tag{18.65}$$

$$\Delta V = 460 \text{ km/s} \tag{18.66}$$

$$L = 0.317 \times L_\odot \times (460)^4 \tag{18.67}$$

$$L = 1.42 \times 10^{10} L_\odot \tag{18.68}$$

$$M_{sun} - M_{galaxy} = 2.5 \log(1.42 \times 10^{10})$$

$$M_{galaxy} = 4.72 - 25.38$$

$$M_{galaxy} = -20.66 \tag{18.69}$$

$$m_{galaxy} = 8.5 \tag{18.70}$$

$$m - M = 5 \log d - 5 \tag{18.71}$$

$$\log d = \frac{m - M}{5} + 1 = \frac{8.5 + 20.66}{5} + 1$$

$$d = 10^{6.832}$$

$$= 6.80 \text{ Mpc} \tag{18.72}$$

(d) As given in the question, the final observed wavelengths will include the effect of Hubble recession velocity.

$$V_H = H_0 d \tag{18.73}$$

$$= 67.8 \times 6.8$$

$$= 460 \text{ km/s} \tag{18.74}$$

Centre of the galaxy recedes with this speed.

$$V = V_H \pm V_{max} \tag{18.75}$$

$$= 460 \pm 230 \text{ km/s}$$

$$\frac{\Delta \lambda}{\lambda_0} = \frac{v}{c} \tag{18.76}$$

$$\lambda = \lambda_0 \left(1 + \frac{V_H \pm V_{max}}{c}\right)$$

$$\lambda_{max} = 656.28 \times \left(\frac{6.9 \times 10^5}{3 \times 10^8}\right)$$

$$\lambda_{max} = 657.79 \text{ nm} \tag{18.77}$$

$$\lambda_{min} = 656.78 \text{ nm} \tag{18.78}$$

Note that both λ_{max} and λ_{min} are greater than λ_0.

(e) At a distance of 30 kpc, velocity is roughly equal to 225 km/s.

$$\frac{v^2}{R} = \frac{GM}{R^2} \tag{18.79}$$

$$M_{dynamic} = \frac{V^2 R}{G}$$

$$= \frac{\left(2.25 \times 10^5\right)^2 \times 3 \times 10^4 \times 3.0856 \times 10^6}{6.672 \times 10^{-11}}$$

$$M_{dynamic} = 7.02 \times 10^{41} \text{ kg} \tag{18.80}$$

$$= 3.53 \times 10^{11} \, M_\odot \tag{18.81}$$

(f) Let there be n stars of $M_{\odot}$ mass.

$$nM_{\odot} = \frac{M_{bary}}{3} \tag{18.82}$$

$$= \frac{M_{dynamic}}{3} \times \frac{4}{(22+4)}$$

$$\therefore \qquad n = \frac{2M_{dynamic}}{39M_{\odot}} \tag{18.83}$$

$$= \frac{2 \times 2.53 \times 10^{11}}{39}$$

$$n = 1.8 \times 10^{10} \tag{18.84}$$

Note that we are estimating stellar mass only till 30 kpc but the galaxy extends much further.

9. Let the distance to the galaxy be d (pc) and let physical separation of the two objects r AU apart within this galaxy correspond to $\theta = 1''$.

$$d = r\theta \tag{18.85}$$

$$1\left(arcsec^2\right) = \left(\frac{r}{d}\right)^2 \tag{18.86}$$

Let the total number of stars in the area of 1 arcsec^2 be N. It is important to note that as you go further from the galaxy, the light intensity goes down as $1/d^2$. But at the same time, the angular area of the galaxy will also decrease as $1/d^2$. Thus, the surface brightness of the galaxy does not depend on the distance is to the galaxy. As all stars are sun-like, the magnitude of one star is

$$m_{star} = M_{\odot} + 5 \log d - 5$$

$$= 4.82 + 5 \log d - 5$$

$$m_{star} = 5 \log d - 0.18 \tag{18.87}$$

$$\text{Now,} \quad m_N = m_{star} - 2.5 \log N \tag{18.88}$$

$$18 = 5 \log d - 0.25 - 2.5 \log N$$

$$18.25 = 2.5 \log \frac{d^2}{N} \tag{18.89}$$

$$\frac{d^2}{N} = 1.995 \times 10^7 \tag{18.90}$$

Now, each of the stars occupies a cross-section of $\pi R_{\odot}^2$. Thus, the fraction will be,

$$f = \frac{A(stars)}{A(total)} = \frac{N\pi R_{\odot}^2}{r^2\theta^2 \times (1AU)^2} \tag{18.91}$$

$$= \frac{NR_{\odot}^2 \pi}{d^2 (1AU)^2}$$

$$= \frac{\pi \times \left(6.995 \times 10^8\right)^2}{1.995 \times 10^7 \times \left(1.496 \times 10^{11}\right)^2}$$

$$\therefore \qquad\qquad f = 3.4 \times 10^{-12} \qquad\qquad (18.92)$$

10. (a) Let the velocity of each galaxy be divided into three orthogonal components: the first along the radius vector, the second along RA and the third along declination ($v = v_r + v_\alpha + v_\delta$). Using the virial theorem for the given isolated, spherical system of N galaxies of mass m each, we get

$$-2\langle K \rangle = \langle U \rangle$$

$$\therefore \qquad\qquad \langle U \rangle = -\frac{2}{N} \sum_{1}^{N} \frac{1}{2} m_i v_i^2$$

$$\frac{U}{N} = -\frac{m}{N} \sum_{1}^{N} v_i^2$$

$$\therefore \qquad\qquad \frac{U}{N} \approx -m\langle v^2 \rangle \qquad\qquad (18.93)$$

$$\approx -m\left(\langle v_r^2 \rangle + \langle v_\alpha^2 \rangle + \langle v_\delta^2 \rangle\right)$$

As the velocities of the galaxies in the cluster are randomly distributed, we have $\langle v_r^2 \rangle \sim \langle v_\alpha^2 \rangle \sim \langle v_\delta^2 \rangle$. Now, we approximate the cluster to a spherical body with uniform mass distribution.

$$\therefore \qquad\qquad \frac{U}{N} \approx -3m\langle v_r^2 \rangle \qquad\qquad (18.94)$$

$$\frac{1}{N} \times \left(\frac{-3GM^2}{5R}\right) \approx -3m\langle v_r^2 \rangle$$

$$-\frac{3}{5}\frac{GMm}{R} = -3m\langle v_r^2 \rangle \quad (\because M = Nm)$$

$$\therefore \qquad\qquad M \approx \frac{5R\langle v_r^2 \rangle}{G} \qquad\qquad (18.95)$$

(b) From the result of the previous questions we have

$$M \approx \frac{5R\langle v_r^2 \rangle}{G} = \frac{5R\sigma_{v_r}^2}{G} \qquad\qquad (18.96)$$

$$= \frac{5\left(\theta d / 2\right)\sigma_{v_r}^2}{G}$$

$$= \frac{5 \times 90 \times 3.0856 \times 10^{22} \times 2\pi \times \left(10^6\right)^2}{180 \times 6.6726 \times 10^{-11}}$$

$$= 7.26 \times 10^{45} \text{ kg}$$

$$= 3.7 \times 10^{15} \, M_\odot \qquad (18.97)$$

(c) Note that as the Sun is a typical main-sequence star, we would expect visible mass to have the same mass to luminosity ratio as the Sun.

$$\frac{M_{virial}}{L_{cluster}} = \frac{3.7 \times 10^{15} \, M_\odot}{5 \times 10^{12} \, L_\odot}$$

$$= 730 \, \frac{M_\odot}{L_\odot}$$

$$= 730 \, \frac{M_{virial}}{L_{cluster}}$$

$$\therefore \frac{M_{virial}}{L_{cluster}} = \frac{1}{730} \qquad (18.98)$$

18.2 Data Analysis

1. First, we estimate physical length of the galaxy per pixel (a'). Given that the distance to the galaxy (d) is 40 Mpc, 1 arcsec angle will be subtended at that distance by 4×10^7 AU at that distance.

$$a' = \theta d \qquad (18.99)$$

$$a' = 40 \times 10^6 \times 0.82 \;\; \text{AU}$$

$$= \frac{32.8 \times 10^6}{3.262 \times 6.324 \times 10^4} \, \text{pc}$$

$$a' = 159 \;\text{pc} \qquad (18.100)$$

For the scale on the x-axis, we note that the two wavelengths which are separated by 2 nm are separated by 20 pixels on the spectrum. Thus, each pixel corresponds to 0.1 nm.

Most spiral galaxies have a nearly circular cross-section. But the image of NGC 7083 shows that it is somewhat elliptical. This tells you that the plane of the galaxy is inclined at some angle θ to the line of sight. We may estimate θ by measuring the vertical and horizontal dimeters of the galaxy.

$$\sin\theta = \frac{6.7}{13.7} = 0.5323 \qquad (18.101)$$

$$\therefore \qquad \theta = 29.68° \qquad (18.102)$$

$$\cos\theta = 0.8723 \qquad (18.103)$$

Also, in this spectrum, we assume that it has been corrected for Hubble expansion and that the only reason for deviation of λ is rotation of the galaxy.

$$V_{obs} = V_{rot}\cos\theta \qquad (18.104)$$

$$\frac{V_{obs}}{c} = \frac{\Delta\lambda}{\lambda} \qquad (18.105)$$

$$\therefore \qquad V_{rot} = \frac{\Delta\lambda c}{\lambda\cos\theta} \qquad (18.106)$$

It can be seen that away from the spherical bulge, of radius r_0, at the centre, $\Delta\lambda$ and hence V_{rot} are almost constant. For $d < r_0$, $\Delta\lambda$ increases nearly linearly with d. As velocity becomes constant about 7–8 pixels away from the central line, we can say

$$r_0 \approx (1.20 \pm 0.07)\,\text{kpc} \tag{18.107}$$

For λ_1 as well as λ_2

$$|\Delta\lambda(d=+r_0) - \Delta\lambda(d=-r_0)| = 0.9 \pm 0.1\,\text{nm} \tag{18.108}$$

Note that Doppler shift for both wavelengths is verified independently. It turns out that for the given observational accuracy, the variation in both wavelengths is the same.

$$\Delta\lambda(d=\pm r_0) = -0.45 \pm 0.05\,\text{nm} \tag{18.109}$$

We can find V_{rot} for both wavelengths and compute the average.

$$
\begin{aligned}
V_{rot,1} &= \frac{(0.45 \pm 0.05) \times 3 \times 10^8}{656.4 \times 0.8723} \\
&= (236 \pm 26)\,\text{km}\,/\,\text{s}
\end{aligned} \tag{18.110}
$$

$$
\begin{aligned}
V_{rot,2} &= \frac{(0.45 \pm 0.05) \times 3 \times 10^8}{656.4 \times 0.8723} \\
&= (236 \pm 26)\,\text{km}\,/\,\text{s}
\end{aligned} \tag{18.111}
$$

$$V_{rot} = (2.4 \pm 0.3) \times 10^5\,\text{m}\,/\,\text{s} \tag{18.112}$$

If the mass of the central bulge of the galaxy is M, then for a test mass m, the outside bulge will be given by

$$\frac{GMm}{(r_0)^2} = \frac{mV_{rot}^2}{r_0} \tag{18.113}$$

$$
\begin{aligned}
M &= \frac{V_{rot}^2 r_0}{G} \\
&= \frac{(2.4 \times 10^5)^2 \times 1.20 \times 3.086 \times 10^{19}}{6.6726 \times 10^{-11}}
\end{aligned}
$$

$$M = 1.6 \times 10^{10}\,M_\odot \tag{18.114}$$

$$\frac{\Delta M}{M} = \frac{2\Delta V_{rot}}{V_{rot}} + \frac{\Delta r_0}{r_0} \tag{18.115}$$

$$= \frac{2 \times 0.3}{2.4} + \frac{0.07}{1.20}$$

$$\Delta M = 0.3 \times 10^{10}\,M_\odot \tag{18.116}$$

$$\therefore \qquad M = (1.6 \pm 0.3) \times 10^{10}\,M_\odot \tag{18.117}$$

EA: Note that there is also a small error due to rounding of constants G and $M_\odot$ and the value of 1 pc in metres. But that is much smaller (one part in thousand) than other quantitites and it is hence ignored.

2. (a) Converting the angular coordinates α and β into mm as per the given scale, we get Table 18.1.

These are used to plot the points on a graph paper, as shown in Fig. 18.2. The ellipse is drawn tracing these points and its major and minor axes are drawn.

(b) What we see is only a projection of an actual elliptical orbit due to inclination of the actual orbit with respect to the observer. Projection of any ellipse is also an ellipse but with a different focus. However, in this case, the focus of the original orbit (i.e., location of Sagittarius A*, which is the origin) lies on the major axis of the projected ellipse. This is only possible when orbital inclination of the orbit is zero, i.e., the orbit of S* around SA* is face-on as seen by us.

(c) i. By measuring the length of the major and minor axes on the graph

$$a = 137 \text{ mm} \tag{18.118}$$

$$= \frac{41}{1200} \times 137 \text{ light days}$$

$$a = 4.68 \text{ light days} \tag{18.119}$$

$$b = 69 \text{ mm} \tag{18.120}$$

$$b = 2.36 \text{ light days} \tag{18.121}$$

$$e_1 = \frac{ae}{a} = \frac{119 \text{ mm}}{137 \text{ mm}}$$

$$= 0.8686$$

Table 18.1   *Coordinates for S* in plane P*

	α mm	β mm
1	140.4	−199.2
2	116.4	−226.8
3	104.4	−230.4
4	92.4	−231.6
5	62.4	−219.6
6	43.2	−200.4
7	0	−144.0
8	−19.2	−99.6
9	−31.2	−49.2
10	−20.4	9.6
11	−4.8	16.8
12	9.6	20.4
13	25.2	14.4
14	44.4	10.8
15	86.4	−28.8
16	105.6	−60.0
17	129.6	−109.2

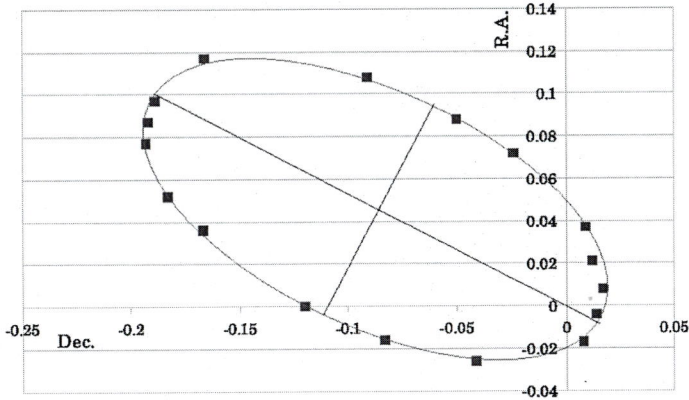

Fig. 18.2   *Motion of S* around Sagittarius A**

$$e_2 = \sqrt{1 - \frac{b^2}{a^2}} = \sqrt{1 - \frac{69^2}{137^2}}$$

$$= 0.8639$$

$$\therefore \qquad e = \frac{0.8686 + 0.8639}{2} = 0.866 \qquad (18.122)$$

ii.
$$R_{min} = a(1 - e) = 4.68 \times (1 - 0.866)$$
$$= 0.63 \text{ light days} \qquad (18.123)$$
$$R_{max} = a(1 + e) = 4.68 + (1 + 0.866)$$
$$= 8.73 \text{ light days} \qquad (18.124)$$

iii. 41 light days subtends 1″.
$$d_S = 41 \times 2.997\,92458 \times 10^8 \times 86\,400 \times 206\,265$$
$$d_S = 2.19 \times 10^{20} \text{ m}$$
$$= 7.10 \text{ kpc} \qquad (18.125)$$

iv. From the graph, *Aellipse* ≈ 28 560 mm². Now, by Kepler's second law, we know

$$T = \frac{\Delta t}{\Delta A} A_{ellipse} \qquad (18.126)$$

We compute these for all successive readings as shown in Table 18.2. Thus, the period is $T = (14.9 \pm 0.2)$ years.

v. By Kepler's third law

$$T^2 = \frac{4\pi^2}{G(M_{S*} + M_{AS*})} \times a^3 \qquad (18.127)$$

$$M_{tot} = \frac{4\pi^2 a^3}{GT^2}$$

$$= \frac{4\pi^2 \times (4.68 \times 2.997\,924\,58 \times 10^8 \times 86\,400)^3}{6.6726 \times 10^{-11} \times (14.94 \times 3.1557 \times 10^7)^2}$$

$$= 4.74 \times 10^{36} \text{ kg}$$
$$M_{tot} = 2.4 \times 10^6 M_{\odot} \qquad\qquad (18.128)$$

Table 18.2 *Period estimation using areas*

Movement	Δt (years)	ΔA (mm^2)	T (years)
1 to 2	2.304	4370	15.0577
2 to 3	0.8	1532	14.9138
3 to 4	0.715	1400	14.5860
4 to 5	1.373	2714	14.4484
5 to 6	0.755	1435	15.0263
6 to 7	1.662	3165	14.9974
7 to 8	0.753	1435	14.9865
8 to 9	0.581	1107	14.9895
9 to 10	0.42	800	14.9940
10 to 11	0.07	135	14.8089
11 to 12	0.079	147	15.3486
12 to 13	0.105	200	14.9940
13 to 14	0.097	185	14.9747
14 to 15	0.567	1080	14.9940
15 to 16	0.538	1025	14.9905
16 to 17	1.019	1942	14.9859

19

Solutions: Extragalactic Astrophysics

19.1 Theory

1. By Wien's law

$$\lambda_{max} T = \text{constant} = b$$

$$\lambda_{\text{max}} = \frac{b}{T} \tag{19.1}$$

$$\frac{\lambda_{observed}}{\lambda_{emitted}} = 1 + z \tag{19.2}$$

$$\lambda_{observed} = \lambda_{emitted} (1 + z)$$

$$\frac{b}{T_{observed}} = \frac{b}{T_{emitted}} (1+z)$$

$$T_{emitted} = T_{observed} (1 + z) \tag{19.3}$$

$$= 2.73 \times (1 + 10)$$

$$T_{emitted} = 30.03 \approx 30K \tag{19.4}$$

2. Let recession velocity of the QSO be v. Then

$$\sqrt{\frac{1 + \dfrac{v}{c}}{1 - \dfrac{v}{c}}} = 1 + z \tag{19.5}$$

$$\frac{1 + \dfrac{v}{c}}{1 - \dfrac{v}{c}} = (1+z)^2$$

$$\therefore \qquad \frac{v}{c} = \frac{(1+z)^2 - 1}{(1+z)^2 + 1} \tag{19.6}$$

$$= \frac{(1.2)^2 - 1}{(1.2)^2 + 1}$$

$$= \frac{0.44}{2.44}$$

$$= 0.18 \qquad (19.7)$$

$$v = H_0 D \qquad (19.8)$$

$$\therefore \qquad D = \frac{v}{H_0} \qquad (19.9)$$

$$= \frac{0.18 \times 3.00 \times 10^5}{67.8}$$

$$\approx 800 \text{ Mpc} \qquad (19.10)$$

3. The recession velocity using the classical relation will be $v_{cla} = z \times c$.

   The relativistic relation for velocity is given by $v_{rel} = \left(\frac{(1+z)^2 - 1}{(1+z)^2 + 1} \right) c$.

   The calculations for the three galaxies are summarised in the following table:

Galaxy	v_{cla} km/s	v_{rel} km/s	$v_{rel}/c \times 100$	$r = v_r/H_0$ Mpc
3C 279	160700	121300	40%	1789
3C 245	308490	182610	61%	2693
4C41.17	1140000	274900	92%	4050

From columns 2 and 3 it is obvious that the relativistic relation gives much better answers. One can note that for 3C245 and 4C41.17, the classical relation gives velocities larger than the speed of light. Further, the difference between the distance calculated by the classical relation and the relativistic relation is about 30%, even for the 'nearby' galaxy 3C 279.

4. As dark energy is the energy of empty space, its energy density remains constant during expansion of the Universe. If a_0 is the scale factor today and a_z is the scale factor at the recombination epoch

$$1 + z = \frac{a_0}{a_z} \qquad (19.11)$$

$$a_z = \frac{1}{1+z} a_0 = \frac{1}{1+1100} a_0$$

$$= 0.00091 a_0$$

On the other hand, all of the normal matter and dark matter was created at the time of the formation of the Universe. So the mass of these components remains constant. Hence, mass densities will change as per the volume of the Universe.

$$\rho_{DM_z} = \frac{\rho_{DM}}{a^3} \qquad (19.13)$$

$$= \frac{2.4 \times 10^{-30}}{(9.1 \times 10^{-4})^3} = \frac{2.4 \times 10^{-30}}{7.5 \times 10^{-10}}$$

$$= 3.2 \times 10^{-21} \, \text{g/cm}^3 \tag{19.14}$$

$$\frac{\rho_{DM}}{\rho_{DE}} = \frac{3.2 \times 10^{-21}}{7.1 \times 10^{-30}} \tag{19.15}$$

$$= 4.5 \times 10^{8} \tag{19.16}$$

5. We should remember that classical Hubble's law would give approximately correct answers only if the galaxy is not too far. Hence, we first check the redshift of the galaxy.

$$z = \frac{\lambda - \lambda_0}{\lambda} = \frac{662.9 - 656.3}{656.3}$$

$$\therefore \qquad\qquad z \approx 0.01 = \frac{v}{c} \tag{19.17}$$

$$H_0 = \frac{v}{d} = \frac{cz}{r} = \frac{3 \times 10^5 \, km/s \times 0.01}{41.67 \, \text{Mpc}}$$

$$H_0 = 72.0 \text{km/s/Mpc} \tag{19.18}$$

$$t_H \approx \frac{1}{H_0}$$

$$= 13.58 \, \text{Gyrs} \tag{19.19}$$

6. Note that Vega is a standard zero magnitude star for Johnson UBV photometry. We know the apparent magnitude and luminosity of the Sun. Combining this information

$$m_\odot - m_{vega} = -2.5 \log\left(\frac{F_\odot}{F_{vega}}\right) \tag{19.20}$$

$$-26.72 - 0 = 2.5 \log\left(\frac{F_{vega}}{F_\odot}\right)$$

$$F_{vega} = 10^{\frac{-26.72}{2.5}} F_\odot = 10^{-10.69} F_\odot$$

$$= 2.05 \times 10^{-11} \, F_\odot \tag{19.21}$$

$$F_{SN} = 1.6 \times 10^{-7} \, F_{vega} \tag{19.22}$$

$$= 1.6 \times 10^{-7} \times 2.05 \times 10^{-11} \, F_\odot$$

$$F_{SN} = 3.28 \times 10^{-18} \, F_\odot \tag{19.23}$$

$$\frac{L_{SN}}{4\pi d_{SN}^2} = 3.28 \times 10^{-18} \frac{L_\odot}{4\pi d_\odot^2}$$

$$d_{SN}^2 = \frac{L_{SN}}{3.28 \times 10^{-18} L_\odot} \times d_\odot^2 \tag{19.24}$$

$$d_{SN} = \sqrt{\frac{5.8 \times 10^9}{3.28 \times 10^{-18}}} \times 1.496 \times 10^{11}$$

$$= 6.3 \times 10^{24} \, \text{m}$$

$$d_{SN} \approx 204 \text{ Mpc} \tag{19.25}$$

If t_H is the Hubble time, then by combining Hubble's law and the approximate relation between redshift and velocity (for low redshift)

$$t_H = \frac{1}{H_0} = \frac{d_{SN}}{v_{SN}} = \frac{d_{SN}}{cz} \tag{19.26}$$

$$= \frac{204 Mpc}{(1\, lyr/yr)(0.05)}$$

$$= 204 \times 10^6 \times 3.262 \times 20 \text{ years}$$

$$= 1.33 \times 10^{10} \text{ years}$$

$$t_H = 13.3 \text{ Gyrs} \tag{19.27}$$

You may note the clever use of speed of light as one light year per year to obtain the answer directly in years. The Hubble time thus obtained is for a non-accelerating Universe and based on the observation of only one galaxy. Thus, we are not surprised by the fact that the answer is lower than the actual age of the Universe.

7. In a flat Universe, classical total energy is zero. For a test particle of unit mass, at the edge of the Universe, we can take R to be the radius of the visible Universe and M as its total mass. Let ρ_c be the critical density of the Universe.

$$KE = - PE \tag{19.28}$$

$$\frac{1}{2}v^2 = \frac{GM}{R}$$

$$\frac{1}{2}(H_0 R)^2 = \frac{4\pi R^3 \rho_c G}{3R}$$

$$\therefore \qquad \rho_c = \frac{3H_0^2}{8\pi G} \tag{19.29}$$

$$= \frac{3 \times (67.80 \times 10^3)^2}{8\pi \times 6.6726 \times 10^{-11} \times (3.0856 \times 10^{22})^2}$$

$$\rho_c = 8.6371 \times 10^{-27} \text{ kgm}^{-3} \tag{19.30}$$

$$m_{dark} = 0.25 m_{total}$$

$$\therefore \qquad \rho_{dark} = 0.25 \rho_c \tag{19.31}$$

$$n_v = \frac{\rho_{dark}}{m_v} = \frac{0.25\rho_c}{10^{-5} m_e} \tag{19.32}$$

$$= \frac{0.25 \times 8.6371 \times 10^{-27}}{10^{-5} \times 9.1 \times 10^{-31}}$$

$$= 2.37 \times 10^8 \text{ m}^{-3}$$

$$n_v \approx 2 \times 10^8 \text{ m}^{-3} \tag{19.33}$$

Note that the final accuracy is rounded to a single digit due to approximation in the mass of neutrino.

8. (a) We have found the equation for critical density in the previous question (see Equation 19.29).

$$\rho_c = \frac{3H_0{}^2}{8\pi G}$$

$$\rho_m = \Omega_m \rho_c = 0.32 \frac{3H_0{}^2}{8\pi G}$$

$$= 0.32 \frac{3 \times (6.78 \times 10^3)^2}{8\pi 6.6726 \times 10^{-11} \times (3.0856 \times 10^{22})^2}$$

$$\rho_m = 2.76 \times 10^{-27} \text{ kg/m}^3 \tag{19.34}$$

(b) The contained in a given volume can be estimated by multiplying the volume by the crictical density. Hence, the escape velocity is

$$v_{esc} = \sqrt{\frac{2GM}{d}}$$

$$= \sqrt{\frac{2G}{d} \times \frac{4\pi\rho_c d^3}{3}}$$

$$= \sqrt{\frac{8\pi G}{3} \times 0.32 \times \frac{3H_0{}^2}{8\pi G} d^2}$$

$$= \sqrt{0.32} H_0 d$$

$$= \sqrt{0.32} \times 67.80 \times 100$$

$$v_{esc} = 3840 \text{ km/s} \tag{19.35}$$

(c) If this galaxy is orbiting around the centre of our local cluster (i.e, the Earth) in a circular orbit, then its velocity is $\frac{1}{\sqrt{2}}$ of its escape velocity and its angular velocity is given by $\omega = v/d$. Thus

$$\omega = \frac{v}{d} = \frac{v_{esc}}{\sqrt{2}d}$$

$$= \frac{\sqrt{0.32} H_0 d}{\sqrt{2}d}$$

$$= \sqrt{0.16} H_0 \tag{19.36}$$

$$= \frac{0.4 \times 67.80}{3.0856 \times 10^{19}}$$

$$\omega = 8.8 \times 10^{-19} \text{ rad/s}$$

$$= 1.81 \times 10^{-13} \text{ arcsec/s} \tag{19.37}$$

(d) From Equation 19.36, it is clear that ω does not depend on the distance d. Therefore, we will never be able to resolve the two galaxies from each other.

9. In the absence of additional information, we take the age of the Universe as 13.77 Gly. However, one should note that this will not be the value of Hubble time in a flat Universe.

$$1+z = \frac{a_0}{a_z} = \left(\frac{t_0}{t_z}\right)^{\frac{2}{3}} \tag{19.38}$$

$$\therefore \quad t_z = \frac{t_0}{(1+z)^{1.5}} = \frac{1.377 \times 10^{10}}{(1+6.03)^{1.5}}$$

$$t = 739 \times 10^6 \text{ years} \tag{19.39}$$

$$t_{form'max} = t - 560 \times 10^6$$

$$= 179 \times 10^6 \text{ years} \tag{19.40}$$

$$t_{form'min} = 139 \times 10^6 \text{ years} \tag{19.41}$$

$$z_{form,min} = \left(\frac{t_0}{t_f}\right)^{\frac{2}{3}} - 1 \tag{19.42}$$

$$= \left(\frac{13770}{179}\right)^{\frac{2}{3}} - 1$$

$$= 17.1 \tag{19.43}$$

$$z_{form'max} = 20.4 \tag{19.44}$$

Epoch of star formation was from $z = 17.3$ to $z = 20.8$.

10. If the assumed model of the Universe is without dark energy, one cannot simply take the present age of the Universe as 13.7 Gyrs. One should go back to the definition of the Hubble constant and start from there. Let T, t and a be the temperature, age and scale factor, respectively, of the Universe. We assume that variation in H is very small and it can be approximated as a constant.

$$H_0 = \frac{1}{a}\frac{da}{dt} \approx \frac{1}{a}\frac{\Delta a}{\Delta t} \tag{19.45}$$

$$\frac{\Delta a}{\Delta t} = H_0 a \tag{19.46}$$

$$T \propto a^{-1} \tag{19.47}$$

$$\frac{\Delta T}{\Delta t} = -H_0 T_i \tag{19.48}$$

$$\Delta t = -\frac{\Delta T}{H_0 T_i}$$

$$= -\frac{(-0.1) \times 3.0856 \times 10^{22}}{67.80 \times 10^3 \times 2.73}$$

$$= 1.667 \times 10^{16} \text{s}$$

$$\Delta t = 528 \text{ Myr} \tag{19.49}$$

Alternatively, one can solve this more rigorously using calculus. In a matter-dominated Universe

$$\rho = \zeta a^{-3} \tag{19.50}$$

$$a \alpha t^{\frac{2}{3}} \tag{19.51}$$

$$\Omega_0 = \frac{8\pi G\rho}{3H^2} = \frac{8\pi G}{3H^2}\frac{\zeta}{a^3} = 1 \tag{19.52}$$

Again using the definition of the Hubble parameter, we obtain the expression for a by integration.

$$\frac{da}{dt} = Ha$$

$$\left(\frac{da}{dt}\right)^2 = H^2 a^2 = \frac{8\pi G\zeta}{3a}$$

$$\therefore \qquad \frac{da}{dt} = \sqrt{\frac{8\pi G\zeta}{3a}} \tag{19.53}$$

$$\therefore \qquad \int \sqrt{a}\, da = \sqrt{\frac{8}{3}\pi G\zeta} \int dt \tag{19.54}$$

$$\frac{2}{3}\left(a_f^{\frac{3}{2}} - a_i^{\frac{3}{2}}\right) = \sqrt{\frac{8}{3}\pi G\zeta}\,\Delta t$$

$$\frac{2}{3}\left(\left(\frac{a_f}{a_i}\right)^{\frac{3}{2}} - 1\right) = \sqrt{\frac{8\pi G\zeta}{3a_i^3}}\,\Delta t$$

$$= H_i \Delta t$$

$$\Delta t = \frac{2}{3}\left(\left(\frac{a_f}{a_i}\right)^{\frac{3}{2}} - 1\right)\frac{1}{H_i} \tag{19.55}$$

$$= \frac{2}{3}\left(\left(\frac{T_i}{T_f}\right)^{\frac{3}{2}} - 1\right)\frac{1}{H_i} \qquad \text{(using Equation 19.47)}$$

$$= \frac{2}{3}\left(\left(\frac{2.73}{2.63}\right)^{\frac{3}{2}} - 1\right)\frac{3.0856 \times 10^{22}}{67.80 \times 10^3}$$

$$= 1.730 \times 10^{16}\ \text{s}$$

$$\Delta t = 548\ \text{Myr} \tag{19.56}$$

11. In this question, it helps if you start with a general solution (i.e, $\beta \neq 0$) then converge to special case $\beta = 0$. Refer to Fig. 9.2. As ϕ, β and θ are very very small angles, the point of bending is very very close to the lens and almost at distance D_L from the observer.

$$\xi \approx \theta D_L$$

$$_1 PS_1 = PS + SS_1$$

$$\theta D_S = \beta D_s + (D_S - D_L)\phi \tag{19.57}$$

$$(\theta - \beta)D_S = (D_S - D_L)\frac{4GM}{\xi c^2}$$

$$= (D_S - D_L)\frac{4GM}{\theta D_L c^2}$$

$$\therefore \quad \theta(\theta - \beta) = \frac{4GM}{c^2}\frac{(D_s - D_L)}{D_L D_s}$$

$$\theta^2(\theta - \beta) = \frac{4GM}{c^2}\frac{(D_S - D_L)}{D_L D_S} \tag{19.58}$$

(a) For a perfect alignment in which $\beta = 0$, we have $\theta = \pm\theta_E$, where

$$\theta_E = \sqrt{\frac{4GM}{c^2}\frac{(D_S - D_L)}{D_L D_S}} \tag{19.59}$$

(b) For the given parameters

$$D_L = 50 - 10 = 40 \text{ kpc} \tag{19.60}$$

$$\theta_E = \sqrt{\frac{4GM}{c^2}\frac{(D_S - D_L)}{D_L D_S}}$$

$$\theta_{E1} = \sqrt{\frac{4 \times 6.6726 \times 10^{-11} \times 1.9891 \times 10^{30}(50 - 40)}{(3 \times 10^8)^2 \times 50 \times 40 \times 3.0856 \times 10^{19}}} \tag{19.61}$$

$$(\because 1 \text{ kpc} = 3.0856 \times 10^{19} \text{ m})$$

$$= 9.8 \times 10^{-10} \text{ rad} \tag{19.62}$$

$$\theta_{E1} = 2.0 \times 10^{-4} \text{ arcsec} \tag{19.63}$$

(c) The resolution of the Hubble space telescope for mean optical wavelength is

$$\theta_{Hubble} = \frac{1.22\lambda}{D} = 1.22 \times \frac{1.22 \times 5 \times 10^{-7}}{2.4}$$

$$= 2.5 \times 10^{-7} \text{ rad} \tag{19.64}$$

$$\theta_{Hubble} > \theta_{E1} \tag{19.65}$$

Hence, the Hubble telescope can not resolve this Einstein ring.

(d) The quadratic equation 19.58 has two distinct roots, namely

$$\theta_1 = \frac{\beta}{2} + \sqrt{\left(\frac{\beta}{2}\right)^2 + \theta_E^2} \tag{19.66}$$

$$\theta_2 = \frac{\beta}{2} - \sqrt{\left(\frac{\beta}{2}\right)^2 + \theta_E^2} \tag{19.67}$$

This implies that there are two images for a single isolated source.

(e) Dividing the above equations by β

$$\theta_{1,2} = \frac{\beta}{2} \pm \sqrt{\left(\frac{\beta}{2}\right)^2 + \theta_E^2}$$

$$\frac{\theta_{1,2}}{\beta} = \frac{1}{2} \pm \sqrt{\left(\frac{1}{2}\right)^2 + \left(\frac{\theta_E}{\beta}\right)^2}$$

$$\frac{\theta_{1,2}}{\beta} = \frac{1}{2} \pm \sqrt{\frac{1}{4} + \frac{1}{\eta^2}}$$

$$= \frac{1}{2}\left(1 \pm \frac{\sqrt{\eta^2 + 4}}{\eta}\right) \tag{19.68}$$

(f) From Equation 19.58

$$\theta^2 - \beta\theta - \theta_E^2 = 0$$

$$(\theta + \Delta\theta)^2 - (\beta + \Delta\beta)(\theta + \Delta\theta) - \theta_E^2 = 0 \tag{19.69}$$

$$(\theta^2 - \beta\theta - \theta_E^2) + 2\theta\Delta\theta - \beta\Delta\theta - \theta\Delta\beta = 0$$

$$(2\theta - \beta)\Delta\theta - \theta\Delta\beta = 0 \tag{19.70}$$

Thus, we get

$$\frac{\Delta\theta}{\Delta\beta} = \frac{\theta}{2\theta - \beta} \tag{19.71}$$

$$\left[\frac{\Delta\theta}{\Delta\beta}\right]_{\theta=\theta_{1,2}} = \frac{\theta_{1,2}}{2\theta_{1,2} - \beta}$$

$$= \frac{\theta_{1,2}/\beta}{2\theta_{1,2}/\beta - 1}$$

$$= \frac{\left(\frac{1}{2}\left(1 \pm \frac{\sqrt{\eta^2 + 4}}{\eta}\right)\right)}{2\left(\frac{1}{2}\left(1 \pm \frac{\sqrt{\eta^2 + 4}}{\eta}\right)\right) - 1}$$

$$= \frac{\eta \pm \sqrt{\eta^2 + 4}}{2(n \pm \sqrt{\eta^2 + 4} - \eta)}$$

$$\left[\frac{\Delta\theta}{\Delta\beta}\right]_{\theta=\theta_{1,2}} = \frac{1}{2}\left(1 \pm \frac{\eta}{\sqrt{\eta^2 + 4}}\right) \tag{19.72}$$

$$F(\lambda_B) = \frac{L_\lambda(\lambda_B)}{4\pi d_L^2} \tag{19.73}$$

$$\lambda_{emitted} = \frac{\lambda_{observed}}{(1+z)} \tag{19.74}$$

Let the monochromatic flux of the galaxy be denoted by $S(\lambda)$, then for small wavelength interval $\Delta\lambda$

$$S(\lambda_{ob})\Delta\lambda_{ob} = \frac{L_\lambda(\lambda_{emitted})}{4\pi d_L^2}\Delta\lambda_{emitted}$$

$$= \frac{1}{4\pi d_L^2} L_\lambda\left(\frac{\lambda_{ob}}{1+z}\right)\frac{\Delta\lambda_{ob}}{1+z} \tag{19.75}$$

$$S_{10}(\lambda) = \frac{L_\lambda(\lambda)}{4\pi d_{10}^2}$$

$$\therefore \qquad \frac{S(\lambda)}{S_{10}(\lambda)} = \left(\frac{d_{10}}{d_L}\right)^2 \frac{L_\lambda\left(\dfrac{\lambda}{1+z}\right)}{L_\lambda(\lambda)}\frac{1}{1+z} \tag{19.76}$$

$$= \left(\frac{d_{10}}{d_L}\right)^2\left(\frac{1}{1+z}\right)^4\frac{1}{1+z}$$

$$\frac{S(\lambda)}{S_{10}(\lambda)} = \left(\frac{d_{10}}{d_L}\right)^2\left(\frac{1}{1+z}\right)^5 \tag{19.77}$$

Here, we have used SED approximation, which is justified by the fact

$$\lambda_{B,min} = 445 - 47 = 398 \text{ nm} \tag{19.78}$$

$$\lambda_{SED,min}\,(1+z) = 250 \times (1+0.5) = 375 \text{ nm} \tag{19.79}$$

$$\therefore \qquad \lambda_{SED,min}\,(1+z) < \lambda_{B,min} \tag{19.80}$$

This, means λ is in the range of SED approximation. Now, evaluting

$$m_B - M_B = -2.5\log\left(\frac{S(\lambda)}{S_{10}(\lambda)}\right) \tag{19.81}$$

$$= -2.5\log\left(\frac{d_{10}}{d_L}\right)^2 - 2.5\log(1+z)^{-5}$$

$$\therefore \qquad M_B = m_B - 5\log\left(\frac{d_L}{d_{10}}\right) - 12.5\log(1+z) \tag{19.82}$$

$$= 20.40 - 5\log\left(\frac{2754\times10^6}{10}\right) - 12.5\log(1.5)$$

$$= -2.5\log\frac{f(\lambda_B)4\pi(10\,\text{pc})^2}{L(\lambda_B)} \tag{19.83}$$

$$= -24.00 \tag{19.84}$$

As normal elliptical galaxies are fainter than this by at least magnitudes, we conclude that this galaxy is not a member of this cluster but is a forground object.

13. (a) Let θ_0 be the horizon distance and let X_r be the physical distance between two points, which are on mutual horizon at recombination epoch. It would be tempting to relate the two by a simple equation like

$$X_r = d\theta_0 = c(t_0 - t_r)\theta_0$$

where d is the distance to the CMB horizon. However, it must be remembered that space itself is continuously expanding. Hence, the light from CMB has in fact travelled a much shorter distance. The physical distance X_r is the real horizon distance at that epoch.

$$X_r = c(t_0 - t_r)\theta_0 \times \frac{a_r}{a_0} \tag{19.85}$$

$$ct_r = c(t_0 - t_r)\theta_0 \times \frac{T_0}{T_r}$$

$$\therefore \quad \theta_0 = \frac{T_r t_r}{T_0(t_0 - t_r)} \approx \frac{T_r t_r}{T_0 t_0} \tag{19.86}$$

$$\approx \frac{3000 \times 3 \times 10^5}{3 \times 1.5 \times 10^{10}}$$

$$\theta_0 \approx 0.02\, rad = 1.15° \tag{19.87}$$

(b) No. It is not possible. As the given separation is more than θ_0

(c) We note that magnitude of the current age of the Universe can be also interpreted as the size of the present Universe in light years. Let S denote the size of the Universe at a given epoch.

$$S_0 = 1.5 \times 10^{10} \times 9.46 \times 10^{15} \text{ m}$$

$$S_r = \frac{a_r}{a_0} S_0 = \left(\frac{t_r}{t_0}\right)^{2/3} S_0 \tag{19.88}$$

$$S_i = \frac{a_i}{a_r} S_r = \left(\frac{t_i}{t_r}\right)^{1/2} S_r \tag{19.89}$$

$$= \left(\frac{t_i}{t_r}\right)^{1/2} \left(\frac{t_r}{t_0}\right)^{2/3} S_0 \tag{19.90}$$

$$= \left(\frac{10^{-32}}{3 \times 10^5 \times 3.1557 \times 10^7}\right)^{1/2} \left(\frac{3 \times 10^5}{1.5 \times 10^{10}}\right)^{2/3} S_0$$

$$= 3.25 \times 10^{-23} \times 7.37 \times 10^{-4} S_0$$

$$= 2.40 \times 10^{-26} S_0$$

$$= 2.40 \times 10^{-26} \times 1.5 \times 10^{10} \times 9.46 \times 10^{15}$$

$$\approx 3.40 \text{ m} \tag{19.91}$$

Thus, the size of the Universe was just 3.4 metres at the end of the inflation period.

19.2 Data Analysis

1. **Virgo Cluster**

   (a) Simply substitute the values and find the answers.

   $$d_{avg} = \frac{\sum\limits_{i=1}^{n} \dfrac{d_i}{s_i^2}}{\sum\limits_{i=1}^{n} \dfrac{1}{s_i^2}}$$

   $$= \frac{55.943}{3.5485}$$

   $$= 15.765 \text{ Mpc} \tag{19.92}$$

   (b) The rms uncertainity will be given by

   $$s_a = \sqrt{\frac{1}{\sum\limits_{i=1}^{n} \dfrac{1}{s_i^2}}} \tag{19.93}$$

   $$= \sqrt{\frac{1}{3.5485}} \text{Mpc} = 0.53 \text{ Mpc}$$

   $$d_{Virgo} = 15.8 \pm .5 \text{ Mpc} \tag{19.94}$$

   (c) The Hubble constant can be found by Hubble's law

   $$H_0 = \frac{v}{d_{avg}} = \frac{1136 \text{ km/s}}{15.765 \text{ Mpc}} \tag{19.95}$$

   $$H_0 = 72.058 \text{ km/sec/Mpc} \tag{19.96}$$

   $$s_H = \left(\frac{s_d}{d_{avg}} + \frac{\Delta v}{v}\right) H_0 \tag{19.97}$$

   $$= \left(\frac{0.53}{15.765} + \frac{1}{1136}\right) \times 72.058$$

   $$= 0.0345 \times 72.058 \tag{19.98}$$

   $$s_H = 2.49 \text{ km/sec/Mpc} \tag{19.99}$$

   $$\therefore \quad H_0 = 72 \pm 2 \text{ km/sec/Mpc} \tag{19.100}$$

   (d) The Hubble time is simply the inverse of the Hubble constant. Thus, the percentage error remains the same as in Equation 19.98.

   $$H_0^{-1} = 72.058^{-1} \times 3.0856 \times 10^{16} \times 10^6 / 10^3$$

   $$= 4.28 \times 10^{17} \text{ sec}$$

$$T_H = 13.57 \text{ Gyr} \tag{19.101}$$

$$e_T = 13.57 \times 0.0345$$

$$e_T = 0.47 \text{ Gyr} \tag{19.102}$$

$$\therefore \quad T_H = 13.6 \pm 0.5 \text{ Gyr} \tag{19.103}$$

20

Solutions: Night Sky Observation

20.1 General Night Sky

1. One is expected to remember the stars that are reasonably close to the celestial equator and then sweep the laser pointer, making an arc passing through the stars. The celestial equator can be remembered as something like this:

   Mintaka (δ Ori), a couple of degrees south of Procyon (α CMi), similarly slightly south of Hydra's head, Porrima (γ Vir), slightly south of Kelb Al Rai (β Oph), Sadalmalik (α Aqr), slightly south of the southern fish of Pisces and south of the head of Cetus.

2. The vernal equinox is located slightly south of the circlet of Pisces. There is no bright star near its exact location; hence it can be identified only through practice.

3. Question self-explanatory.

4. α - And

5. Question is self-explanatory.

6. Question is self-explanatory.

7. The constellations shown were: Cygnus (Cyg), Corona Borealis (Crb), Pisces Australis (Psa), Delphinus (Del), Saggitarius (Sgr).

8. The equatorial constellations visible in the projected sky were: Virgo (Vir), Serpens (Ser), Ophiuchus (Oph), Aquila (Aql), Aquarius (Aqr), Pisces (Psc) and Cetus (Cet).

Table 20.1 *Angular distance*

Pairs of Stars	Angular Distance (degrees)
1 (Errai) and 2 (Alfirk)	$\approx 11°$
1 (Errai) and 3 (Alderamin)	$\approx 18°$

Table 20.2 *Star magnitudes*

Star Name	Apparent Visual Magnitude
2 (Alfirk)	3.2–3.3 (actual answer 3.23)
3 (Alderamin)	2.4–2.6 (actual answer 2.47)

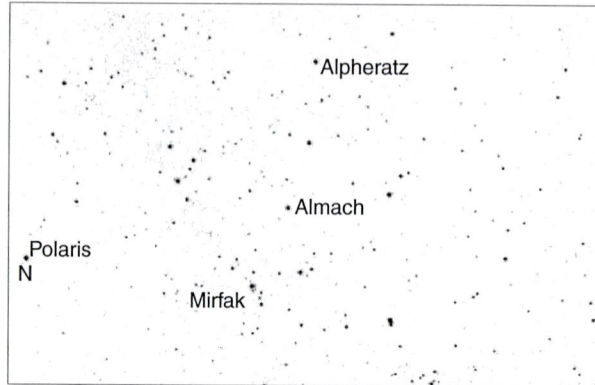

Fig. 20.1   *Sky map for Scorpio and surrounding regions*

9. Fig. 20.1 shows the missing stars put back at their positions.

10. **Equal area star chart:** You are given an equal area sky map as shown in Fig. 20.2. The map represents the sky in Suceava (latitude 47°39′ North, longitude 26°15′ East) at 19:00 UT on the day of the test. The observer who made the sky map was at a very high altitude above Suceava; the zenith point is at the centre of the chart.

   (a) Answer is shown in Fig. 20.2.

   (b) Answer is shown in Fig. 20.2.

   (c) Answer is shown in Fig. 20.2.

   (d) Answer is shown in Fig. 20.2.

1	Name of the star: α Boo (Arcturus)
2	Name of the star: α Lyr (Vega)
3	Name of the star: α Aur (Capella)
4	Name of the star: α Aql (Altair)

   (e) Answer is shown in Fig. 20.2.

   (f) Answer is shown in Fig. 20.2.

   (g) We note that the vernal equinox is at the eastern horizon. Thus, sidereal time is 18 hours.

   (h) We note that Altair is about 2 hours past the meridian and slightly north of the equator. Thus, approximate equatorial coordinates of Altair (as estimated from the map) are

$$\alpha = t_s + H = 18^h + 2^h$$
$$\alpha = 20^h \tag{20.1}$$
$$\delta = 10° \tag{20.2}$$

   Note that this is an approximate estimate. An error of ± 30 minutes in RA and ± 5 degrees in declination is natural.

11. The students were expected to place the missing stars in the proper location and associate the correct name with the correct position. Similarly, they were expected to draw the

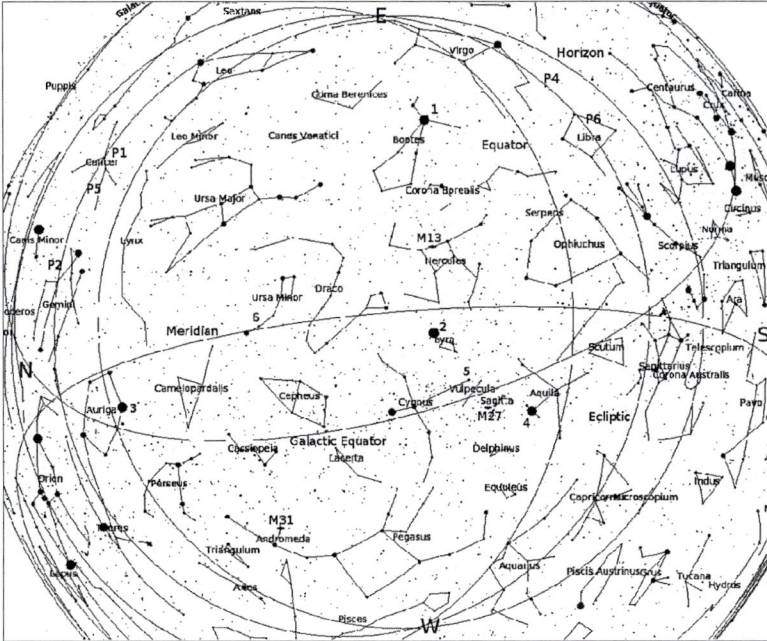

Fig. 20.2 *Equal area star chart*

boundaries of constellations by remembering that all constellation boundaries are along constant RA or constant declination.

12. Answers are given in Fig. 20.3.

20.2 Magnitude and Angular Size

1. Mirfak (α -Per).   (I07-O05-A)
2. 3.7–3.8 (actual answer 3.75).
3. Answers given Table 20.1 and Table 20.2.

20.3 Instrument Aided Observations

1. (a) See Table 20.3.

   (b) 21. d   22. c

      23.1. b   23.2. a

      24. c   25. b

      26. c

   (c) 27. Magnification: $M = \dfrac{f}{f_{\text{eyepiece}}} = 32X$

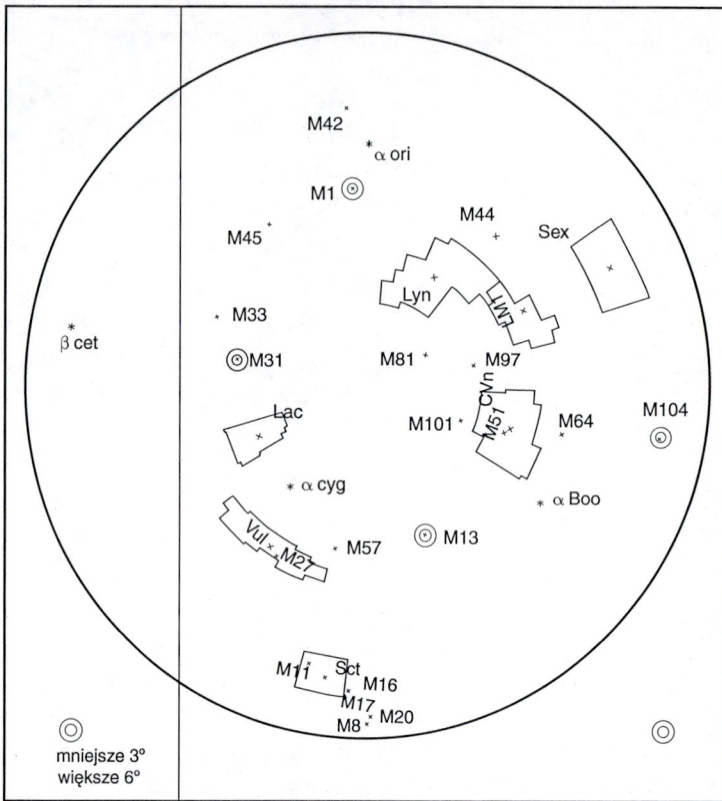

Fig. 20.3 *Solution for IOAA 2011 group task 1*

28. Focal ratio : 5 or f/5

29. Resolution (in arcseconds) : $r = \dfrac{1.22\lambda}{D} = 1.73$ arcsec

30. Limiting magnitude: 11.5 mag to 12 mag

2. Question is self-explanatory.

3. Brighter: Yellow and Dimmer: White/blue

4. Brighter: Yellow and Dimmer: Blue

5. Night 1:

   Object 1 (M22)   Object 2 (M8)   Object 3 (M7)   Object 4 (M57)

   Night 2:

   Object 1 (M4)   Object 2 (M8)   Object 3 (M6)   Object 4 (M57)

6. You are expected to recognise the constellation of Sagitta and point the telescope at γ Sagitta, which is the brightest star in the constellation. After the first part of the task, we notice that the two targets have very similar Right Ascension. Thus, one can point to M27 by shifting the direction of the telescope by about 3 degrees towards Polaris, while keeping the RA knob fixed.

Table 20.3   *Parts of telescope*

Item name		Letter
	(example) Tripod	M
1.	Counterweight	L
2.	Right Ascension Setting Circle (RA Scale)	C
3.	Declination Setting Circle (Declination Scale)	K
4.	Right Ascension locking knob	B
5.	Declination locking knob	J
6.	Geographical latitude scale	A
7.	Finder scope	F
8.	Focuser tube	H
9.	Focuser knob	G
10.	Eyepiece	I
11.	Declination Axis	XX
12.	Right Ascension Axis (Polar Axis)	XY
13.	Right Ascension slow motion adjustment	E
14.	Declination flexible slow motion adjustment	D
15.	90° diagonal mirror	T
16.	Azimuth adjustment knobs	P
17.	Altitude adjustment screws	R
18.	Lock screw	O
19.	Spirit level bubble	W
20.	Eyepiece reticle light switch and brightness control	U

7. ν – Scorpii will be resolved into four components at this magnification.

8. About 13'.

9. Scale and orientation of M31 should be exact, as shown in Fig. 20.4.

10. The idea is to measure time taken by the selected star to cross the diameter of the field of the telescope. For example, if we choose Capella ($\delta = 46.0°$) and it transits the field in $t = 3^m31^s = 3.53$ min, we get

$$\text{FoV} = \omega \times t \times \cos(\delta) \tag{20.3}$$

$$= \frac{360°}{23^h56^m4^s.1} \times 3.53 \times \cos\left(46°\right)$$

$$= 0.615° = 37' \tag{20.4}$$

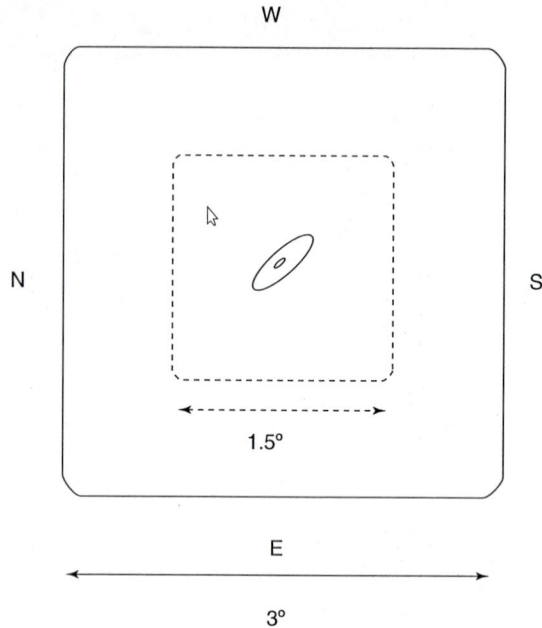

Fig. 20.4   *Drawing of Andromeda Galaxy*

EA: For better accuracy, it is advisable that multiple readings of transit time should be taken. However, the time constraint given to complete the task may not allow this.

11. It is critical to note RA and declination readings for Caph before moving the telescope. This will help in eliminating zero errors. After pointing the telescope to the next star, note the readings again and hence find the RA and declination of the star. Knowing current date and time, RA can be easily converted into hour angle.

12 About 24'.

13. About 7.8.

14. The correct sequence of steps would be as follows:

- Level the tripod with the help of a spirit level.
- Place the the equatorial mount on the telescope.
- As it is a vernal equinox day, the declination of the Sun is $0°$. Hence, the declination dial of the mount should be set to $0°$and fixed. The declination axis is now calibrated.
- Now move the telescope around the RA axis to make the tube horizontal. Use a spirit level to check if it is exactly horizontal. Note the reading on the RA dial.
- Move the telescope by exactly $90°$ around the RA axis by looking at the RA dial. If the telescope was duly pointing North, this movement would bring the telescope exactly to the meridian. However, as we do not know the northern direction presently, the telescope may not be aimed towards any point on the meridian.
- Move the telescope in the horizontal plane (around the azimuthal axis), such that it faces some point in the meridian. The sun will now be directly above or below the direction of the telescope. The telescope's polar axis is now along the North–South line.
- Now move the latitude axis of the telescope to move the telescope along the meridian and bring the Sun in FoV. The polar axis is now aligned.

15. Solving this question without the actual CCD and related software is impossible. However, we will briefly state the motivation behind the question. With three different exposure times, students can choose the best image, identify different stars in the image and by identifying the faintest star in the image, they can obtain an imperical estimate of the limiting magnitude. The particular software used (The Sky) includes magnitudes of bright individual stars within the clusters.

20.4 Planetarium Based Questions

1. Student can estimate the phase of the Moon. As the Moon is present in the evening sky, it is in the waxing phase. Hence the age of the Moon can be determined. Next, one can check the zodiacal sign in which Moon is present. By the age of the Moon and current zodiacal sign, one can find out the zodiacal sign of the Moon on new moon day. This will be the same as the zodiacal sign of the Sun. Thus, the month is determined.

2. (a) First arc was the equator with segment length of 15° and second arc was the local meridian with segment length of 10°. The meridian would pass through zenith and hence would be easy to identify, and the equator can be identified by its inclination (and the fact that it is exactly passing through the East and the West cardinal points) or by identifying the stars along its path. Segment length can be estimated by counting the segments.

   (b) Local sidereal time can be estimated as approximately $13^h\ 30^m$ by noting the zodiacal constellation on the meridian.

   (c) The corresponding month for this sky at 18:00 UT would be June.

Serial No.	Object No.	Type	Constellation
1	M101	1	Uma
2	M57	2	Lyr
3	M92	4	Her

Serial No.	Star Name	Type	Constellation
1	β UMi (Kochab)	1	UMi
2	γ Leo (Algieba)	2	Leo
3	α CVn (Cor Caroli)	2	CVn

3. (a) Question is self-explanatory.
   (b) Following objects were visible:

α Cyg – Deneb	o Cet – Mira	δ CMa – Wezen
δ Cep – Alrediph	β Per – Algol	M44 – Praesepe
		(Beehive Cluster)

   (c) Question is self-explanatory.
   (d) The sky was set for $\phi = 50°$ and $LST = 5^h\ 25^m$. Approximate time of the year was either January or February.
   (e) The two objects were M45 and Regulus (α Leo).

(f) α CMa: A3 $= 340° \pm 2°$; $h_3 = 20° \pm 1°$

   M31: A4 $= 108° \pm 2°$; $h_4 = 41° \pm 2°$

(g) $\alpha = 3^h24^m \pm 15^m$; $\delta = 49° \pm 3°$

4. (a) Areographic latitude of the observer is $\phi = 22.5°$

   (b) Pollux (β Gem): $h_u = 61° \pm 0.5°$;$h_l = -75° \pm 1°$ (calculated)

      Deneb (α Cyg) : $h_u = 32° \pm 0.5°$;$h_l = 13° \pm 0.5°$

   (c) Give the areocentric (Martian) declination of:

      Regulus (αLeo) $\delta = -22.5° \pm 0.5°$

      Toliman (α Cen) $\delta = -48° \pm 0.5°$

   (d) One way to work out declinations can be as shown below.

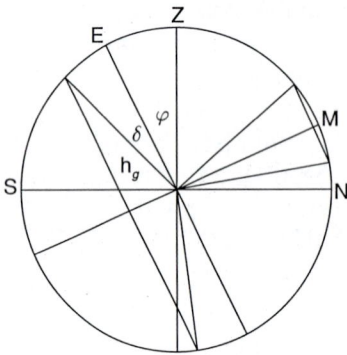

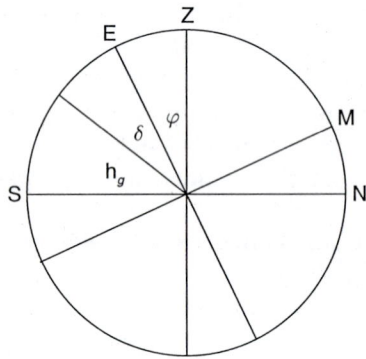

   (e) Question is self-explanatory

   (f) Azimuth of the observer was $A = 150°$.

   (g) The base on Mars was located near the northern Tropic circle.

   (h) It was roughly the spring season.

Appendix A

Syllabus of IOAA

A.1 General Notes

1. Extensive contents in basic astronomical concepts are required in theoretical and practical problems.
2. Basic concepts in physics and mathematics at high-school level are required in solving the problems. Standard solutions should not involve use of calculus and/or the use of complex numbers and/or solving differential equations.
3. Astronomical software packages may be used in practical and observational problems. The contestants will be informed of the list of software packages to be used at least 3 months in advance. The chosen software packages should preferably be freeware or low-cost ones enabling all countries to obtain them easily for practice purpose. The chosen software should preferably be available on multiple OSs (Windows / Unix / GNU-Linux / Mac).
4. Concepts and phenomena not included in the Syllabus may be used in questions but sufficient information must be given in the questions so that contestants without previous knowledge of these topics would not be at a disadvantage.
5. Sophisticated practical equipment likely to be unfamiliar to the candidates should not dominate a problem. If such devices are used in the questions, sufficient information must be provided. In such cases, students should be given the opportunity to familiarise themselves with such equipment.
6. The original texts of the problems have to be set in SI units, wherever applicable. Participants will be expected to mention appropriate units in their answers and should be familiar with the idea of correct rounding off and expressing the final result (s) and error (s) with correct number of significant digits.

A.2 Theoretical Part

Symbol (Q) is attached to some topics in the list. It means "qualitative understanding only". Quantitative reasoning / proficiency in these topics is not mandatory.

The following theoretical contents are proposed for the contestants.

A.2.1 Basic Astrophysics

Contents	Remarks
Celestial Mechanics	Newton's laws of gravitation, Kepler's laws for circular and non-circular orbits, Roche limit, barycentre, 2-body problem, Lagrange points
Electromagnetic Theory and Quantum Physics	Electromagnetic spectrum, Radiation laws, Blackbody radiation
Thermodynamics	Thermodynamic equilibrium, Ideal gas, Energy transfer
Spectroscopy and Atomic Physics	Absorption, Emission, Scattering, Spectra of celestial objects, Doppler effect, Line formations, Continuum spectra, Splitting and broadening of spectral lines, Polarisation
Nuclear Physics	Basic concepts including structure of atom, Mass defect and binding energy, Radio activity, Neutrinos (Q)

A.2.2 Coordinates and Times

Contents	Remarks
Celestial Sphere	Spherical trigonometry, Celestial coordinates and their applications, Equinox and Solstice, Circumpolar stars, Constellations and Zodiac
Concept of Time	Solar time, Sidereal time, Julian date, Heliocentric Julian date, Time zone, Universal Time, Local Mean Time, Different definitions of "year", Equation of time

A.2.3 Solar System

Contents	Remarks
The Sun	Solar structure, Solar surface activities, Solar rotation, Solar radiation and Solar constant, Solar neutrinos (Q), Sun–Earth relations, Role of magnetic fields (Q), Solar wind and radiation pressure, Heliosphere (Q), Magnetosphere (Q)

Contents	Remarks
The Solar System	Earth–Moon System, precession, nutation, libration, Formation and evolution of the Solar System (Q), Structure and components of the Solar System (Q), Structure and orbits of the Solar System objects, Sidereal and Synodic periods, Retrograde motion, Outer reaches of the solar system (Q)
Space Exploration	Satellite trajectories and transfers, Human exploration of the Solar System (Q), Planetary missions (Q), Sling-shot effect of gravity, Space-based instruments (Q)
Phenomena	Tides, Seasons, Eclipses, Aurorae (Q), Meteor Showers

A.2.4 Stars

Contents	Remarks
Stellar Properties	Methods of Distance determination, Radiation, Luminosity and magnitude, Colour indices and temperature, Determination of radii and masses, Stellar motion, Irregular and regular stellar variabilities-broad classification and properties, Cepheids and period–luminosity relation, Physics of pulsation (Q)
Stellar Interior and Atmospheres	Stellar equilibrium, Stellar nucleosynthesis, Energy transportation (Q), Boundary conditions, Stellar atmospheres and atmospheric spectra
Stellar Evolution	Stellar formation, Hertzsprung–Russell diagram, Pre-Main Sequence, Main Sequence, Post-Main Sequence stars, supernovae, planetary nebulae, End states of stars

A.2.5 Stellar Systems

Contents	Remarks
Binary Star Systems	Different types of binary stars, Mass determination in binary star systems, Light and radial velocity curves of eclipsing binary systems, Doppler shifts in binary systems, interacting binaries, peculiar binary systems

Contents	Remarks
Exoplanets	Techniques used to detect exoplanets
Star Clusters	Classification and Structure, Mass, age, luminosity and distance determination
Milky Way Galaxy	Structure and composition, Rotation, Satellites of Milky Way(Q)
Interstellar Medium	Gas (Q), dust (Q), **HII** regions, 21cm radiation, nebulae (Q), inter stellar absorption, dispersion measure, Faraday rotation
Galaxies	Classifications based on structure, composition and activity, Mass, luminosity and distance determination, Rotation curves
Accretion Processes	Basic concepts (spherical and disc accretion) (Q), Eddington luminosity

A.2.6 Cosmology

Contents	Remarks
Elementary Cosmology	Expanding Universe and Hubble's law, Cluster of galaxies, Dark matter, Dark energy (Q), Gravitational lensing, Cosmic Microwave Background Radiation, Big Bang (Q), Alternative models of the Universe (Q), Large scale structure (Q), Distance measurement at cosmological scale, cosmological redshift

A.2.7 Instrumentation and Space Technologies

Contents	Remarks
Multi-wavelength Astronomy	Observations in radio, microwave, infrared, visible, ultraviolet, X-ray, and gamma-ray wavelength bands, Earth's atmospheric effects
Instrumentation	Telescopes and detectors (e.g. charge-coupled devices, photometers, spectrographs), Magnification, Focal length, Focal ratio, resolving and light gathering powers of telescopes, Geometric model of two element interferometer, Aperture synthesis, Adaptive optics, photometry, astrometry

A.3 Practical Part

This part consists of two sections: observations and data analysis. The theoretical part of the Syllabus provides the basis for all problems in the practical part.

The observations section focuses on contestant's experience in

1. Naked-eye observations
2. Usage of sky maps and catalogues
3. Application of coordinate systems in the sky, magnitude estimation, estimation of angular separation
4. Usage of basic astronomical instruments–telescopes and various detectors for observations but enough instructions must be provided to the contestants. Observational objects may be from real sources in the sky or imitated sources in the laboratory. Computer simulations may be used in the problems but sufficient instructions must be provided to the contestants.

The data analysis section focuses on the calculation and analysis of the astronomical data provided in the problems. Additional requirements are as follows:

1. Proper identification of error sources, calculation of errors, and estimation of their influence on the final results.
2. Proper use of graph papers with different scales, e.g., polar and logarithmic papers. Transformation of the data to obtain a linear plot and finding the best fit line approximately.
3. Basic statistical analysis of the observational data.
4. Knowledge of the most common experimental techniques for measuring physical quantities mentioned in Part A.